TECHNIQUES OF CHEMISTRY

ARNOLD WEISSBERGER, *Editor*

VOLUME I

PHYSICAL METHODS OF CHEMISTRY

PART IB
*Automatic Recording and Control,
Computers in Chemical Research*

TECHNIQUES OF CHEMISTRY

ARNOLD WEISSBERGER, *Editor*

TECHNIQUES OF CHEMISTRY

VOLUME I

PHYSICAL METHODS OF CHEMISTRY

INCORPORATING FOURTH COMPLETELY REVISED AND AUGMENTED
EDITION OF TECHNIQUE OF ORGANIC CHEMISTRY,
VOLUME I, PHYSICAL METHODS OF ORGANIC CHEMISTRY

Edited by

ARNOLD WEISSBERGER
AND
BRYANT W. ROSSITER

Research Laboratories
Eastman Kodak Company
Rochester, New York

PART IB
Automatic Recording and Control,
Computers in Chemical Research

WILEY-INTERSCIENCE

A DIVISION OF JOHN WILEY & SONS Inc.

New York · London · Sydney · Toronto

Library of Congress Catalog Card Number: 77-114920

ISBN 0 471 92725 2

Printed in the United States of America

10 9 8 7 6 5 4 3 2 1

PLAN FOR
PHYSICAL METHODS OF CHEMISTRY

PART I

Components of Scientific Instruments, Automatic Recording and Control, Computers in Chemical Research

PART II

Electrochemical Methods

PART III

Optical, Spectroscopic, and Radioactivity Methods

PART IV

Determination of Mass, Transport, and Electrical-Magnetic Properties

PART V

Determination of Thermodynamic and Surface Properties

AUTHORS OF PART I

LEROY L. BLACKMER

Research Laboratories, Eastman Kodak Company, Kodak Park, Rochester, New York

CURTIS E. BORCHERS

Department of Chemistry, Northwestern University, Evanston, Illinois

JOHN FIGUERAS

Research Laboratories, Eastman Kodak Company, Kodak Park, Rochester, New York

MURRAY C. GODDARD

Research Laboratories, Eastman Kodak Company, Kodak Park, Rochester, New York

ROBERT J. LOYD

Department of Chemistry, Northwestern University, Evanston, Illinois

LEON F. PHILLIPS

Department of Chemistry, University of Canterbury, Christchurch, New Zealand

DAVID R. SIMONSEN

Manufacturing Experiments, Kodak Park, Rochester, New York

DONALD E. SMITH

Department of Chemistry, Northwestern University, Evanston, Illinois

NEW BOOKS AND NEW EDITIONS OF BOOKS OF THE TECHNIQUE OF ORGANIC CHEMISTRY SERIES WILL NOW APPEAR IN TECHNIQUES OF CHEMISTRY. A LIST OF PRESENTLY PUBLISHED VOLUMES IS GIVEN BELOW.

TECHNIQUE OF ORGANIC CHEMISTRY
ARNOLD WEISSBERGER, *Editor*

INTRODUCTION TO THE SERIES

Techniques of Chemistry is the successor to the Technique of Organic Chemistry Series and its companion—Technique of Inorganic Chemistry. Because many of the methods are employed in all branches of chemical science, the division into techniques for organic and inorganic chemistry has become increasingly artificial. Accordingly, the new series reflects the wider application of techniques, and the component volumes for the most part provide complete treatments of the methods covered. Volumes in which limited areas of application are discussed can be easily recognized by their titles.

Like its predecessors, the series is devoted to a comprehensive presentation of the respective techniques. The authors give the theoretical background for an understanding of the various methods and operations and describe the techniques and tools, their modifications, their merits and limitations, and their handling. It is hoped that the series will contribute to a better understanding and a more rational and effective application of the respective techniques.

Authors and editors hope that readers will find the volumes in this series useful and will communicate to them any criticisms and suggestions for improvements.

Research Laboratories　　　　　　　　　　　　　　　ARNOLD WEISSBERGER
Eastman Kodak Company
Rochester, New York

PREFACE

Physical Methods of Chemistry succeeds, and incorporates the material of, three editions of *Physical Methods of Organic Chemistry* (1945, 1949, and 1959). It has been broadened in scope to include physical methods important in the study of all varieties of chemical compounds. Accordingly, it is published as Volume I of the new Techniques of Chemistry Series.

Some of the methods described in *Physical Methods of Chemistry* are relatively simple laboratory procedures, such as weighing and the measurement of temperature, refractive index, and determination of melting and boiling points. Other techniques require very sophisticated apparatus and specialists to make the measurements and to interpret the data; x-ray diffraction, mass spectrometry, and nuclear magnetic resonance are examples of this class. Authors of chapters describing the first class of methods aim to provide all information that is necessary for the successful handling of the respective techniques. Alternatively, the aim of authors treating the more sophisticated methods is to provide the reader with a clear understanding of the basic theory and apparatus involved, together with an appreciation for the value, potential, and limitations of the respective techniques. Representative applications are included to illustrate these points, and liberal references to monographs and other scientific literature providing greater detail are given for readers who want to apply the techniques. Still other methods that are successfully used to solve chemical problems range between these examples in complexity and sophistication and are treated accordingly. All chapters are written by specialists. In many cases authors have acquired a profound knowledge of the respective methods by their own pioneering work in the use of these techniques.

In the earlier editions of *Physical Methods* an attempt was made to arrange the chapters in a logical sequence. In order to make the organization of the treatise lucid and helpful to the reader, a further step has been taken in the new edition—the treatise has been subdivided into technical families:

Part I   Components of Scientific Instruments, Automatic Recording and Control, Computers in Chemical Research
Part II   Electrochemical Methods
Part III   Optical, Spectroscopic, and Radioactivity Methods

Part IV   Determination of Mass, Transport, and Electrical-Magnetic Properties
Part V   Determination of Thermodynamic and Surface Properties

The changes in subject matter from the Third Edition are too numerous to list in detail. We thank previous authors for their continuing cooperation and welcome the new authors to the series. New authors of Part I are Dr. Leroy L. Blackmer, Dr. Curtis E. Borchers, Dr. John Figueras, Mr. Murray C. Goddard, Mr. Robert J. Loyd, Dr. Leon F. Phillips, and Dr. Donald E. Smith.

We are also grateful to the many colleagues who advised us in the selection of authors and helped in the evaluation of manuscripts. They are for Part I: Mr. D. C. Barton, Dr. E. R. Brown, Mr. M. C. Goddard, Mr. W. K. Grimwood, Mr. H. O. Hoadley, Mrs. A. Kocher, Dr. W. R. Ruby, and Mr. J. G. Streiffert.

The senior editor expresses his gratitude to Bryant W. Rossiter for joining him in the work and taking on the very heavy burden with exceptional devotion and ability.

ARNOLD WEISSBERGER
BRYANT W. ROSSITER

January 1970
Research Laboratories
Eastman Kodak Company
Rochester, New York

CONTENTS

TECHNIQUES OF CHEMISTRY

ARNOLD WEISSBERGER, *Editor*

VOLUME I

PHYSICAL METHODS OF CHEMISTRY

PART IB
Automatic Recording and Control,
Computers in Chemical Research

Chapter VI

DETECTION (TRANSDUCERS)
Leon F. Phillips

1   THE NATURE OF THE DETECTION PROCESS

Electrical Detection

The term detection has two fundamentally different meanings in relation to the components of scientific instruments. In the commoner sense detection is simply the process of observing a change in some physical property of a system and converting this change into an electrical signal. The device that responds to the change in the physical property by producing an electrical

1

signal is called a transducer, and most of this chapter is, in fact, concerned with the nature and characteristics of transducers for measuring changes in different physical properties. In a more technical and strictly electronic sense detection is the process of extracting the information that is present in a modulated ac signal and expressing this information as a dc analog signal. It is not uncommon for both forms of detection to occur in the same instrument, for whenever a transducer is used to respond to a chopped signal—a chopped light beam, for example—it is necessary at some stage to convert the resulting ac signal back to dc. Detection in the electrical sense is seen to be essentially the same as rectification but with the difference that a rectifier is designed with a view to obtaining the most efficient conversion of ac power to dc, whereas a detector is more likely to be designed with the emphasis on linearity and fidelity, that is, faithful conversion of the information content of the signal from ac to dc.

In many applications of electrical detection it is sufficient to employ a simple diode detector, as in Fig. 6.1a, with a capacitor filter to provide peak-rectifier action. In the old-fashioned crystal radio the combination of "cat's whisker" and germanium crystal formed a point-contact diode that served to rectify the rf signal received from the antenna; essentially the same system is now used in most microwave spectrometers. More recently it has been common for radio receivers to incorporate a grid-leak (or "leaky-grid") detector for the same purpose. This form of detector, illustrated

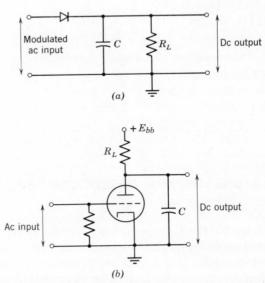

Fig. 6.1 Simple detector circuits: (a) diode detector; (b) grid-leak detector.

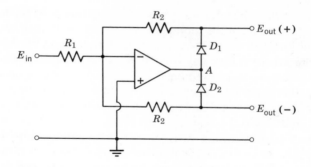

Fig. 6.2 Ultralinear rectifier based on an operational amplifier.

in Fig. 6.1b, uses a vacuum tube with the grid biased at the same potential as the cathode so that only the negative-going part of the input signal is amplified by the tube. When the grid attempts to swing positive with respect to the cathode, the grid-cathode diode is forward-biased, grid current flows, and the positive-going part of the input signal is lost.

The nonlinearity of the rectifying elements in the circuits of Fig. 6.1 would be tolerable in many scientific instruments. Extremely linear rectifier action for critical applications is provided by the operational amplifier circuit of Fig. 6.2. This circuit is basically an inverting amplifier in which the voltage gain measured at point A is always $(R_2 + r)/R_1$, where r is the forward resistance of one of the diodes. If the input signal is positive, the output signal is negative, diode D_1 is reverse-biased, and the gain at A is fixed by the feedback loop containing D_2. When the input signal is negative, D_2 is reverse-biased and the gain at A is then fixed by the feedback loop containing D_1. With a positive input signal the diode D_2 is forward-biased and a fraction $R_2/(R_2 + r)$ of the signal at A appears at the negative output terminal, the over-all gain between the input and this terminal therefore being just $-R_2/R_1$, which is independent of r. At the same time the diode D_1 is reverse-biased, its reverse resistance being R, and a fraction $R_2/(R_2 + R)$ of the negative output signal appears at the positive output terminal; the over-all gain between the input and this terminal is $-R_2(R_2 + r)/R_1(R_2 + R)$. Suppose D_1 and D_2 are both type 1N456 general-purpose silicon diodes, with $R > 1000$ M at room temperature and $r < 25$ Ω (at a forward voltage > 0.7 V); let us set $R_1 = 10$ K and $R_2 = 100$ K. Then, with a positive input signal, the voltage gain at the negative output terminal is -10.0 and the maximum voltage gain between the input and the positive output terminal is -1×10^{-3}. With a negative input signal these figures would be reversed, the positive output terminal having the gain of -10.0.

For linearity at high frequencies it would be preferable to set $R_1 = R_2 = 10$ K, thereby optimizing the loop gain. We may note that the nonlinearity of the diode forward resistance r and, in particular, the requirement of a forward voltage drop before any current will flow, have almost no effect on the output of this circuit. Suppose that the open-loop voltage gain of the amplifier at the signal frequency is 10^4; it can be seen that an input error signal of 50 μV will be sufficient to provide a forward voltage of 0.5 V across one of the diodes at the output of the amplifier. To ensure stability of the circuit at high frequencies it is possible to insert small capacitors in parallel with the resistors R_2, but this will not usually be necessary because the same purpose is served by any smoothing capacitors introduced between the output terminals and ground.

It often happens that the most interesting measurements to be made with a scientific instrument are those that are near the limits of detection and therefore most affected by noise. In Chapter IV we noted that the signal-to-noise ratio in an ac signal can be improved by decreasing the bandwidth of the signal-handling system, and that with very small signals it is helpful to add some of the chopping waveform to the input to ensure that the phase of the signal passed by the narrow-band system is governed by the phase of the input signal rather than by the phase of any random noise that may be present. A further improvement in the final signal-to-noise ratio can usually be obtained by employing a *phase-sensitive detector* to convert the ac signal back to direct current.

A simple form of phase-sensitive detector circuit is shown in Fig. 6.3. A phase-sensitive detector is basically a switch operated in time with the chopper of the input signal. In Fig. 6.3 the FET has a drain-source resistance that is at most 60 Ω when the gate signal is at 0 V and at least 10^{10} Ω (at room temperature) when the gate is at -4 V. Therefore, when the gate is at 0 V (i.e., the switch is closed), the input signal is attenuated by a factor of 10^3, whereas with the gate at -4 V the input signal appears almost unchanged at the output. Since the input and the gate signal in this example

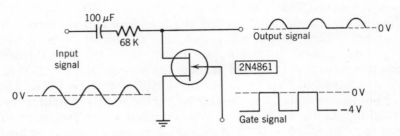

Fig. 6.3 Basic phase-sensitive detector using an FET.

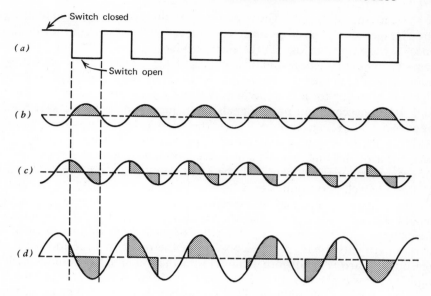

Fig. 6.4 Waveforms in a phase-sensitive detector: (a) switching waveform; (b) signal of correct frequency and phase; (c) signal 90° out of phase; (d) signal of wrong frequency.

are 180° out of phase, it follows that only the positive-going portion of the input waveform appears in the output. To see how the use of a phase-sensitive detector can improve the signal-to-noise ratio we consider the waveforms of Fig. 6.4. The switching waveform is shown at (a), and a waveform for an input signal exactly in phase with the switching waveform is shown at (b). The portion of the input signal that appears in the output is shaded. In practice the output of the detector would be taken to a smoothing, that is, integrating, network and the result would be a positive dc signal. If the relative phase of the switching waveform and the input signal were gradually varied from zero, some of the negative-going portion of the input would begin to appear at the output, and the size of the positive dc output after smoothing would gradually decrease. With a 90° phase difference between the input and the switching waveform, as in (c), the smoothed output would be zero, while with a 180° phase difference a maximum negative dc signal would be obtained. Since noise signals are of random phase, it follows that signals due to noise of exactly the same frequency as the input must give a zero contribution to the integrated dc output, provided only that a reasonably long averaging period is used. A signal of different frequency from the switching waveform, as shown at (d), also gives a zero average contribution to the smoothed dc output. The number of switching cycles required to bring the average exactly to zero is inversely proportional to the frequency difference; for example, in Fig. 6.3 the signal (d) has a period 20% longer than the switching frequency, and five cycles of (d), or six of the switching frequency, are required for the output to be exactly zero. Thus, if the output signal is averaged for a long period, by using a smoothing network with a long RC time constant, noise signals of frequency close to the switching frequency will average to zero. This is the same as having a narrow bandwidth in the detection system, the effective bandwidth being given by the reciprocal of the time constant of the smoothing or integrating network. An integrating network can easily be constructed to have a time constant of 1 min, which corresponds to a bandwidth of less than 0.02 Hz centered on the switching frequency. To construct an amplifier with so narrow a bandwidth and to keep the narrow passband centered on the switching frequency would be exceedingly difficult. For most electrical measurements it is convenient to have a time constant of the order of 1 sec to obtain a reasonably narrow bandwidth without losing the ability to follow moderately rapid changes in the quantity being measured. Even with a 1-Hz bandwidth it is far easier to integrate the final dc output than to attempt to fix the position of the passband of a sharply tuned amplifier.

Almost any electrical switching device can be used as the basis of a phase-sensitive detector; for example, one of the transistor choppers of Fig. 4.60, an electromagnetic relay, a ring modulator (Fig. 4.77), or a tube with more than one control grid. An interesting development of the method* is shown in principle in the block diagram of Fig. 6.5. At very low light levels a photomultiplier tube is capable of giving an output in the form of discrete pulses, each pulse in excess of the random pulses due to dark current being the result of the arrival of a single photon at the photocathode. In Fig. 6.5 the light beam is chopped at a low frequency (typically 1.0 Hz) and the output pulses are taken to a reversible decade scaler, or "up-down" counter. During the time that the beam is interrupted the pulses are fed into the negative input of the counter so that they subtract from the total count, and then while the beam is not interrupted the pulses are fed into the positive input where they add to the total count. The accumulated count therefore contains a contribution from pulses due to photons, which averages to a finite value, and a contribution from pulses due to the dark current of the multiplier, which averages to zero. The effective bandwidth of the system is the reciprocal of the time in seconds during which counts are accumulated.

In its more usual sense, the term detection covers a large variety of physical operations, with a similarly wide range of associated problems. An extreme

* E. D. Morris, Jr., and H. S. Johnston, *Review of Scientific Instruments*, **39**, 620 (1968).

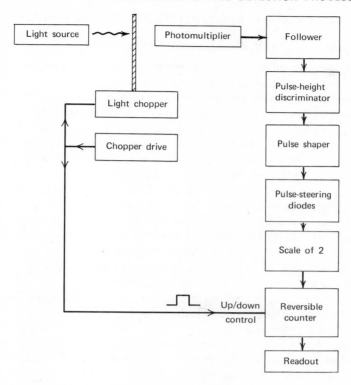

Fig. 6.5   Block diagram of a digital phase-sensitive detection system for handling pulses from a photomultiplier. The circuit described in the reference (footnote 1) includes a second counter for measuring the signal that is 90° out of phase with the chopper-drive waveform and an analog-digital converter for use when the photocurrent is too large to be treated as a series of discrete pulses.

example would be the estimation of 1 part in 10^9 of a hydrocarbon in a stream of argon or the detection of 10^{-11} W of infrared radiation from an exothermic reaction. Obviously not all of the methods of detection that are used in scientific instruments can be discussed here because of space limitations, but many are described in other chapters and volumes in this series. We shall therefore be content to describe and consider the limitations of several of the more important kinds of transducer under the headings (a) detectors of electromagnetic radiation, (b) nuclear detectors, (c) pressure, composition, and field transducers. The devices considered here are almost all input transducers; output transducers, including meters, oscilloscopes, and recorders, are discussed in Chapters III and VII.

2   DETECTORS OF ELECTROMAGNETIC RADIATION

Radiofrequency and Microwave Detectors

The primary element of a detection system for radiofrequency or microwave radiation in free space is the *antenna*, which can be defined as a network that serves to transfer energy from circuits to space or vice-versa. In chemical instrumentation it is most often necessary to detect energy due to microwave radiation within a waveguide or a resonant cavity rather than in free space; we shall return to this point shortly. The effectiveness of energy transfer between an antenna and the adjacent circuitry is governed by the input and output impedances in the usual way; the effectiveness of transfer between an antenna and space, on the other hand, is governed by more complex factors, which include the polarization of the radiation and the antenna gain. For a radiating or receiving antenna the gain is the ratio of the measured radiative intensity in a particular direction to the intensity that would be observed if the radiation were distributed equally in all directions. The gain of an antenna is governed mainly by its size, an antenna that is large in comparison with the wavelength of the radiation normally having a high gain. An extreme example of a large, high-gain antenna is provided by the 1000-ft-diameter radio telescope at Arecibo in Puerto Rico. Two elementary forms of antenna, the monopole over ground, and the dipole, are shown in Fig. 6.6, and a group of high-gain antennas, including the familiar Yagi television antenna, are shown in Fig. 6.7. The first element of a receiver circuit is invariably a tuned *LC* network, the tuning being adjusted to select signals of a particular frequency from the complex sea of radiation that washes against the antenna. A degree of selectivity may also be provided by the polarization of the antenna; for example, AM radio

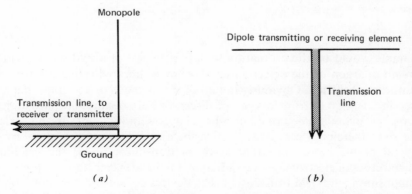

Fig. 6.6   Elementary forms of antenna for radiofrequency radiation: (*a*) monopole over ground; (*b*) dipole.

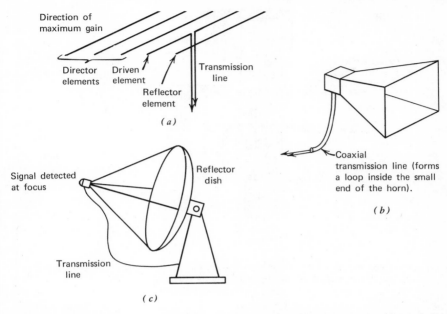

Fig. 6.7   High gain antennas: (*a*) Yagi antenna; (*b*) microwave horn antenna; (*c*) parabolic reflector antenna.

broadcasts are usually vertically polarized and FM and television broadcasts horizontally polarized (this is not true in the United Kingdom).

The detection of microwave energy in a cavity or waveguide is best accomplished with a point-contact *crystal diode*, consisting of a silicon (or sometimes germanium) crystal in contact with a tungsten whisker. A typical arrangement is shown in Fig. 6.8. The crystal detector comes as a plug-in cartridge with the tungsten whisker preadjusted and in contact with the cartridge's inner conductor. When the cartridge is inserted in the holder, the inner conductor extends across the waveguide to a coaxial plug and acts as an antenna for the microwave radiation inside the guide. The body of the crystal is in contact with the outside of the cartridge, which in turn is in contact with the grounded waveguide walls. The point-contact diode rectifies the microwave signal with an efficiency, or *conversion gain*, that is typically about 25%. It is usual to modulate the microwave signal at about 100 kHz so that the output of the detector is also modulated. The radiation source itself (commonly a klystron) may be modulated, or the molecular spectrum that is being studied can be modulated by way of the Stark effect or, in the case of the spectrum of a free radical such as OH or OD, the Zeeman effect.

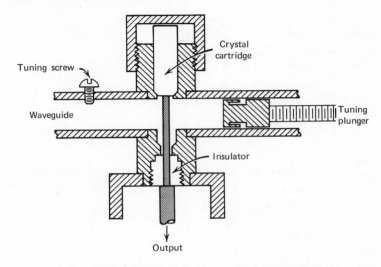

Fig. 6.8   Holder for a crystal detector of microwave radiation (adapted from T. M. Sugden and C. N. Kenney, *Microwave spectroscopy of gases* Van Nostrand, London, 1965).

Other devices for detecting microwave energy include the maser (the forerunner of the now familiar laser which operates at optical frequencies) and the Josephson junction, which shows particular promise as a detector of very short wavelength radiation, intermediate between the microwave and far infrared regions of the spectrum. Both devices are normally operated at temperatures near 4°K and have correspondingly low thermal noise levels. Microwave energy can also be detected directly through its heating effects; for example, by measuring the resistance change in a *bolometer* in the form of a grid of very fine wire when it is exposed to the radiation.

Infrared Detectors

The infrared spectral region is a large one extending from the red end of the visible at a wavelength of about 8000 Å (800 nm in *Système International* units) to the ill-defined boundary with the microwave region at a wavelength about 0.1 mm. At the short wavelength end, below about 1.2 μ, the preferred detection methods are the same as those used for visible and ultraviolet radiation and are not considered in this subsection.* The detectors used at longer wavelengths may be classified as quantum detectors, which depend on internal photoconductive effects resulting from the excitation of electrons

---

* 1.2 μ, or 1.2 microns, is properly written 1.2 μm; however the *micron* (10^{-6} m) is so widely used by spectroscopists that we have retained it.

2 DETECTORS OF ELECTROMAGNETIC RADIATION   11

within a crystal, or thermal detectors, in which the radiation produces a heating effect that alters some physical property of the detector.

Quantum detectors are particularly useful at the short wavelength end of the infrared region, lead sulfide detectors being sensitive to radiation below 3 μ at room temperature, lead telluride below 4 μ, and lead selenide below 5 μ. These long wavelength limits are increased by about 50% on cooling the detectors to 20°K. Indium antimonide is useful below 7.5 μ at room temperature (6.5 μ at 90°K). Doped germanium and silicon detectors, cooled to 4°K, have been shown to possess useful sensitivity at wavelengths as great as 120 μ, the maximum being fixed mainly by the choice of doping element. The lead salt photoconductors consist of thin layers of micro-crystals that have been vacuum-evaporated or (more often) chemically deposited on a suitable substrate. Indium antimonide and doped silicon or germanium detectors consist of single crystals prepared with impurities controlled at the 1 part in 10^8 level by standard semiconductor techniques. The long wavelength limit of sensitivity is in each case fixed by the size of the energy gap across which an electron in the crystal must be excited if an incident photon is to create a carrier of electric current. As noted above, in the case of the doped detectors the size of the energy gap can be controlled by the choice of doping element: pure indium antimonide is an intrinsic semiconductor with an energy gap of 0.18 eV. A doped detector must be cooled to the point at which the thermal excitation across the energy gap is negligible or sensitivity is lost; with cooling by liquid nitrogen alone the theoretical response is limited to wavelengths below about 12 μ.

The most important parameters associated with a radiation detector, in addition to its wavelength response, are noise equivalent power (NEP), or minimum detectable energy (MDE), and response time τ, defined by the formula

$$S_f = S_0(1 + 4\pi^2 f^2 \tau^2)^{-\frac{1}{2}}, \tag{6.1}$$

where S_f is the peak voltage signal obtained when the incident radiation is modulated at a frequency f and S_0 is the signal obtained at zero frequency. With lead sulfide the response time sets an upper limit of a few kilohertz to the frequency at which the radiation can usefully be chopped. The response times of the other detectors are much shorter; for lead selenide and telluride they are usually less than 10 μsec, for indium antimonide less than 0.1 μsec, and for doped silicon and germanium of the order of 1 nsec. By use of a doped germanium detector it is possible to build a rapid-scanning infrared spectrometer with sufficient speed of response to be useful for kinetic spectroscopy following flash photolysis.*

* K. C. Herr and G. C. Pimentel, *Appl. Optics*, **4**, 25 (1965).

Noise equivalent power, or minimum detectable energy (strictly the minimum detectable power), is defined for a particular detector area as the amount of incident radiation required to give a signal-to-noise ratio of unity in a 1-Hz bandwidth. Noise in a photoconductor is of three types, namely Johnson or thermal noise in the resistance, flicker-effect or $1/f$ noise (sometimes called current noise), and radiation noise, due to the random exchange of quanta with the surroundings. The Johnson noise can usually be overcome by applying a large enough voltage across the detector (typically 100 V for the lead salt detectors) to swamp it with current noise. In a detector limited by current noise we have

$$N_f = \text{constant} \times \frac{1}{f}, \tag{6.2}$$

so that the signal-to-noise ratio in terms of power is given by

$$\left(\frac{S_f}{N_f}\right)^2 \times \text{constant} = \frac{f}{1 + 4\pi^2 f^2 \tau^2}. \tag{6.3}$$

The right-hand side of (6.3) is a maximum at $f = 1/(2\pi\tau)$. For an uncooled lead sulfide detector this corresponds to an optimum chopping frequency near 1 kHz. The response time is increased by cooling; however, N_f is also decreased and a net improvement in the signal-to-noise ratio usually results. With the other lead salts the optimum frequency is greater than can easily be obtained with a mechanical chopper. Indium antimonide and the doped semiconductor detectors give much less flicker noise, and it appears that in principle these detectors may be limited by radiation noise, which can be reduced by placing the cooled detector within a small enclosure at the same temperature. For such purposes as cooling infrared detectors there are now available small Joule-Thomson refrigerators (e.g., Air Products and Chemicals "Cryo-Tip" units), which are convenient for temperatures of 4°K (using helium gas) or between 20 and 77°K (using hydrogen gas), and are reasonably economical to operate. Reported values of NEP vary by one or two orders of magnitude for different experimenters with different detectors of the same type. For a detector of 1×1 mm area reported values for PbS at the wavelength of peak sensitivity near room temperature (ca. 2.3 μ) normally range between 10^{-11} and 10^{-13} W; some cooled detectors are reported to have sensitivities of the order of 5×10^{-14} W. The NEP has been shown to be proportional to the square root of the detector area; this is sometimes incorporated into the definition by quoting performance in terms of the *detectivity*, $D^* = (\text{NEP})^{-1} \times \text{area}^{1/2}$, in units of W^{-1} cm $Hz^{1/2}$. The NEP limit imposed by radiation noise at room temperature is about 5×10^{-14} W. For PbTe at 90°K values of NEP between 10^{-11} and 10^{-13} W have been reported, and for PbSe at 90°K values between 10^{-11} and 10^{-12} W.

For the detectors with extended wavelength response the magnitude of the radiation noise is correspondingly greater at any given temperature. For indium antimonide at room temperature an NEP of the order of 10^{-9} W at $6\,\mu$ appears to be fairly typical; cooling to 77°K improves this figure by one or two orders of magnitude. For the doped semiconductor detectors, with detector and enclosure cooled to 20°K or less, the NEP can be of the order of 10^{-13} W.

The basic forms of *thermal radiation detector* are the thermocouple, the Golay detector, and the bolometer. Thermal detectors have a uniform response over the whole spectral region in which the light-absorbing part of the detector can be regarded as black. The form of thermocouple used in many commercial infrared spectrometers is illustrated in Fig. 6.9. It consists of a small piece of blackened gold foil, to absorb the radiation, welded to the tips of two wire leads made of dissimilar metals chosen to give a large thermoelectric emf. The Schwartz thermopile is a particularly sensitive version of the thermocouple in which the lead materials are semiconductors, one having a large positive thermoelectric power with respect to gold and the other a large negative power. The leads are made long and thin and the whole assembly is contained in an evacuated enclosure (with

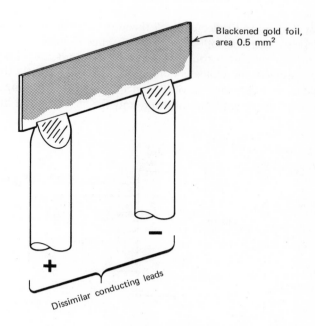

Blackened gold foil, area 0.5 mm²

Fig. 6.9   Active part of a thermocouple radiation detector.

an infrared window) so that heat losses are minimized. A typical high-sensitivity thermocouple detector would have a sensitive area of 0.5 mm², a response time of 40 msec, a dc resistance between 10 and 200 Ω, and an NEP of 10^{-10} W at a chopping frequency of 5 Hz. Because of the low impedance of the thermocouple the Johnson noise is extremely low, and for the best over-all signal-to-noise ratio it is usual to follow the thermocouple with a voltage step-up transformer to increase the size of the signal and at the same time increase the impedance level to the point at which the Johnson noise is equal to the intrinsic input noise of the low-frequency tuned amplifier.

The heart of a Golay detector is illustrated in Fig. 6.10. The infrared radiation passes through the small window, which may be quartz, potassium bromide, diamond, or other suitable material for the wavelength range of interest, and is absorbed by a thin rigid membrane. The absorbing membrane is typically only 2-mm square, but it has an angular aperture of about 60° and generally the detector must be used with a system of condensing mirrors to concentrate the radiation. Behind the absorbing membrane is a small volume of inert gas whose temperature and pressure fluctuate in time with the radiation falling on the membrane. At the far end of the membrane is a flexible mirror which is distorted when the gas pressure rises. To amplify the distortions of the mirror a beam of light is focused through a grid onto the surface and reflected back through the grid to a vacuum photocell which drives a cathode-follower. In the absence of radiation the focus is such that no light returns through the grid to the photocell. Then, when the mirror is distorted, the image is defocused and consequently the photocell receives some light. The output of the detector is at the low impedance level characteristic of the cathode-follower, and the signal is at a high enough level for

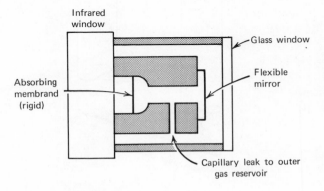

Fig. 6.10   Heart of a Golay detector.

the noise properties of subsequent amplifier stages to be no longer critical. The small capillary leak which connects the sensitive volume with the main gas reservoir is needed to make the device insensitive to changes of ambient temperature. The response time of the Golay detector depends on the nature of the inert gas present but is typically of the order of 20 msec, corresponding to an optimum chopping frequency of about 15 Hz. The NEP is commonly between 3 and 30 × 10^{-11} W, that is, similar to the figure for a sensitive thermocouple. The Golay cell has been used throughout the infrared range and until recently was the only detector suitable for use in the very far infrared or submillimeter region.

A bolometer is a device whose electrical resistance changes as a result of the gross temperature change it undergoes on absorption of radiation and not simply as a result of direct excitation of electrons into a conduction band. The resistance of a typical metal increases with temperature at the rate of about 0.35 % per degree, whereas the resistance of a semiconductor decreases by about 7 % per degree; hence a bolometer for use as an infrared detector is a semiconductor. This is commonly in the form of a small carbon flake or a single crystal of doped germanium. Alternatively, it is possible to use a superconducting bolometer in which high sensitivity results from the very rapid change of resistance that occurs with increasing temperature near the superconducting transition temperature of a material such as niobium nitride. Still another type of bolometer is the electron bolometer, in which absorbed radiation increases the effective temperature of the electrons in a pure crystal at a low temperature without appreciable transfer of energy to the crystal lattice. The response time of the electrons in a crystal is very short (of the order of 10 nsec), and it is this fast response that distinguishes the effect from ordinary bolometer action, which has a response time of the order of 1 msec. The effect has been observed in both indium antimonide and germanium crystals and provides a fast detector that is potentially useful in a band extending through the far infrared into the microwave region. For a carbon flake bolometer at 2°K the NEP can be as low as 10^{-11} W; for a single crystal bolometer at 4°K or for a superconducting bolometer the value of NEP may be two or three times smaller than this. For further information about these detectors, and about still more exotic devices such as the magnetically tunable doped indium antimonide detector, the reader is referred to [2] and [3] in the list of references at the end of this chapter.

Detectors of Visible and Ultraviolet Radiation

Visible and uv radiation can be detected by its chemical, photographic, or photoelectric effects on matter. Chemical radiation detectors, or *actinometers*, consist of chemical systems in which the absorption of sufficiently energetic radiation brings about a photochemical reaction of precisely known quantum yield. Several different systems have been standardized for use in this manner,* the best known being the uranyl oxalate actinometer in which the conversion of oxalate ion to CO and CO_2 occurs with a quantum yield of about 0.5 when the system absorbs light of wavelength between 2500 and 4500 Å (250 and 450 nm). By this it is understood that the absorption of 6.02×10^{23} quanta leads to the removal of 0.5 moles of oxalate ion. In practice the actinometer and the system whose emission intensity or quantum yield of reaction following absorption is to be determined are placed in the same light-tight enclosure, in such a way that the geometrical placing of the test system and the actinometer does not affect the measurement, and the whole arrangement is left for a sufficient time to produce a measurable quantity of reaction products. The extent of reaction in the actinometer is thus a measure of the integrated light intensity during the period of the experiment. For most actinometers the quantum yield is a function of the wavelength of the photolyzing light and it is necessary to determine the spectral energy distribution of the source in a separate experiment.

A photographic detection system also integrates light intensity over a period of time (though this time can be very short) and has the further advantage of being two-dimensional; that is, one photographic exposure can give information about the relative intensity of light emission from several different regions of an extended source. The basis of the photographic process is an emulsion of silver halides, consisting predominantly of silver bromide, in gelatin. According to the current theory of the photographic process, the silver halide is present in the form of fine crystals on the surface of which are impurity centers, each containing at least 10 molecules of silver sulfide. The Ag_2S may be introduced intentionally or be formed by interaction of the silver salt with sulfur compounds contained in the gelatin. When a light quantum is absorbed by a halide crystal during exposure, it causes the promotion of an electron from the crystal's valence band to an empty conduction band. The resulting mobile electron may return to the conduction band after a time or be trapped in an impurity center, where it converts an Ag^+ ion to an atom of silver. The halogen atom, which is an incidental product of this process, is removed by reaction with the gelatin. After exposure to light the emulsion therefore contains a *latent image* in the form of a large number of silver atoms located in small clusters at the impurity centers. During the usual development process a weak reducing agent, such as alkaline hydroquinone, converts the silver halide to black metallic silver, beginning preferentially with the halide surrounding the small groups

* For a useful summary see J. C. Calvert and J. N. Pitts, *Photochemistry*, New York, Wiley, 1966.

of 4 to 10 silver atoms that constitute the latent image. Reduction is stopped after a time found by trial to yield the optimum development of the image; for precise control of developing time with an alkaline developer it is convenient to transfer the plate, film, or print from the developer solution to a stop-bath that consists mainly of a 2% solution of acetic acid. The unreacted silver halide is then removed with a fixing solution, of which the basic ingredient is "hypo," that is, sodium thiosulfate. Once the unreacted halide has been dissolved the excess chemicals are removed by washing in running water and the image may be safely exposed to light. The image formed initially is a negative in which blackening is most intense in the regions on which most light has fallen, and if a positive print is required the whole process must be repeated with an image formed by focusing light through the negative. In the remarkable "Polaroid" process developed by E. H. Land a positive black-and-white print can be obtained directly from the camera 15 sec after exposure. The film pack contains sacs or "pods" of a viscous developer which is released and spread evenly on the exposed film when the latter is squeezed between metal rollers inside the camera. The light-sensitive layer is pressed against a nonsensitive paper impregnated with dry developer: the viscous developer first develops the negative image, then dissolves the remaining crystals and transfers them to the nonsensitive paper on which they are developed to form the positive print. In the present state of the art the resulting image is somewhat delicate, and for long-term stability it is necessary to apply a protective coating to the print to prevent physical damage or loss of detail due to gradual reversal of the development process. A similarly remarkable process has been developed for making a complete color print within one minute of exposure.

The important quantities to be specified for photographic materials for scientific use are the spectral sensitivity, speed, contrast, and resolving power. The spectral sensitivity of a silver halide emulsion is limited by the failure of the silver halides to absorb light at the long-wavelength end, and by the lack of transparency of the gelatin at the short wavelength end. The maximum response is obtained with blue light of a wavelength near 4200 Å (420 nm). For wavelengths below about 2300 Å special plates, such as Ilford Q or Eastman Kodak SWR, are available with emulsions that contain greatly reduced amounts of gelatin. Alternatively, it is possible to coat an emulsion with a material that fluoresces with light below 2500 Å. Orthochromatic and panchromatic emulsions have their long-wavelength limits extended to about 5600 and 6200 Å, respectively, by the addition of sensitizers in the form of dyes that absorb the radiation and in the process transfer electrons to the conduction bands of the silver halide crystals on which the dye molecules are adsorbed. With different sensitizers it has been possible to extend the long wavelength limit into the infrared as far as 13,000 Å

(1.3 μ). Infrared emulsions usually have such low absolute sensitivity that it is necessary to hypersensitize them just before use, generally by first bathing the plate or film in cold dilute ammonia solution and then in methanol or ethanol. With some emulsions it is sufficient to use plain water in place of the ammonia; for details of the best procedure in any particular case it is advisable to consult the manufacturer's data sheets. Most sensitized emulsions have very uneven sensitivity through the visible region, and this can seriously distort the appearance of a band spectrum when the material is used in photographic spectroscopy. Some representative sensitivity curves for Kodak spectroscopic plates are given in Fig. 6.11. Infrared sensitive emulsions are gradually affected by thermally activated processes at room temperature and should be stored in a deep freeze until a few hours before use, with just sufficient time being allowed before opening to prevent condensation of moisture. All photosensitive materials are best stored in a refrigerator to prevent deterioration and should be processed as soon as possible after exposure to minimize fading of the latent image.

A typical characteristic curve, which shows the relationship of optical density D [= log (incident light/transmitted light)] of a final developed image to the logarithm of the product of exposure time and light intensity,

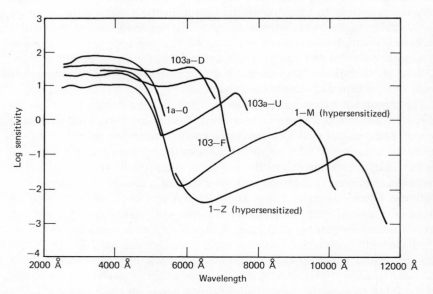

Fig. 6.11 Spectral sensitivities of some Kodak spectroscopic plates. Sensitivity is defined as the reciprocal of exposure (in erg cm^{-2}) required to produce a density D above gross fog. Curves shown are for $D = 0.6$. (Note $D = \log I_0/I$; I = light transmitted by image, I_0 = incident light.) Exposure times all 1.3 sec.

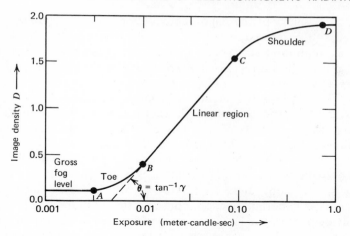

Fig. 6.12   Characteristic curve of a photographic emulsion.

is given in Fig. 6.12. The graph shows that there is a minimum threshold value of exposure at the point marked A, below which there is no detectable optical density above the "gross fog" that appears when an unexposed plate is developed. Above the threshold at B the curve becomes almost linear, and it is in the linear region from B to C that quantitative measurements of light intensity based on the density of blackening are usually made. The slope of the linear portion is designated "gamma" (γ) and is a numerical measure of the relative amounts of contrast between light and dark portions of the image and of the object being photographed. Gamma depends on the manner in which the emulsion is used, as shown in Fig. 6.13; in general, for a given average density, the highest contrast is obtained by short exposure

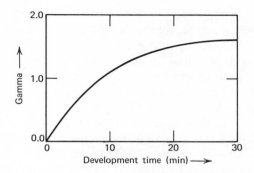

Fig. 6.13   Typical dependence of gamma on development time.

and long development. In the region above C on the characteristic curve the emulsion is overexposed, and with complete overexposure the density reaches a maximum value at the point D. In a region well above D the density may begin to decrease with increasing exposure. The ability of an emulsion to detect a very small amount of light is reflected in the threshold exposure value at A. The usual quoted measure of relative sensitivity, however, is a quantity S_A, defined as the reciprocal of the exposure in meter·candle·seconds required to produce a density of 0.6 above gross fog with an exposure time of 1 sec, using tungsten radiation and specified development conditions. The optical density of 0.6 has been found to be the minimum value for optimum detection and measurement of weak images in astronomy and is also relevant to spectroscopy under conditions in which precise wavelength measurement is as important as the simple detection of radiation.

The resolving power of an emulsion can be measured by photographing a reduced image of a scale containing sets of equally spaced parallel lines and observing the result with a microscope. For best resolving power the density of the image should be in the range 0.7 to 2.0. The resolving power of commonly used plates and films varies from less than 50 lines/mm for low resolving power materials to more than 130 lines/mm for very high resolving power materials. For applications requiring ultrahigh resolution special plates with resolving powers near 2000 lines/mm are available. Related to resolving power is graininess, which is an expression of the lack of uniformity of an image arising from the fact that it is composed of small discrete grains of silver. Graininess is usually an undesirable quality; for example, it adds noise to a microdensitometer trace of an image. Emulsions are classified in terms of graininess on a scale ranging from *coarse* to *extremely fine*; generally, maximum graininess is associated with highest emulsion sensitivity and most energetic development. For minimum graininess it is best to work with exposures near the lower end of the linear region in the characteristic curve. A further quantity related to resolving power is sharpness, or acutance, which is a measure of the ability of a material to give a sharp boundary, that is, a steep density gradient, between exposed and unexposed areas.

In measurements based on the density or the position of a photographic image there are several potential sources of systematic error. With density measurements the most important source of error is usually *reciprocity failure*; that is, the failure of the degree of blackening to be a function only of the exposure E given by the product of light intensity and exposure time. Reciprocity failure is usually manifested in the observation that at very low light intensity and long exposure time the emulsion's sensitivity falls off; thus for precise intensity comparisons it is advisable to use the same exposure time with both light sources. A similar decrease in sensitivity is observed with very short duration exposure to an extremely intense light source and is of some importance in laser or spark photography. The reciprocity behavior of an emulsion is conveniently summarized in graphs of the amount of light required to produce a fixed density of blackening in the form shown in Fig. 6.14, in which vertical axes are lines of constant light intensity and 45° axes are lines of constant exposure time. If reciprocity effects were absent, the characteristic curves would all consist of horizontal straight lines. Reciprocity failure also appears in the form of an intermittency effect, in which a continuous exposure and one that is interrupted to give the same average intensity do not produce the same density of blackening. This effect disappears if the number of interruptions of the more intense light signal is large enough, say more than 100. In general, for reliable intensity measurements it is necessary to compare sources under conditions of exposure that are as similar as possible from the point of view of the emulsion, to avoid subjecting an exposed emulsion to any further influences, such as heat or infrared radiation, that might affect the chemical changes initiated by the exposure, and to allow a fixed time under standard storage conditions between exposure and processing.

Two main effects might lead to error in determining the relative positions of different parts of a photographic image on a plate, film, or print. The first arises from the dimensional stability, or lack of it, of the emulsion and the material used to support it, and the second from the possibility that some parts of a photographic image might receive especially favorable or unfavorable treatment during the development process. Detectable changes of size can occur with photographic papers, and to a lesser extent with film, as a result of changes of temperature and humidity. For precise work it is

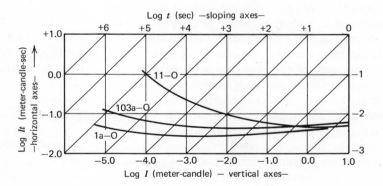

Fig. 6.14 Reciprocity characteristics of some Kodak spectroscopic plates. The curves show the variation with exposure time t or light intensity I of the exposure $E = It$ required to produce a density D of 0.6 above gross fog. From the above curves it can be deduced that the 1a-0 emulsion is suitable for making long exposures at low light intensity and the 11-0 emulsion is unsuitable.

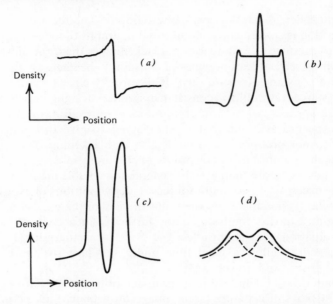

Fig. 6.15 Image displacements occurring during developing: (*a*) edge effect, due to the edge of a dense image being better supplied with developer; (*b*) the edge effect causes a small image to appear relatively dense and narrow in comparison with a larger image; (*c*) depletion of developer between two dense images causes them to appear further apart; (*d*) overlap of latent images causes two faint images to appear closer together.

therefore necessary to use photographic plates whose glass backing typically has a linear thermal expansion coefficient of only 0.001 % and is entirely independent of humidity. Provided the emulsion adheres to the glass, its linear dimensions will be similarly stable. During development it is to be expected that the concentration of developer will be significantly lower and the concentrations of reaction products higher in the vicinity of a dense image than in a region in which exposure has been light. This is true even when the developing process is carried out with the recommended amount of agitation of the solution. Some examples of how this can affect the measured size and position of an image are illustrated in Fig. 6.15.

In recent years there has been an increasing tendency for photographic methods of detecting and measuring light to give way to photoelectric ones. Nevertheless the convenience of a photographic record, the ability of a photograph to distinguish light arriving from different parts of an extended source, and the ability of an emulsion to integrate incoming photons for a period of hours or days ensure that photographic methods will continue to be widely used despite the sources of error mentioned in the preceding paragraphs. It follows that skill in the art of photography will continue to repay the effort spent in acquiring it.

The form of *photoelectric detector* most often used in scientific work is the photomultiplier. Other photoelectric devices that may be encountered are the vacuum photocell, the gas-filled photocell, and various semiconductor devices such as the phototransistor, the avalanche photodiode, the cadmium sulfide photoconductive cell, and the silicon photovoltaic cell. We consider first the three phototubes which depend for their operation on the observation that a material irradiated with light in vacuum is caused to emit electrons—that is, on the photoelectric effect. If a second electrode held at a positive potential is present and an external circuit allows the electrons lost from the first electrode to be continuously replaced, then a steady current will flow. The result is essentially a vacuum photocell or "vacuum photodiode." If the emitting surface is a metal (Fig. 6.16a) it is observed that the maximum energy of the ejected electrons is given by the equation

$$E = h\nu - \phi, \tag{6.4}$$

where $h\nu$ is the energy of the quantum absorbed and ϕ, known as the work function of the metal, is the depth of the Fermi surface below the level corresponding to zero energy in a vacuum. If the energy per quantum is less than the work function, no electrons can be ejected; thus it follows that a detector based on the photoelectric effect will have a long wavelength limit of sensitivity. At very short wavelengths the sensitivity is usually limited by the transparency of the window material. The quantum efficiency of pure metals for electron emission following absorption of visible radiation is 0.1% or less, whereas for semiconducting mixtures such as Cs–Sb or

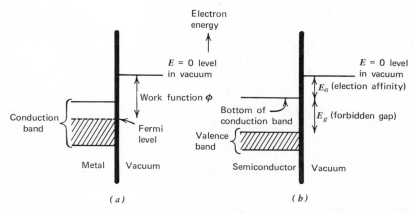

Fig. 6.16 Models used to discuss the photoelectric effect in a metal (a) and a semiconductor (b).

Ag–O–Cs it can be as high as 30%. Consequently the photoemissive surfaces of practical phototubes are invariably composed of such mixtures. For a semiconductor (Fig. 6.16b) a light quantum of energy between E_g and $(E_g + E_a)$ can cause internal photoconduction, but for photoemission it is necessary that the energy per quantum exceed $(E_g + E_a)$, the sum of the energy gap and electron affinity of the material. By appropriate choice of the photoemissive surface and material of which the tube envelope is composed it is possible to vary the spectral response of a phototube over a wide range of wavelengths below about 11,000 Å (1.1 μ). Some response curves for photocathodes of tubes intended for use in the visible and near ultraviolet are given in Fig. 6.17. For work below 3000 Å "solar blind" photomultipliers, such as the EMR type 541G (Electromechanical Research Inc. Princeton, New Jersey), are available, in which the photocathode is made of cesium

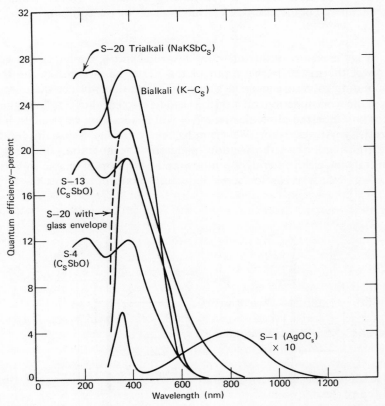

Fig. 6.17 Representative spectral response curves of photocathodes used in EMI photomultipliers. (EMI Electronics Ltd, England.)

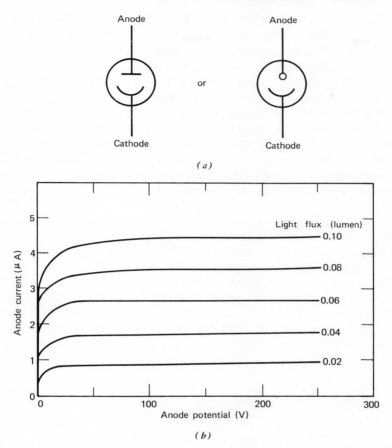

Fig. 6.18   Vacuum photocell: (*a*) alternative circuit symbols; (*b*) characteristics RCA type 929.

or rubidium telluride or iodide and is insensitive to radiation of wavelength greater than 2800 Å.

A typical *vacuum photocell*, such as the RCA types 929 or 935, consists of a photocathode deposited on the inner surface of a support in the form of a half cylinder, with an anode in the form of a single thick wire at the center of the cylinder. The anode is usually connected to a pin at the tube socket, but with tubes for applications in which leakage currents inside the glass envelope might be a source of significant error the anode is connected to a cap on top of the envelope. This is the case with the 935. Alternative circuit symbols for a vacuum photocell are given in Fig. 6.18*a*, and the characteristics of the 929 are shown in Fig. 6.18*b*. The 929 tube has a sensitivity of

45 μA/lm, which is essentially independent of the applied voltage in the usual operating range. At very low light intensities the usefulness of a phototube is limited by the *dark current*, which for the 929 is stated to be 0.0125 μA maximum and for the 935, 0.0005 μA maximum. Thus, although the sensitivity of the 935 is only 35 μA/lm, it is much more useful than the 929 at low light levels. A factor that contributes to the larger dark current of the 929 is its longer wavelength response, the 929 having an S-4 response, with maximum sensitivity at 400 ± 50 nm, and the 935 an S-5 response, with maximum sensitivity at 350 ± 50 nm. A vacuum photocell is a stable and useful device for measuring relative intensities of moderately weak light sources. It behaves as a high-impedance current generator and in critical applications should therefore be used in conjunction with an electrometer, as in the precision fluorimeter of Fig. 6.19.

In a gas-filled photocell some of the stability and precision of operation of the vacuum photocell is sacrificed for increased sensitivity. In a tube containing a small amount (ca. 0.1 torr) of a gas such as argon the electrons accelerating away from the photocathode are able to ionize the gas partially and thus produce further electrons and ions that add to the ionizing current. Further, when positive ions strike the cathode, they can cause the emission of secondary electrons and the whole process may be repeated. Provided the anode voltage is kept low enough to prevent a continuous discharge from being formed, the resulting device is a reasonably stable photocell,

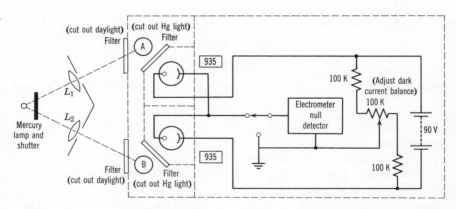

Fig. 6.19 Precision fluorimeter with low dark-current vacuum photocells. Readings are taken from a micrometer-controlled aperture on lens L_1, the aperture of L_2 being fixed. In practice the dark currents are first equalized with the shutter in position; the shutter is then removed and the aperture adjusted to equalize the currents due to fluorescence from solutions A and B. [See W. H. Melhuish and W. S. Metcalf, *Journal of the Chemical Society* (London), **157**, 976 (1954).]

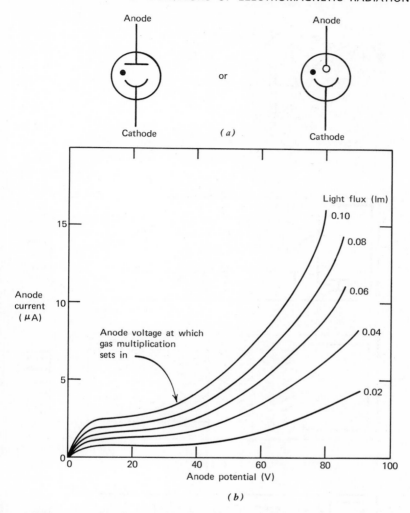

Fig. 6.20   Gas photodiode: (*a*) alternative circuit symbols; (*b*) characteristics of RCA type 930.

with an internal amplification factor of the order of 10 due to the presence of the gas. The frequency response of such a tube is limited to the range below 10 kHz because of the finite time required for ionization to disappear when the illumination is cut off. Circuit symbols and characteristics of a typical gas-filled photocell, or "gas photodiode," are given in Fig. 6.20.

In a *photomultiplier tube* the phenomenon of secondary emission of electrons from a surface bombarded with electrons or ions is exploited to

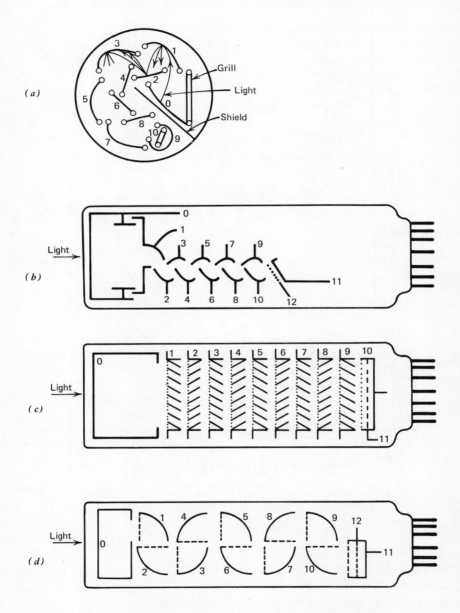

Fig. 6.21 Dynode configurations in photomultipliers. In each configuration the photocathode is numbered 0 and the anode has the highest number: (*a*) is the compact focused "squirrel-cage" structure, as used in the side-window RCA tubes 1P21 or 1P28; (*b*) is the kind of focused structure used in the EMI 9594B; (*c*) is the venetian blind structure used, for example, in the EMI 9514S; (*d*) is the box and grid structure used, for example, in EMI type 9698.

produce a device than can have an internal amplification factor up to 10^8. The principle of operation of a photomultiplier is that electrons ejected from a photocathode are accelerated by a potential of the order of 100 V and made to strike a *dynode*. This is an electrode whose surface is of Be–Cu, Cs–Sb, or some similar material, such that for each electron that strikes the surface initially several secondary electrons are emitted. The secondary electrons emitted from the first dynode are then accelerated by another 100-V potential difference to strike a second dynode, where they bring about further multiplication of the current by secondary emission, and so on. The final electrode is an anode from which the output current is taken to a high-resistance load. The number of secondary emission stages is commonly between 5 and 15, and the over-all sensitivity can be 2000 A/lm or more, with a total voltage drop from anode to cathode of 1 to 2 kV. The four commonest arrangements of electrodes in a multiplier are shown in Fig. 6.21.

Each initial photoelectron resulting from the absorption of a quantum at the photocathode gives rise to a burst of about 10^6 electrons at the anode, the transit time between absorption of the photon and arrival of the shower being typically in the range 10 to 100 nsec. The spread of transit times, that is, the width of an output current pulse with an infinitely sharp input light pulse, is between 20 and 50% of the transit time, the actual figure depending on the number of stages and the degree of focusing of the beam of electrons at the first dynode. The rise time of a sharp pulse is limited by the capacitance from the anode to other electrodes, which is generally around 6 pF, and by the spread of transit times, and is typically in the range of 2 to 20 nsec. These times are short enough to allow a photomultiplier to be used as a quantum counter at very low light levels (up to about 10^6 quanta/sec striking the photocathode) in a circuit such as that in Fig. 6.5. At higher light levels it is usual to measure the output as a steady current by amplifying the voltage produced when the current flows through a load resistor, which is typically in the range 100 K to 100 M. Alternatively, it is possible to employ an analog-to-digital converter, such as that shown in Fig. 6.22, and count the output pulses from the converter.

A photomultiplier is normally operated from a high-voltage power supply with a chain of resistors between the high voltage and earth potential to provide the correct voltage steps for the dynodes. The current through the dynode chain should be at least 10 and preferably 100 times the maximum value of anode current that is likely to flow, since the electrons ejected from the dynodes by the secondary emission process have to be replaced from the power supply via the dynode-resistor chain, and it is necessary for the dynode potential to remain constant while this happens. In pulse applications it is often helpful to insert capacitors of the order of 0.01 μF in parallel with the last few resistors in the chain. The commonest arrangement for connecting

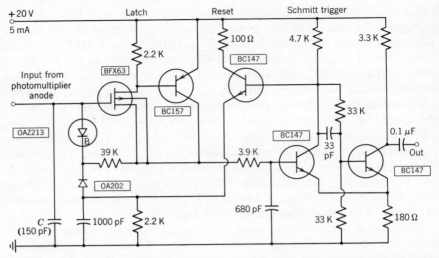

Fig. 6.22 Analog-to-digital converter for photomultiplier output, sensitivity 1 Hz/nA, range 0.01 nA to 100 μA. The OAZ213 zener diode (12 V) is selected for low leakage; the emitter-base diode of a selected planar transistor would serve well in this position. Output pulses from the Schmitt trigger are 20 V deep and 2 μsec in length. Different ranges can be obtained by switching the capacitor C. Circuit designed by C. H. Rowe.

a photomultiplier to its power supply is to set the photocathode at a large negative potential and connect the anode to ground through the load resistor, as in Fig. 6.23a. With this arrangement a standard dc amplifier can be used to measure the output voltage, or, if a chopped light source is being used, a capacitor with a low voltage rating will serve to connect the anode load to the ac amplifier. A flaw of this arrangement is that with end-window type photomultipliers the high electrostatic fields in the neighborhood of the photocathode may be distorted by grounded conductors in contact with the tube envelope. To overcome the effects of electrostatic fields, and of magnetic fields that can also have an adverse affect on the tube gain, it is a good practice to mount the photomultiplier inside a shield of mu-metal with the shield at cathode potential. The mounting of this shield is greatly simplified if the cathode and shield are both at ground with the anode at a large positive potential, as in Fig. 6.23b. With this arrangement it is necessary to couple the anode through a high-voltage capacitor to subsequent amplifying circuits, and therefore the incident light must be chopped or be at a level low enough to be handled by pulse-counting methods. For optimum tube performance in terms of gain stability, transit-time spread, and resistance to disturbance by magnetic fields it is advisable to ensure that the recommended cathode-D_1 voltage is maintained even when the over-all voltage

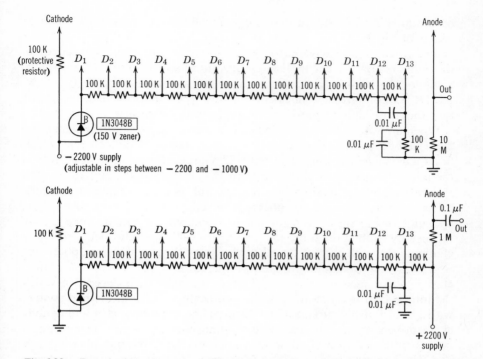

Fig. 6.23a Dynode chains for a 13-stage photomultiplier tube; for example, EMI type 9514S, with anode grounded and cathode grounded. The zener diode can be replaced with a 100-K resistor in most applications.

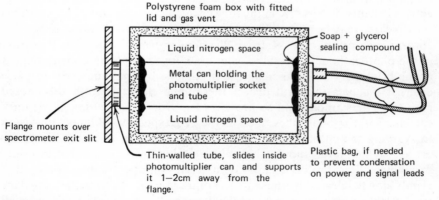

Fig. 6.23b A simple arrangement for cooling a photomultiplier tube, devised by H. P. Broida. Moisture inside the photomultiplier can condenses on the metal surface, which is cooled first, and the entry of further moisture is restricted by the spectrometer slit. The dynode chain at the multiplier socket is "potted" with epoxy resin.

on the tube is reduced as a means of controlling sensitivity. In the dynode chains of Fig. 6.23a the cathode-D_1 voltage is fixed by a zener diode. The chains in the figure have equal values of resistance along the length of the chain; in high current applications it is often useful to double the resistance value for the last one or two steps or to use a series such as $R, R, \ldots, R, 2R, 3R, R$. For further refinements of this type for use with a particular tube the reader should consult the manufacturer's data sheets.

When a photomultiplier is used to measure a very small light signal, the main factor that limits the accuracy is the presence of the dark current, which flows independently of incident light. The largest source of dark current is thermionic emission of electrons from the photocathode, and tubes with spectral response extending into the red will, in general, have worse dark current characteristics than tubes whose sensitivity is limited to the blue and ultraviolet. Since the emission is thermionic, it can be very greatly reduced by cooling the tube, and cooling to $-40°C$ is sufficient to virtually eliminate the dark current for all tubes except those with S-1 response, for which cooling to liquid nitrogen temperature is necessary. Some quite elaborate arrangements for cooled operation have been devised in which the tube is held in a dewar, with the photocathode area in thermal contact with a cooled metal surface under vacuum and the tube socket and dynode chain projecting into an enclosure at atmospheric pressure. This arrangement is intended to prevent condensation on the photomultiplier window and to avoid the possibility of forming a low-pressure glow discharge around the tube socket. For many purposes, however, the simple arrangement shown in Fig. 6.23b is perfectly satisfactory. A small component of the dark current arises from secondary radiation following the decay of radioactive elements such as ^{40}K in the tube envelope, and for critical applications the envelope may be made of fused silica which has a much lower potassium content than ordinary glass. In applications in which only a small portion of the photocathode is actually being used, for example, in a measurement of the brightness of a star image, it is possible by trial and error to place external magnets that will deflect thermionic electrons from the unused regions of the cathode and so prevent them from contributing to the dark current. Some special tubes, such as the ITT type FW118, make provision for varying the effective area of the photocathode in this way. Tubes for use at low light levels should always be stored in the dark, for after exposure to ambient light the photocathode material contains trapped energy that is only slowly released by the emission of thermionic electrons, and the dark current after such exposure may take days to fall to a steady value. A small component of the dark current can develop from ohmic leakage around the tube socket, especially if care is not taken to keep the socket clean and dry, to avoid touching the insulation, and so on. Another form of dark current, which can be significant in a tube being used at the upper limit of applied voltage, arises from the exposure of the photocathode to light due to ionization of residual gas or to fluorescence of the tube envelope when it is struck by stray electrons. This is often termed regenerative dark current, since there is positive feedback between the tube current and the light it produces, and in severe cases the dark current may build up until the tube is destroyed.

Under normal operating conditions the gain per stage is large enough so that all noise in the output of a photomultiplier comes from the photocathode and first dynode. Johnson noise in the load resistor is relatively unimportant. The largest contribution to this tube noise is the shot noise in the sum of photocurrent and dark current, which shows an increase by a factor of about 1.5 over the normal shot noise given by (4.66) due to randomness in the secondary emission process. At very low light levels the statistics of the arrival of photons governs the time required to obtain a given amount of precision in an intensity measurement. As usual, the signal-to-noise ratio can be optimized by a combination of light modulation and phase-sensitive detection with long-term averaging. When pulse-counting methods are used, the signal-to-noise ratio can often be improved significantly by pulse-height discrimination, which eliminates noise due to thermionic emission from the dynodes, though dark current pulses from the photocathode itself are not discriminated against. Measurements made over a period of hours or days are likely to be affected by photomultiplier fatigue, that is, a gradual loss of sensitivity of the tube during exposure to light, with only a relatively slow return of sensitivity during periods of darkness. The effect appears to be greatest at moderately high light levels (photocurrents of the order of 100 μA or more) and also to be most pronounced just after exposure to light has commenced. Some commercial instruments incorporate a small "fatigue light" in the belief that steady illumination will prevent rapid fatigue effects without detracting from the ability of the multiplier to detect small signals. The rate of recovery after illumination ceases is largely independent of any application of high voltage. Photomultiplier fatigue is not properly understood, but it appears that the long-term loss of sensitivity is a direct function of the total charge that the dynodes have been required to pass, which suggests that irreversible changes occurring on the photocathode and dynode surfaces may be a major factor.

The solid-state photoconductive cells based on cadmium sulfide are similar in principle to the lead salt cells, which were described in the subsection dealing with infrared detectors, except that the material used is such that the devices have their peak sensitivity in the visible region. The over-all sensitivity is much less even than that of a vacuum photocell, and cadmium sulfide cells are therefore used only in situations in which ruggedness and

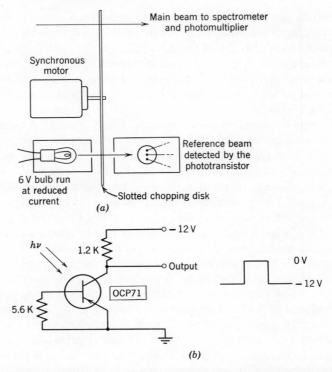

Fig. 6.24 Use of a phototransistor to provide a reference signal for a phase-sensitive detector: (*a*) arrangement of reference beam and chopper; (*b*) circuit used with the phototransistor.

simplicity of operation are more important than sensitivity. A silicon photo-voltaic cell, or "solar cell," consists essentially of a large-area *pn* junction. When the cell is illuminated, carriers are excited across the junction and are then unable to return unless they flow through the external circuit because of the potential difference that results from diffusion at the depletion layer (cf. Fig. 4.26). Consequently the cell behaves as a voltage source with an optimum output voltage of about 0.46 V. Cells of this type are used to generate small amounts of power, for example, in space applications, and as light sensors in data processing systems. In a *phototransistor* such as the Mullard OCP71 the carriers that are excited across the reverse-biased collector-base junction as a result of light absorption constitute a base current that is amplified by normal transistor action. The transistor can be biased completely off in the absence of light and be made to turn fully on in the presence of a small amount of red or near infrared illumination. Consequently the phototransistor is a convenient form of optically controlled switch, for example, for providing a reference signal from the light chopper in a phase-sensitive detection system. A typical circuit for this purpose is shown in Fig. 6.24. The avalanche photodiode is a promising device for the detection of light modulated at very high frequencies, as would be required in television communication via a laser beam. As in the photovoltaic cell, carriers are optically excited across a *pn* junction, but in this instance a large reverse-bias voltage is applied, to accelerate the carriers sufficiently to bring about avalanche breakdown. Provided the bias voltage is not too high, the result is an internal multiplication of the photocurrent by a factor of 50 or 100.

Table 6.1 Short Wavelength Transmission Limits of Some Common Window Materials

	Angstroms
LiF	1040
MgF_2	1120
CaF_2	1220
Synthetic sapphire	1410
Synthetic fused quartz	1600
Atmospheric oxygen	1900
Vycor glass	2200
Ordinary glass	3000

These devices are capable of quantum efficiencies of 60% or more at 6328 Å (the helium-neon laser wavelength), they have an NEP of the order of 10^{-12} W in unit bandwidth at a modulation frequency of 1 GHz (10^9 Hz) and they have a gain-bandwidth product of 100 GHz or more.

Detectors of Vacuum Ultraviolet Radiation

In the wavelength region below 2000 Å (200 nm) optical studies become more difficult because of strong absorption of radiation by oxygen in the air and because of the progressive loss of transmission of most optical materials. The short-wavelength transmission limits of some common optical window materials are listed in Table 6.1. Below 1000 Å and in the x-ray region it is necessary to work without windows except for relatively narrow bands in which it is possible to use metal films a few hundred or a few thousand Ångstroms thick. (For the range 150–750 Å films of aluminum, deposited on fine nickel mesh, are available from Sigmatron Inc., Goleta, California.)

Once the problem of getting the light to the detector has been overcome the chemical, photographic, and photoelectric effects which served to detect visible and near ultraviolet radiation continue to work as well below 2000 Å, while at wavelengths below 1700 Å a further type of detector, based on photoionization, is available. At present there are no chemical actinometers for the vacuum ultraviolet that can be used with the same confidence as those available above 2000 Å, but this situation will improve as a result of continuing studies of the photolysis of simple gases such as N_2O and CO_2. Photographic plates and films for use at short wavelengths must, as previously noted, have most of the gelatin eliminated or be coated with a fluorescent material. The fluorescent lacquer supplied by Eastman Kodak Company for coating their type 103-0 film has a virtually constant quantum efficiency between 1000 and 2200 Å.

When it is necessary to use a photomultiplier at wavelengths below 2000 Å there are several alternative possibilities. The first and often the easiest is to use a blue-sensitive photomultiplier in conjunction with a sodium salicylate phosphor. A film between 1 and 2 mg cm^{-2}, made by evaporating a saturated solution of sodium salicylate in methanol, is easily deposited on the vacuum side of an exit window from the light source, or on the outside of the photomultiplier itself if it can be included within the vacuum chamber. Such a film is stable, provided the vacuum is clean and free of oil vapors, and has a fairly uniform quantum efficiency between 300 and 3000 Å and a fluorescence output that peaks at 4200 Å, the wavelength of maximum sensitivity of an S-11 photocathode. The absolute quantum efficiency is normally between 60 and 90 % and the decay time of fluorescence is approximately 10 nsec. Many other phosphors can, in principle, serve the same purpose, but of those that have been tried so far sodium salicylate has been found to possess the optimum combination of quantum efficiency, output wavelength, and resistance to deterioration under vacuum. When extremely weak light signals are to be detected, the solar-blind photomultipliers, with lithium fluoride windows and photocathodes of cesium iodide or telluride, are more sensitive than the combination of a phosphor with an S-11 photomultiplier because of their very low dark currents (3×10^{-12} and 2×10^{-11} A for the 18-stage EMR type 541F and 541G photomultipliers, respectively, at an over-all gain of 10^6). Other photoelectric detectors that have been used for the vacuum ultraviolet include vacuum photodiodes with gold photocathodes, the Bendix magnetic electron multiplier of the type originally designed for use with the time-of-flight mass spectrometer, and the Bendix or Mullard "Channeltron" in which the secondary multiplication surface is on the inside of a narrow, curved, tubular channel, down which secondary electrons are accelerated following the impact of photons or ions at the entrance to the tube. The channel is made of high-resistance material and the accelerating voltage, which is typically 2 kV, is simply applied between the two ends of the tube. Other multipliers designed primarily for use as particle detectors, for example, the EMI tubes designated 9603B and 9707, are also useful as windowless detectors for electromagnetic radiation in the x-ray and vacuum ultraviolet regions, with a long wavelength limit at about 2900 A. These tubes have Be–Cu or Ag–Mg–O dynodes (the first dynode serves as the photocathode when the tube is used to detect photons) which can withstand exposure to dry air for short periods without deterioration and can be regenerated by exposure to atomic oxygen in a discharge at about 1 torr.

Detectors based on photoionization are of two types, namely, ionization chambers and photon counters. The difference is that in an ionization chamber the steady current produced by ionization of the gas in the chamber is measured with an electrometer, whereas in a counter the individual bursts of ionization due to the arrival of single photons are counted as pulses. Ionization detectors are completely inert to radiation of wavelength longer than the photoionization threshold of the gas, but at shorter wavelengths the efficiency of detection can be close to 100%. The construction and a typical current-voltage characteristic of one form of ionization chamber are given in Fig. 6.25. The form of the characteristic shows that with this particular chamber a potential of a few volts between the electrodes is sufficient to ensure that essentially all of the primary ions produced by the incident radiation are collected and that at a potential difference of about 150 V gas multiplication, as in a gas-filled photocell, sets in. It is often convenient to operate with a gas gain of about 50. By suitable choice of the window materials and the filling gas an ionization chamber or photon counter can be constructed to be sensitive to radiation in only a relatively narrow band of wavelengths.*

A photon counter is essentially the same as the Geiger-Müller and proportional counters that are used to detect nuclear radiation: for a discussion of the mode of operation of these devices the reader is referred to the next section. Because of the difficulty of obtaining suitable windows combining strength with transparency, photon counting has not been feasible for radiation between 300 Å and the lithium fluoride cut-off (1040 Å).

Summary

The methods of detection used for electromagnetic radiation range from the antenna and tuned circuit at one end of the spectrum to the ionization chamber at the other. The transition from detectors that depend entirely on the wave properties of the radiation, through heat detectors, such as bolometers, thermocouples, or Golay detectors, to the different forms of quantum detectors is a simple reflection of the increasing predominance of particle behavior over wave properties as the energy per quantum increases.

* See J. H. Carver and P. Mitchell, *J. Sci. Instr.*, **41**, 555 (1964).

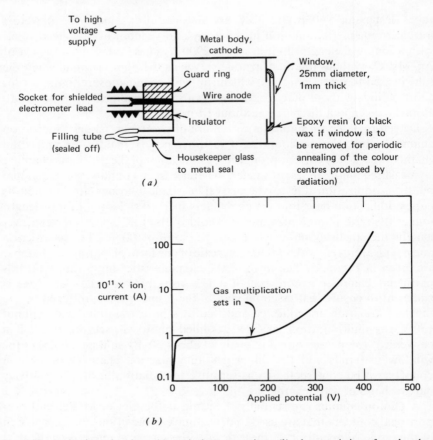

Fig. 6.25 Ionization chamber: (*a*) typical construction; (*b*) characteristics of a chamber filled with 20 torr of nitric oxide.

Just as at the radiofrequency end it is difficult to find effects that depend on the presence of discrete quanta, so with x-rays is it difficult to find effects that depend on the electromagnetic waves. Thermal detectors, which make no distinction between waves and quanta, are applicable over the whole frequency range and are used, for example, even in the vacuum ultraviolet when absolute intensity measurements are required. The different forms of quantum detector—photoconductive, photoemissive, photographic, photochemical, and photoionization—have definite long-wavelength limits of sensitivity that are set by the minimum size of the quantum capable of producing an effect. However, the practical short-wavelength limits of these detectors are not intrinsic limitations but are fixed by the transmission of window or support materials. When windows or suitable phosphors are available at short wavelengths these detectors can continue to serve, and in the next section, which deals with detectors for nuclear radiation, we consider essentially the same devices in the form of semiconductor radiation detectors, scintillation counters, nuclear emulsions, chemical dosimeters, and Geiger-Müller tubes.

3   NUCLEAR DETECTORS

The Properties of Nuclear Radiation

Nuclear radiation can consist either of particles of matter—neutrinos, electrons, protons, α-particles, or fission fragments, for example—or of electromagnetic radiation, termed gamma radiation if it arises from radiative transitions within atomic nuclei and x-radiation if it arises from transitions of orbital electrons. A beam of radiation has properties that depend strongly on its energy, which is a reflection of the particle momentum in the one case and of the radiation frequency or wavelength in the other. Directly related to the energy is the penetrating power of the radiation when it passes through matter in bulk. The energy of a nuclear particle or quantum may range from a fraction of an electron volt, as for a "thermal" neutron, to several MeV or even GeV (1 electron volt (eV) per particle = 23.06 kcal per mole of particles). The distance a particle may travel in air can vary from infinity, in the case of a neutrino, to a small fraction of a millimeter, in the case of a low-energy charged particle. Massive charged particles, such as deuterons, alpha particles, or fission fragments, travel in straight lines through air and for a given energy have a well-defined range with only a small degree of straggling, that is, variation of range from particle to particle in a mono-energetic beam. This is because the main stopping mechanism for such particles involves scattering collisions with electrons, and the electrons have such a small mass that the extent of deflection of the heavier particle in the collision is negligible. Electrons (β-particles), on the other hand, suffer large deflections in their passage through matter and can lose up to half their kinetic energy in a single collision with a stationary electron, so that they travel in crooked paths and usually appear to have a variable range. Gamma rays, x-rays, and neutrons have no definite range, but instead show an exponential falling-off of beam intensity with distance from the source. The specific ionization of a particle or photon in a medium is the number of ion pairs produced per unit path length. It depends on the nature of the particle and the medium and decreases with increasing particle energy except at very high energies.

The ability of a nuclear particle to penetrate matter is directly related to the variety of interactions the particle can enter into. Thus a neutrino, whose sole contact with other matter is through the exceedingly feeble *weak interaction* responsible for β-decay, can be detected only with great difficulty by observing the products of occasional reactions such as

$$v_e + Cl^{37} \rightarrow Ar^{37} + e^- \qquad (6.5a)$$

or

$$\bar{v}_e + p \rightarrow e^+ + n \qquad (6.5b)$$

A beam of neutrons owes its considerable penetrating power to the fact that the neutron lacks an electrical charge and therefore experiences no coulomb forces. The neutron, however, is capable of affecting other matter via the medium of the short-range (10^{-13} cm) *strong nuclear interaction* and can therefore undergo elastic or inelastic scattering collisions with atomic nuclei. Neutrons can be classified as fast ($E > 100$ keV), thermal ($E \sim 0.04$ eV at 20°C), or epithermal (E between these values), and for many purposes it is desirable to slow fast neutrons to thermal energies with the aid of a *moderator*. In a moderator the neutrons are made to undergo successive elastic collisions, which are most effective in removing energy when the colliding partners are of similar mass; hence it is a common practice to use hydrogen-containing materials such as water or paraffin as neutron moderators in nuclear reactors. When a neutron is inelastically scattered by an atomic nucleus, the result is a simple form of nuclear reaction, such as (n, n), leaving the scattering nucleus in a metastable excited state, or $(n, n\gamma)$, in which the excited nucleus has a short lifetime. More complicated reactions are also possible; for example, (n, γ), the process of neutron capture, which can be very efficient within a narrow energy range, $(n, 2n)$, which is possible only at energies above 10 MeV, (n, f), that is, fission of the compound nucleus, which can occur when the atomic weight is large enough, and (n, α), which occurs readily with some light nuclei, notably Li^6 and B^{10}. Other fairly common types of reaction include (n, p) and (n, d), which are most likely with fast neutrons. The probability of interaction with the nucleus is expressed in terms of a cross section σ, defined by the expression

$$I = I_0 \cdot e^{-N\sigma d}, \qquad (6.6)$$

where N is the number of target nuclei per square centimeter, I_0 is the intensity of the incident neutron beam, and I is the intensity of the beam after it has penetrated a distance d into the target. The microscopic cross section σ is normally stated in barns, where 1 barn = 10^{-24} cm^2. When several different processes can contribute to σ, the quantity obtained experimentally by measurements of beam attenuation is the total cross section. The variation of total cross section with energy for neutrons in boron and hydrogen is shown in Fig. 6.26.

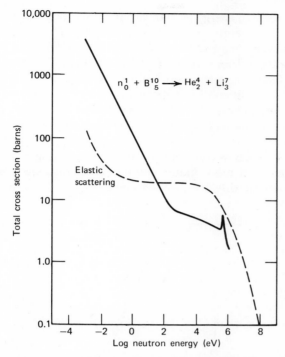

Fig. 6.26   Total cross section as a function of energy for neutrons in boron (solid line) and hydrogen (broken line). (Adapted From D. J. Hughes and J. A. Harvey, *Neutron Cross Sections*, McGraw-Hill, New York, 1955.)

Gamma rays and x-rays can interact with charged particles via the long-range electromagnetic interaction, which is intermediate in strength between the strong and weak nuclear interactions. A beam of high-energy photons passing through matter is described by an equation identical with (6.6), but with the product of N and σ normally given the symbol μ and termed the total linear absorption coefficient. The total absorption coefficient μ can be separated into components, τ, σ, and κ, arising, respectively, from the photoelectric effect, the Compton effect, and pair-production. With an exponential fall-off of intensity it is possible to define a mean range $\bar{R}$ equal to $1/\mu$. At low photon energies the photoelectric effect predominates, at intermediate energies the Compton scattering process

$$\gamma\,(h\nu) + e^- \rightarrow \gamma\,(h\nu') + e^-, \qquad (\nu' \ll \nu) \qquad (6.7)$$

is most important, and at high energies pair production according to

$$\gamma + \text{nucleus} \rightarrow e^+ + e^- + \text{nucleus} \qquad (6.8)$$

takes over. The minimum energy for pair-production is two electron masses, or 1.02 MeV, and this energy reappears as two 0.51-MeV photons when the positron is annihilated. The energy variation of τ, σ, κ, and μ is illustrated in Fig. 6.27 for γ-rays in lead and in aluminum. Whenever a beam of γ-rays loses energy, the main outcome is the production of fast electrons or of photons of lower but still considerable energy, which can in turn produce fast electrons. Consequently the effects that follow the stopping of the secondary electrons in matter may be more obvious than the primary effects of the γ-rays themselves.

Charged particles such as electrons, β- and α-particles, and fission fragments also interact with other matter via the long-range electromagnetic interaction, in this case directly through coulomb forces. In general, the

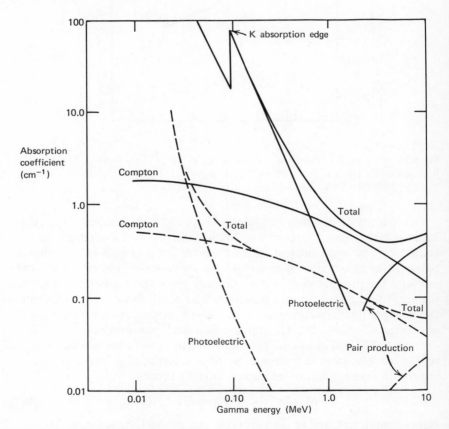

Fig. 6.27   Linear absorption coefficients for gamma rays in lead (solid lines) and aluminum (broken lines). (After A. R. White, National Bureau of Standards, Circular #583, 1957.)

main sources of energy loss are ionization and excitation of the absorbing materials, for which it can be shown that the stopping power of the material, defined as the energy loss per unit path, is given by the equation

$$-\frac{dE}{dx} = \frac{4\pi e^4 z^2 ZNB}{mv^2},$$ (6.9)

where ze, E, and v are the charge, kinetic energy, and velocity of the primary particle, m is the electron mass, N is the number of absorber atoms per cubic centimeter, Z is the atomic number of the absorber, and the stopping number B is a slowly varying function of v, Z, and the nature of the charged particle. With fission products the net charge Ze, which may be as great as $+25\ e$ initially, decreases steadily as the fragment is slowed down; similarly, the charge of an α-particle below 0.1 MeV can vary through electron capture and loss. The effect of the mass of a particle with a given energy appears mainly through the presence of the factor v^2 in the denominator in (6.9); for 1-MeV particles the range in air is approximately 5 mm for an α-particle, 10 mm for a deuteron, a small fraction of millimeter for a fission fragment, and 300 cm for an electron. The energy loss w per ion pair formed in air appears to be almost constant at 35 ± 1 eV for electrons, protons, and α-particles. In condensed media the value of w is in the neighborhood of 5 eV. In addition to producing ionization and excitation, electrons can also lose energy in the form of *bremsstrahlung* at moderate and high energies and in the form of Cerenkov radiation in transparent materials at relativistic energies. Bremsstrahlung radiation arises directly from the deceleration of the electron as it encounters matter, and the energy per quantum emitted can range from zero up to almost the total electron energy. The ratio of radiative and collisional energy losses for electrons is approximately equal to $EZ/800$, where Z is the atomic number of the target and E is the energy in MeV. Thus in lead, with $Z = 82$, radiative losses predominate above 10 MeV. Heavy particles do not give *bremsstrahlung* until the GeV range (formerly BeV) is reached. Cerenkov radiation, which is produced as a sort of "sonic boom" when a particle exceeds the speed of light in a transparent medium (without, of course, exceeding the speed of light in vacuum), is not significant as a mode of energy loss from fast particles but does provide a useful means of detecting such particles.

Ionization Detectors: Proportional Counters and Geiger-Müller Counters

The principle of the ionization chamber has already been discussed in connection with detectors of vacuum ultraviolet radiation. There it was mentioned that to obtain a larger output current it is possible to turn up the applied voltage until gas multiplication becomes significant. In the region in which the gas multiplication amounts to a factor of 10 or less (the *proportional-counter* region, Fig. 6.28) the height of an output pulse is a function of the ability of the detected particle to produce a large amount of ionization in a short space, that is, of its specific ionization, so that with the aid of a pulse-height discriminator it is possible to distinguish particles of different type and different energy. This kind of discrimination is also possible in the ionization chamber region indicated in Fig. 6.28, but here the output pulses are so small that it is preferable to treat the output as a steady current and to measure it with an electrometer. With applied voltages that are above the proportional region, and also above the subsequent region of limited proportionality, there is a region in which any small amount of ionization is sufficient to produce a very large avalanche of ions and electrons

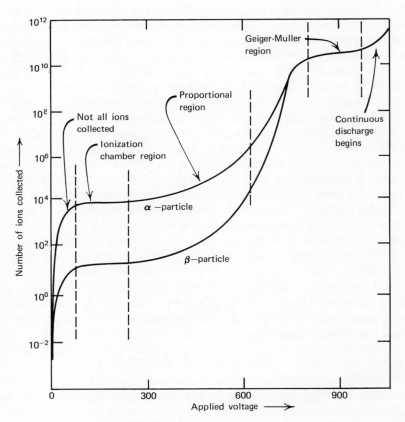

Fig. 6.28   Modes of operation of an ionization chamber at various applied voltages. (Adapted from W. J. Price, *Nuclear Radiation Detection*, McGraw-Hill, New York, 1958.)

within the chamber, and the resulting burst of current forms a massive pulse whose size is independent of the energy or nature of the initiating particle. This is the Geiger-Müller (G-M) region, which occupies the short plateau in the tube characteristic just before the region in which the applied voltage is sufficient to maintain a continuous discharge. The onset of a continuous discharge is inhibited, and the length of time during which the G-M tube continues to respond to the passage of a single ionizing particle is reduced to about 10^{-4} sec, by the addition of a small amount of a "quenching" gas such as 10% ethyl alcohol or, better still, 0.1% of a halogen (chlorine or bromine) to the usual argon or neon filling. Tubes with organic quenchers have lives of the order of 10^{10} counts before all the quencher is used up by free radical reactions; halogen-quenched tubes have lives in excess of 10^{13} counts, for when the halogen has become dissociated, in the process of removing slow-moving ions that would cause the discharge to continue, the atoms merely recombine and the quencher is available for further use. In the G-M region the tube is a sensitive and undiscriminating detector of any particle that will produce some ions to initiate a pulse and is widely used for counting electrons and β-particles and γ- and x-rays, which are relatively difficult to detect otherwise because of the small amounts of ionization they produce. Alpha-particles and highly ionizing particles can also be counted with a G-M tube, provided a thin enough window is used or if the source is placed inside the tube. Some different forms of G-M tube are shown in Fig. 6.29.

The output of a G-M tube consists of negative pulses of amplitude up to 10 V and duration 50 to 100 μsec. These pulses can be counted precisely with the aid of scaling circuits such as those described in Chapter IV. Alternatively, when the requirement is a rapid, low-precision estimate of the rate of arrival of pulses, it is possible to use a ratemeter, or frequency meter, to read the counting rate directly. A typical ratemeter circuit is shown in Fig. 6.30. The heart of the circuit is the *diode pump* which contains the diodes D_1 and D_2 and the capacitors C and C_1. The output pulses from the G-M tube are first standardized by the univibrator, which may be preceded by a preamplifier and a height discriminator in case a proportional counter, or other type of counter, is to be used with the same electronics. The diode D_1 acts as a dc restorer (cf. Chapter IV) for the train of negative-going pulses emerging from the univibrator via C_1, so that after each pulse has passed the potential at the cathode of D_2 is restored to ground level. The negative pulses themselves flow through D_2, each pulse adding an increment of charge $-q$ to the capacitor C. It is necessary for the voltage produced across C by the charge $-q$ to be small in comparison to the amplitude of the negative pulses; this condition, which results in the magnitude of q being essentially independent of the number of pulses already stored on C, is met by having

C much larger than C_1. In the steady state, in which each of r pulses per second delivers a charge $-q$ to C, the voltage across C is equal to $-rqR$. This voltage, which is independent of C, except that the time constant RC governs how long it will take to establish the steady state, is amplified and supplied to the voltmeter at the output. For a numerical estimate of the voltage developed across C per pulse per second suppose that the output resistance which governs the current available from the univibrator is 5K and that the output pulses have amplitude -10 V and duration 50 μsec. The charge delivered per pulse is therefore $(-10 \times 50 \times 10^{-6})/(5 \times 10^3)$, or -10^{-7} C. Therefore, with R equal to 3.3 M, a steady count of one pulse per second would develop 0.33 V across the capacitor. The basic ratemeter circuit can also be used as a frequency meter for any repetitive signal, if the pulses needed to actuate the univibrator in this case are obtained by

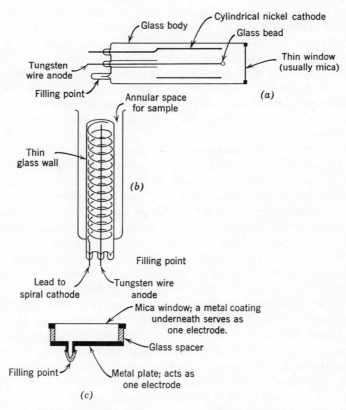

Fig. 6.29 Forms of Geiger-Müller tube: (*a*) end window type; (*b*) liquid sample counter; (*c*) large-area type.

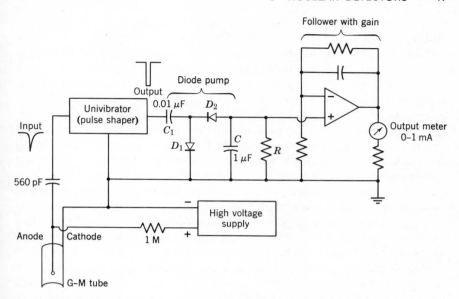

Fig. 6.30 Block diagram of a ratemeter. The resistor R can be switched to vary the time constant RC between approximately 3 sec (low counting rates) and 10^{-4} sec (high counting rates). The output of the univibrator may also drive a small loudspeaker.

differentiating the output of a Schmitt trigger whose input is the repetitive signal in question.

Proportional counters, which operate in the region in which gas multiplication is significant but not catastrophic, are able to count about 200 times as fast as the G-M counter because much less time is required for the system to return to equilibrium after delivering a pulse. They are used in situations in which it is necessary to discriminate between α- and β-particles; in addition, most windowless gas-flow counters are designed to operate in the proportional region. In a windowless flow counter the sample is placed within the ion chamber, the chamber is purged with an initial rapid flow of counter gas (e.g., 10% methane in argon), and a slow steady flow of gas is maintained during counting. Such a counter is particularly suitable for distinguishing and counting low energy α- and β-radiation.

Scintillation Counters

In a scintillation counter some of the energy acquired by the medium when a nuclear particle is absorbed is in the form of electronic excitation of fluorescent molecules and is subsequently emitted as a pulse of visible or near ultraviolet light. This light is observed by a photomultiplier, either directly or through an internally reflecting lightpipe of Lucite (Perspex), and the output of the photomultiplier therefore consists of a train of pulses, with one output pulse for each particle detected. The size of the pulse produced by a given particle depends on the strength of its interaction with the medium and its energy, and as a result the scintillation detector has excellent discrimination properties. Further, the decay time for the fluorescence is typically only 10^{-8} sec, so that the counting rate can be very high. The output pulses from the photomultiplier are, however, generally much smaller than those obtained with a G-M tube, and therefore it is invariably necessary to insert a preamplifier between the photomultiplier and any subsequent ratemeter or scaling circuitry. Many special types of photomultiplier have been developed primarily for use in scintillation counting. Some of these tubes have photocathodes 15 cm or more in diameter to facilitate their use with large volumes of scintillator material. An extreme example is the EMI type 9545B, which has a 30-cm diameter envelope, shaped like a TV picture tube, with a photocathode diameter of 25 cm.

Many different materials have been used as scintillators, including the rare gases, pure organic crystals, solid and liquid solutions of organic materials, and crystalline inorganic halides. Crystalline organic scintillators are usually aromatic hydrocarbons, such as anthracene, whose blue fluorescence is in a convenient spectral region. Phosphorescence is an undesirable property because of its slow decay, which limits the time resolution of the scintillator. Organic liquid scintillators, consisting of dilute solutions of aromatic substances such as p-terphenyl in solvents such as toluene, xylene, or dioxane are most convenient and economical for applications in which a large detection volume is required. Terphenyl has also been used successfully as a solid solution in polystyrene. The inorganic scintillators, such as NaI(Tl) (sodium iodide doped with thallous iodide), are best for detecting gamma rays because of their high density, which gives a high probability of absorption. A simple and convenient form of scintillation detector consists of an end-window photomultiplier with a doped sodium iodide crystal in contact with the window, the whole detector being covered with black masking tape to exclude visible light but allow the penetration of nuclear radiation. For counting α-particles the best scintillator is a thin layer of silver-activated zinc sulfide, which may be coated on the envelope of the photomultiplier or on the outside of a light pipe leading to the photomultiplier. Electrons or β-particles can be detected by all types of scintillator, but the organic liquids are usually preferred because of their short decay times, which are typically two or three orders of magnitude less than the decay times of the inorganic halides. Both ^{13}C and ^3H, which are low energy ("soft") beta emitters, are commonly counted by dissolving the organic compound in which they are incorporated in a suitable liquid scintillator.

The only limitation here is that the compound should not quench the fluorescence of the scintillator to an appreciable extent. (Electrons can also be counted directly with an electron multiplier, the multiplier being windowless or provided with a window thin enough for electrons to penetrate.) Scintillators for detecting neutrons all depend on the production of a secondary particle to which the scintillator can respond directly. For fast neutrons the $H(n, n)$ proton scattering process is commonly exploited in this way, while for slow neutrons the transmutation reactions $^6Li(n, \alpha)$ or $^{10}B(n, \alpha)$ are effective. The main difficulty with detectors for neutrons develops from the need to distinguish neutrons from γ-rays; for this reason zinc sulfide, which has a low sensitivity to γ-rays, is more suitable than NaI(Tl) as a host for ^{10}B in a neutron scintillation detector. Before the development of semiconductor detectors the scintillation counter was by far the most versatile and widely used form of nuclear detector; at the time of writing it is still the most widely used.

Semiconductor Detectors

The most recent type of nuclear detector to be developed is the semiconductor detector, of which the lithium-drifted silicon and germanium detectors are examples. This type normally consists of a reverse-biased pn junction, which may be operated at 77°K or below to reduce thermal excitation of carriers and noise and to overcome problems associated with the dissipation of energy in the crystal. As with the avalanche photodiode and silicon photovoltaic cell, the working of this device depends on the ability of an incident particle or photon to excite carriers across the energy gap in the crystal and thus produce a pulse of current. The size of the current pulse that results is a sensitive indication of the energy of the particle; typical quoted figures for energy resolution of a detector 3-mm thick are 3.8 keV for electrons, 600 eV for x-rays, and 20 keV for protons. The value of the resolution quoted is derived from the width at half-maximum of a peak in the energy spectrum of particles from a given source, and is usually abbreviated into the form 600 eV FWHM. The major advantages of the semiconductor detector are its high stopping power, linearity of pulse-height as a function of energy of the incident particle, short response and recovery times, and low cost. Other advantages include insensitivity to magnetic fields, convenient size, and possession of a rugged but thin window. The semiconductor radiation detector has largely revolutionized nuclear spectroscopy and has many potential applications in chemical studies involving energetic particles, ions, or photons.*

* For a discussion of a complete Ge(Li) γ-ray spectrometer see M. G. Strauss, I. S. Sherman, S. J. Rudnick, R. N. Larsen, and H. M. Mann, *Rev. Sci. Instr.*, **38**, 725 (1967).

Chemical Dosimeters

The dosimeter is the nuclear radiation analog of the actinometer used with visible and ultraviolet light. A chemical dosimeter, which employs a well-studied system under the same conditions as the system being investigated, is a convenient means of energy calibration in radiochemical studies. The dosimeter most often used in practice consists of a 2×10^{-3} molar solution of ferrous sulfate in 0.4 molar sulfuric acid, with 10^{-3} molar NaCl to stabilize the ferrous ion. The amount of ferrous ion converted to ferric as a result of irradiation is conveniently determined with a spectrophotometer from the intensity of the absorption maximum at 3040 Å (304 nm). The yield of reaction in a chemical dosimeter is expressed as a value of G, which is the number of molecules transformed per 100 eV of energy absorbed. For the ferrous sulfate dosimeter the value of G for x-rays, γ-rays, and electrons is close to 15.5; with heavy particles the yield is lower, the difference being approximately a factor of 2 for α-particles. Other chemical processes used in dosimetry include the reduction of ceric ions to cerous in 0.4 molar H_2SO_4 and the decomposition of gaseous nitrous oxide to nitrogen and oxygen. At high dose rates ceric sulfate is to be preferred over ferrous sulfate because of its lower yield.

Nuclear Emulsions and Track Visualization

Photographic emulsions contain heavy atoms such as silver and bromine which give them high stopping power, are rugged, of convenient size, and can integrate data over a long period. These qualities make them attractive devices for the detection of high-energy radiation. Ordinary photographic emulsions are not ideal for this purpose, but special nuclear emulsions, which contain very small grains of silver bromide and have up to four times the normal silver halide content, have been developed. Special emulsions with a high content of ^{10}B are available for detecting neutrons. Nuclear emulsions are commonly used in the form of a thick stack, and the emulsion may be purchased either with a glass backing, so that the stack is similar to a pile of ordinary photographic plates, or as a "stripped emulsion" up to about 1-mm thick, with no glass backing. Special development techniques are required to ensure even development of a thick emulsion throughout its volume and to control shrinkage.* The developed emulsion is finally examined with a high-powered microscope. Particles of low specific ionization may not produce any developable grains, since it appears that more than one impurity center must be activated before a grain can be reduced to metallic silver; in some emulsions there is a maximum energy, dependent on the nature of the particle, above which no track will be produced.

* See, for example, F. R. Gilbert, *Rev. Sci. Instr.*, **29**, 318 (1958).

Other track visualization devices for nuclear radiation include the cloud chamber, in which ions produced by the radiation act as condensation nuclei for liquid droplets in a supersaturated vapor, the bubble chamber, in which the ions act as nuclei for bubbles in a liquid that a sudden drop in pressure has rendered supersaturated with vapor, and the spark chamber, in which the trail of ions formed between metal plates in a three-dimensional grid provides a path for visible electrical sparks between adjacent pairs of plates. Cloud and bubble chambers have the advantage, in comparison to a nuclear emulsion, that the track of a particle is not noticeably distorted by its collisions with atoms in the medium so that the momentum of a charged particle can be determined precisely by measuring the curvature of its path in an applied magnetic field. These specialized forms of nuclear detector do not seem likely to find direct application in chemistry, in which their main interest stems from the information they provide concerning the different kinds of possible behavior for energetic particles in matter.

4   PRESSURE, COMPOSITION, AND FIELD TRANSDUCERS

Pressure Transducers

For the measurement of pressure between about 30 atm and a few torr (1 torr = $\frac{1}{760}$ of a standard atmosphere*) the most direct and obvious procedure is to use a simple manometer (Fig. 6.31a) with mercury as the manometer fluid over most of the range and oil, or dibutyl phthalate, as the fluid below about 5 torr. For work with corrosive materials it is possible to use inert fluorocarbon oils such as Kel-F or to have an intermediate pressure-transmitting device such as a glass or metal diaphragm. With a wide-bore (1-cm) tube to reduce surface tension effects and careful avoidance of contamination the position of the meniscus in such a manometer can be read reliably to 0.1 mm or better. At high pressures the length of the column becomes prohibitive, and devices have been developed to allow the pressure at the bottom of the column in one measurement to be transferred to the top of the column in the next measurement and so on. Such a method of measuring pressure is tedious and has been limited mainly to the calibration of other measuring systems at pressures up to 2500 atm. A slightly less accurate device for use at pressures up to about 20,000 atm is the free-piston gage (Fig. 6.31b) in which the pressure transmitted by a liquid to one end of a piston is balanced by weights placed on the other end. The piston must fit accurately into its cylinder to prevent leakage and is usually rotated

---

* The S.I. unit of pressure is the Newton per square meter, or "Pascal," where 133.32 Pascal = 1 Torr = 1 mmHg. At present very few pressure gages are calibrated in S.I. units.

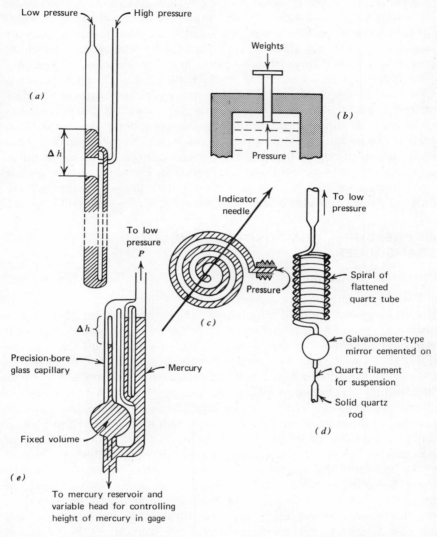

Fig. 6.31 Non-electrical forms of pressure transducer: (*a*) mercury manometer for precision measurements above about 10 torr; (*b*) free-piston high-pressure gage; (*c*) common form of metal-spiral Bourdon gage; (*d*) sensitive quartz-spiral Bourdon gage; (*e*) McLeod gage: $(\Delta h + P)/P = V/\Delta V$.

continuously to reduce friction. The effective area of the piston appears to increase slightly with increasing pressure, and for precise measurements the free piston gage should be calibrated against a mercury column. The Bourdon spiral gage (Fig. 6.31c and d) is commonly used as a direct-reading instrument to measure pressures up to 5000 atm, when the spiral is made of metal, and below 1 atm, when the spiral is often made of quartz. The most sensitive quartz spiral gages can detect pressure changes of the order of 10^{-4} torr. The accuracy of a Bourdon gage is generally better than $\pm 1\%$ of the full-scale reading, although above 3000 atm there may be a considerable amount of hysteresis when the gage is cycled between large and small pressure readings. Somewhat better precision than is available from the quartz spiral gage can be obtained with a gage based on a thin metal diaphragm, such as the Pace transducer or the Consolidated Electrodynamics micromanometer, in which a flat stainless-steel diaphragm is bowed by a pressure difference. In the Consolidated micromanometer the diaphragm forms part of a parallel-plate capacitor in an ac bridge and the distortion of the diaphragm produces an imbalance in the bridge. The pressure difference is determined from the size of the dc voltage which must be applied across the capacitor to counteract the gas pressure. The range of the Consolidated gage is 10^{-3} to 0.5 torr; within this range the pressure can be read to 0.0001 torr. In the Pace system an inductance change is converted to a frequency change in a tuned oscillator. At pressures below about 1 torr the only direct and absolute means of pressure measurement is the McLeod gage (Fig. 6.31e), in which the mass of gas in a known volume is measured by determining the volume to which it is compressed by a known head of mercury. The McLeod gage has the disadvantage of requiring a large amount of expensive and toxic mercury and is not accurate to better than $\pm 10\%$ below 10^{-4} torr. In addition, the vapor pressure of mercury (10^{-3} torr at room temperature) limits the vacuum attainable, unless a cold trap, which may introduce further error, is inserted between the gage and the system whose pressure is being measured. The gage is insensitive to condensable vapors such as water, and pressure readings cannot be taken continuously because of the need to fill the standard volume with gas before each measurement. Nevertheless, the McLeod gage is virtually the only absolute pressure gage available for the region below 0.1 torr and as such is normally used to calibrate the electrical forms of vacuum gage we are to consider shortly. Quite recently another method of calibration, based on the pressure drop produced by gas flow through a standard orifice, has begun to compete with the McLeod gage.

An accurate electrical method of measuring pressures up to at least 25,000 atm is available in the form of a gage made of manganin wire, whose resistance changes by about 0.2% per 1000 atm. It was shown by Bridgman that such a gage is linear up to 13,000 atm and that the deviation from linearity at 25,000 atm is only 2%. A manganin gage can be used for recording pressure continuously; it is relatively cheap and combines good accuracy with rapid response. The change in resistance is conveniently followed with a Wheatstone bridge circuit (cf. Chapter III), of which one of the most useful forms is available commercially as a *strain-gage bridge.* This type of bridge is widely used in conjunction with a flat or spiral coil of strain-sensitive wire to measure linear strains, that is, load-induced linear distortions, of supporting members in buildings and large constructions. The electrical resistance of a thin wire invariably increases when the wire is stretched. Devices similar to strain gages are also used in such instruments as dynamometers and accelerometers. To reduce errors due to resistance changes with temperature in a manganin pressure gage or a strain gage it is helpful to have temperature compensation in the form of an unused "dummy gage" included in an arm of the bridge opposite the test gage and placed as close to it as possible, as in Fig. 6.32.

An electrical resistance change is used as a measure of pressure in two forms of vacuum gage, namely the Pirani gage and the thermistor gage. In these devices the resistance of an electrically heated element, either a thin wire spiral or a small thermistor bead, is a function of its temperature, which in turn is dependent on the pressure of gas that is available to remove heat by conduction. In the thermocouple gage the temperature of a heated wire is measured directly with a thermocouple. Typical forms of the three types of thermal conductivity gage are illustrated in Fig. 6.33. With Pirani

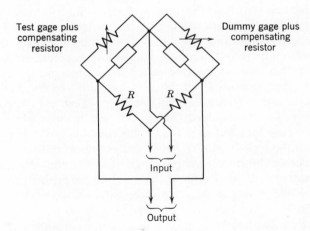

Fig. 6.32 Temperature-compensated bridge for use with a strain gage or manganin wire pressure gage.

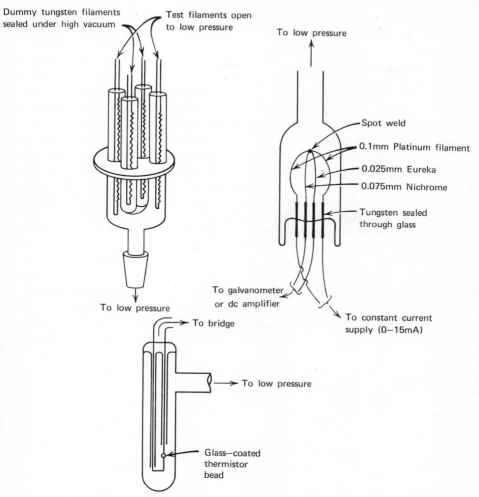

Fig. 6.33   Thermal conductivity pressure transducers: (*a*) Pirani gage; (*b*) thermistor gage; (*c*) thermocouple gage.

and thermistor gages the pressure is read from the deflection of a galvanometer in a temperature-compensated Wheatstone bridge circuit, whereas with a thermocouple gage the output may be read directly with a galvanometer or, if greater robustness is required, a dc amplifier and moving-coil meter. Thermal conductivity gages have the advantages of small volume, continuous reading, and sensitivity to condensable as well as noncondensable vapors (unlike the McLeod gage). They have the disadvantages that the calibration depends on the nature of the gas (the rate of thermal transfer is roughly proportional to the square root of the molecular weight), that the calibration may alter if the gage is contaminated (this effect is most pronounced with Pirani gages and is almost absent with glass-enclosed forms of thermistor gage), and that the lowest pressure that can be measured reliably is about 10^{-3} torr.

For electrical measurements of gas pressure below 10^{-3} torr it is usual to employ an ionization gage, which may have a heated filament to emit thermionic electrons for ionizing the gas, as in the Bayard-Alpert gage, may use a cold-cathode discharge in a magnetic field to ionize the gas, as in the Penning gage, or may even use nuclear radiation from a long-lived isotope to ionize the gas, as in the Alphatron gage. In each instance the pressure measurement involves a measurement of the current of ions produced under fixed discharge conditions. If price is not a major consideration, it is possible to attach the ion source to a small mass spectrometer (generally of the quadrupole type, though magnetic spectrometers have also been used) so that the partial pressures of individual components in the gas may be determined separately. Many "residual gas analyzers" of this type are now available commercially. We here restrict our consideration to the simple forms of ionization gage, of which there are many variants, using the Penning, Bayard-Alpert, and Alphatron gages as illustrative examples.

A common form of Penning gage is illustrated in Fig. 6.34. It consists of a flat metal box, of which the larger pair of walls forms a parallel-plate cathode,

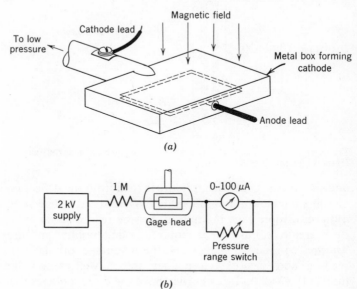

(a)

(b)

Fig. 6.34 Penning vacuum gage: (*a*) Common form of gage head; (*b*) Operating circuit.

and an open metal frame that serves as the anode. A magnetic field of about 400 Oe is maintained between the cathode plates by an external permanent magnet. A sharp metal point may be provided to help the gas break down when the discharge is being started. The voltage between anode and cathode may be as high as 2 kV and the pressure can be measured down to about 10^{-5} torr simply by measuring the total discharge current with a micro-ammeter. The purpose of the magnetic field is to force the electrons in the discharge to travel in a spiral path so that the probability of ionizing gas molecules on their way to the anode is increased. The Penning gage shares with all ionization gages the defect that the ionization current at a given gas pressure is dependent on the nature of the gas via the cross section for ioniza-tion by electron impact. This is not always a disadvantage, since the pressure reading will change when the gas is changed from air to oxygen, helium, or an organic compound, and the gage can be used for leak hunting in conjunction with a probe blowing out oxygen or helium gas or with a wash-bottle spraying a fine stream of alcohol. Several other types of cold-cathode gage have been developed, some of which have an extended low pressure range, but the Penning gage is representative of the class.

The usual form of construction of a Bayard-Alpert ionization gage is shown in Fig. 6.35a and a block diagram of an ionization gage control unit is shown in Fig. 6.35b. This form of gage can be used to measure pressure between 10^{-3} and 10^{-11} torr. The mode of operation is that electrons emitted from the filament are attracted to the grid by a potential difference of about $+150$ V, and on the way they ionize a small proportion of whatever gas is present. The resulting positive ions are gathered by a collector electrode in the form of a thin wire at the center of the open spiral grid, the potential of the collector being typically -30 V with respect to the filament. The pressure is determined by measuring the ion current with an electrometer. The gage head can be baked free of adsorbed gas at the start of pump-down by heating the grid to red heat with a current of about 10 A; subsequently the heat radiated from the filament keeps the walls reasonably well outgassed. For more even heating of the walls the filament may be placed at the center of the glass envelope, with the grid and collector off-center. To be sure of making reasonably reliable pressure measurements in the ultrahigh vacuum region (below 10^{-8} torr) it is necessary to take a number of precautions, and for details the reader should consult the specialized literature in this field (see [8] in the list at the end of this chapter). The original form of ionization gage was just a triode tube, with the plate operated at cathode potential to collect some of the positive ions formed by electrons on their way from the cathode to the positively charged grid. This kind of gage is not capable of indicating pressures below about 10^{-8} torr because electrons striking the grid cause the emission of soft x-rays, which in turn bring about

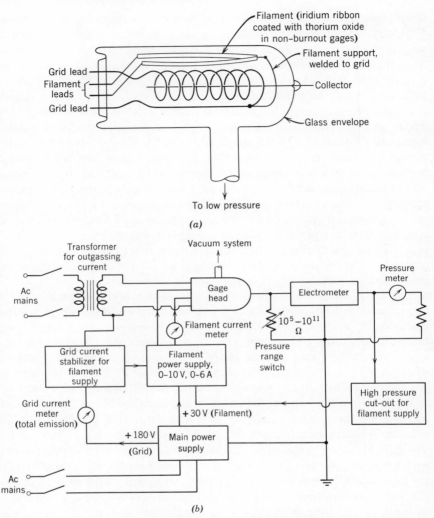

Fig. 6.35 Bayard-Alpert ionization gage: (a) typical construction; (b) block diagram of control circuit.

emission of photoelectrons from the large-area collector. The current of electrons leaving the collector is entirely equivalent from the viewpoint of the external circuit to a current of positive ions arriving. By reducing the collector electrode to the dimensions of a thin wire Bayard and Alpert succeeded in reducing the emission of photoelectrons to an insignificant level.

The Alphatron gage (Fig. 6.36) is essentially an ionization chamber with the electrodes in the form of two open grids, on one of which a radioactive source is mounted. A potential difference of 40 V between the electrodes is sufficient to ensure that the gage is operating in the plateau of the ionization chamber region (Fig. 6.28). The radioactive source normally consists of a radium-gold alloy containing about 0.2 mg of radium in a capsule thin enough to allow α-particles to escape but able to prevent the escape of the radon gas formed when the radium decays. Typically the ionization current at 1 torr is 2×10^{-10} A, and using a common type of electrometer the low-pressure limit for accurate measurements is therefore about 10^{-3} torr, or about 10^{-5} torr with a vibrating-reed electrometer. With a more powerful source of radiation the lower limit has been reduced by two more orders of magnitude. The upper pressure limit may be as high as 1000 torr, and the ionization current is a linear function of the gas pressure from 10^{-3} to at least 100 torr. The disadvantages of this type of gage are its high price and the potential hazard of the radioactive source.

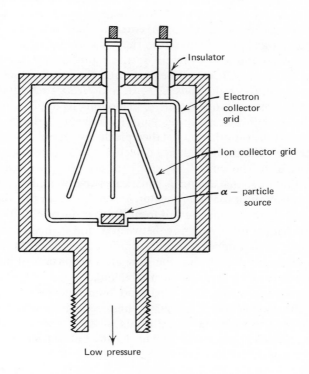

Fig. 6.36 Alphatron gage head.

Before leaving pressure transducers it is necessary to mention that the piezoelectric effect in materials such as quartz or barium titanate, which was discussed in Chapter V in connection with the generation of ultrasonic radiation, can also be used in reverse, as in the crystal microphone, to detect pressure changes associated with sound waves.* Piezoelectric crystals are also used in some forms of accelerometers and strain gages.

Composition Transducers

A better title for this subsection might be "detectors for gas chromatography," since it is in connection with the analysis of mixtures by gas chromatography that transducers sensitive to the composition of a gas mixture have had their most extensive development. It is not intended here, however, to give an exhaustive account of detectors for gas chromatography but rather to discuss the principles of operation of the more important detectors and to point out some similarities to devices that we have already considered.

The *gas density balance* shown in Fig. 6.37 constitutes an ingenious extension of the principle of the Wheatstone bridge. At the left-hand gas inlet pure carrier gas (nitrogen) enters and at the right hand inlet the stream of carrier gas plus sample from the gas chromatograph is introduced. If an organic compound is present in the right-hand stream, the mass balance of the U-tube $ABCD$ will be upset and the gas flow between X and Y will alter. In practice the rods E, F, G, and H are first adjusted to give a zero flow between X and Y (this is analogous to adjusting the four resistance arms of a Wheatstone bridge) and the imbalance due to arrival of the compound at the right-hand inlet then produces a small flow through the detector path XY. The bridge balance detector is an anemometer of the form shown in Fig. 6.38. The wires X–J_1 and Y–J_2 are of copper and the J_1–J_2 wire is of constantan, so that J_1 and J_2 constitute two opposed thermocouple junctions. The position of the small heater K is adjusted in the absence of a gas flow so that there is no net output from the thermocouples; that is, they are at the same temperature. Any flow between X and Y then produces a temperature difference that appears as an output voltage from the thermocouples. The arrangement is such that the flow always consists of pure carrier gas. The sensitivity of this form of detector is similar to that of the thermal conductivity detector to be described next, and both detectors are commonly used in applications in which extremely high sensitivity is not required. They are able to detect organic components in the carrier gas at concentrations of the order of 1 part in 50,000. The density balance has the advantage that the

---

* For an example of piezoelectric pressure measurements see K. W. Ragland and R. E. Cullen, *Rev. Sci. Instr.*, **38**, 740 (1967).

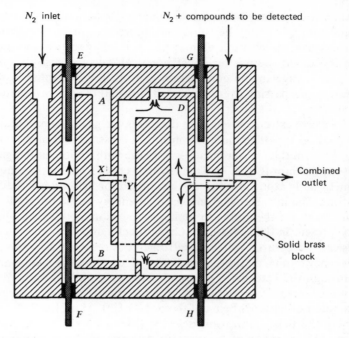

N_2 inlet N_2 + compounds to be detected

Combined
outlet

Solid brass
block

Fig. 6.37   Gas density balance (Martin's density meter).

response is directly related to a simple property, namely vapor density, of
the component being sensed.

We previously noted that a disadvantage of thermal conductivity gages
for measuring gas pressure is that the sensitivity varies with the nature of
the gas in the vacuum system. This property is turned to advantage in the
thermal conductivity cell, or katharometer, for detecting components in
gas chromatography. Many different forms of katharometer are available
commercially or have been built by individual chemists. The body of the

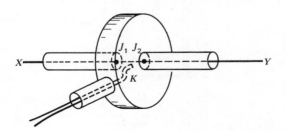

Fig. 6.38   Anemometer balance indicator for Martin gas-density balance.

katharometer may be of glass or metal; a metal body is better for temperature uniformity but may be ruled out if corrosive materials are to be detected. The sensitive element itself may be a wire, as in the Pirani vacuum gage, or a glass-coated thermistor. Most practical detectors use the principle of the dummy gage in the comparison arm of a Wheatstone bridge, with pure carrier gas passing over one heated wire and the gas chromatograph effluent passing over the other.

Several extremely sensitive detectors for gas chromatography have been based on the differences in ionization cross section mentioned as a source of error in the measurement of pressure with an ionization gage. The argon β-ray detector (Fig. 6.39) depends for its operation on the long lifetime of the metastable atoms produced when argon (or helium) is irradiated with electrons. The metastable atoms have an energy of the order of 20 eV, which is sufficient for the atoms to ionize by collision any organic species that may be present in the gas stream. Consequently an additional ion current, which is easily measured with an electrometer or sensitive dc amplifier, is observed whenever one of the components of the mixture being analyzed passes through the detector. The argon detector is able to measure 1 part in 10^9 of an organic compound in the inert gas stream, the minimum detectable amount of material being of the order of 10^{-12} moles.

In the flame ionization detector (Fig. 6.40) the carrier gas is hydrogen, and the operation of the detector depends on the large increase in electron

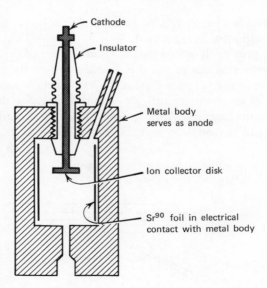

Fig. 6.39   Argon β-ray detector (Lovelock detector).

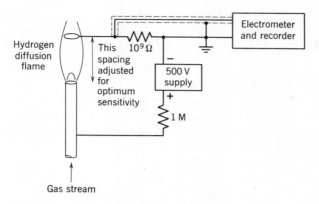

Fig. 6.40 Flame ionization detector.

and positive ion concentration that results when a trace of hydrocarbon is added to a hydrogen-air flame. The dc electrical conductivity of the flame is usually measured directly by measuring the current that flows when a high voltage is applied between the burner tube and a probe inserted in the flame gases. The ion current is small enough to require an electrometer. The most sensitive form of flame ionization detector, which has a performance comparable to that of the argon detector, uses two flames, one burning pure carrier gas and the other the chromatograph effluent. The electrical circuitry is based on a pair of electrometer tubes in the long-tailed pair configuration.

A fairly recent development in the field of detectors for gas chromatography is the use of a rapid-scanning mass spectrometer to monitor continuously the output from the chromatograph column and to provide identification as well as a concentration estimate for each component. As an alternative to continuous monitoring with the mass spectrometer alone, it is possible and often preferable to divide the gas stream into two uneven parts, taking the larger part to a conventional form of detector and scanning the mass spectrometer through the ions produced by electron bombardment of the smaller sample whenever the detector shows that a peak is leaving the column. One difficulty encountered when a mass spectrometer is attached directly to the output of a gas chromatograph is that the pressure of carrier gas in the ion source of the spectrometer can be no larger than about 5×10^{-5} torr, if the instrument is to operate normally. Hence the partial pressure of the component to be identified may be only 10^{-13} torr, which is two or three orders of magnitude below the minimum detection limit of most mass spectrometers. The method of overcoming this problem is to use some sort of fractionation system, such as diffusion through a porous plug, to increase the relative concentration of the heavier organic components relative to the low molecular weight carrier gas. Several commercial manufacturers now produce combinations of gas chromatographs and mass spectrometers with appropriate "interface" units for bridging the concentration gap.

Field Transducers

In Chapter V several devices that can be regarded as examples of field transducers were considered (i.e., devices in which the input signal is in the form of an electric or magnetic field and the output signal is impressed on another form of energy, for example, a light beam). Thus a piezoelectric transducer can be used to transform energy from an oscillating electric field into ultrasonic vibrations, and a Kerr cell or electro-optic light modulator is a transducer that converts an electrical signal into an optical one. There are many direct ways of determining the intensity of electric fields, and electric-field transducers in general are important mainly as devices for changing electrical energy into some other form. With magnetic fields, on the other hand, field transducers based on the Hall effect, magnetoresistance, or nuclear magnetic resonance, are important as devices for obtaining information about the field itself.

A number of effects may occur when a metal or semiconductor through which an electron or phonon current is flowing is placed in a magnetic field. The observed effects are classified as galvanomagnetic when the current is electrical, thermomagnetic when it is thermal, and magnetoacoustic when it is in the form of sound vibrations. With electrical and thermal currents the nature of the effect also depends on whether measurements are made parallel or perpendicular to the direction of the field and whether the field is applied parallel or perpendicular to the direction of the current. There are in fact 12 inter-related effects, and we shall consider just two of them, namely the *Hall effect* and *magnetoresistance*. In Chapter IV the Hall effect was mentioned as a means of determining the sign of the majority carriers in a semiconductor by measuring the sign of the voltage developed across a ribbon of the material in a direction at right angles to both an applied magnetic field and a current from an external source. The *Hall coefficient* R_H of a material is defined by

$$R_H = \frac{E_y}{I_x H_z}, \tag{6.10}$$

where E_y is the observed Hall emf in the y-direction when the current is I_x in the x-direction and the field is H_z in the z-direction. It can be shown by considering the Lorentz force on the charge carriers as they move through the field that

$$R_H = \frac{1}{Nqc}, \tag{6.11}$$

where N is the number of charge carriers per unit volume, q is the charge they carry, and c is the velocity of light. In terms of gaussian units (mechanical quantities in cgs units, electrical quantities in esu, and magnetic fields in gauss or oersted) the quantity R_H is of the order of -10^{-24} for free electrons, the negative sign arising from the sign of the charge q. For carriers in a solid the Hall coefficient usually is about 50% of the value given by (6.11) because of scattering of carriers by the lattice.

When a substance of known Hall coefficient is used, the Hall effect provides a convenient means of measuring an unknown magnetic field. Hall effect probes can be made with extremely small sensitive areas, so that detailed mapping of a magnetic field is possible, and can be operated at low temperatures. Figure 6.41 shows a Hall-effect probe* of vacuum-deposited indium antimonide or indium arsenide, having a sensitive area 25×25 μ and capable of measuring fields between 1 G and 50 kG at temperatures down to 4.2°K and below.

When an electrical conductor is placed in a magnetic field, its resistivity changes by an amount $\Delta\rho$. The ratio $\Delta\rho/\rho$, which is normally positive, is termed the magnetoresistance of the conductor. The *transverse magnetoresistance* is a measure of the change in resistivity at right angles to the applied field, that is, in the same direction as the Hall emf in Fig. 4.12, whereas the *longtitudinal magnetoresistance* is a measure of the change in the same direction as the magnetic field. Magnetoresistance is a second-order effect, arising from the action of the field in forcing individual electrons in the conductor to follow curved paths rather than straight ones, and varies as H^2 in weak fields. To a first order of approximation the effect of the magnetic field on the carriers is canceled by the Hall emf. As pointed out in the reference in the footnote on this page, the Hall effect is fundamentally superior as a means of measuring magnetic fields, but both have been used.

For very precise measurements of magnetic-field intensity it is usual to employ a magnetometer based on nuclear magnetic resonance, of which the commonest is the *proton resonance magnetometer* (Fig. 6.42). The frequency of electromagnetic radiation such that the spacing of the energy levels $m_I = +\frac{1}{2}$ and $m_I = -\frac{1}{2}$ is just equal to $h\nu$ is 4257.8 Hz/G for ^{1}H. For ^{7}Li it is 1654.6 Hz/G. In practice the probe, which contains glycerol or dilute aqueous $MnSO_4$, is placed in the magnetic field and the frequency of the rf signal applied to the probe coil is varied with a tuning capacitor until absorption of rf energy is observed. The resonance frequency is then determined by beating the rf signal with a frequency standard or by converting the sinusoidal signal into a pulse train and using a digital counter. Between 1 and 100 MHz this can be done fairly easily to 1 part in 10^6. Proton resonance

---

* See J. E. Simpkins, *Rev. Sci. Instr.*, **39**, 570 (1968).

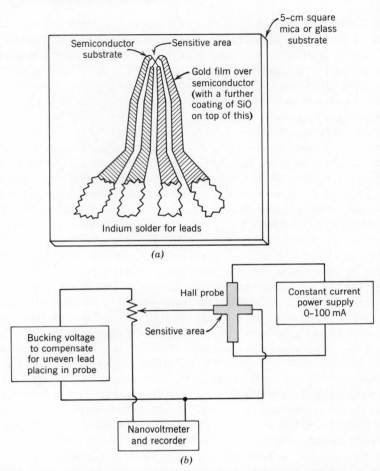

Fig. 6.41 Hall probe for magnetic field measurements: (a) construction of probe; (b) operating circuit. (Adapted from reference in footnote on page 65.)

works well in the range 100 to 20,000 G; an electron-spin resonance probe using DPPH (α,α-diphenyl-β trinitrophenyl-hydrazyl) is to be preferred for the range of 0.5 to 100 G. For very low fields, as in geomagnetic measurements, a fairly large water sample is used as a probe, and the sample is first exposed to a relatively strong field (100 G) to line up the spin axes of the protons in the low-energy state. The strong field is then suddenly removed, and the spinning protons begin to precess around the weak field, thereby inducing a signal in a nearby coil. While the distribution of proton-spin directions is relaxing toward its thermal value, a process that requires 1 or 2 sec for completion, the frequency of precession is measured.

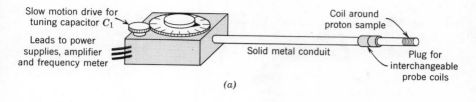

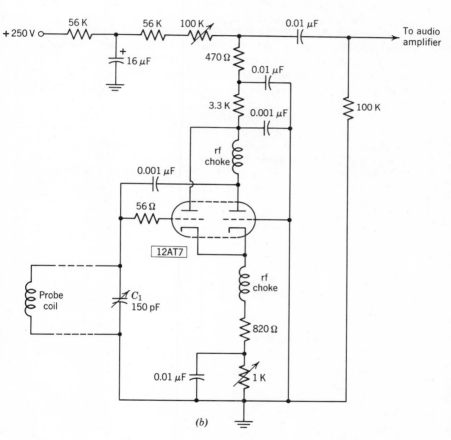

Fig. 6.42 Proton resonance magnetometer: (*a*) typical appearance; (*b*) oscillator drive circuit given by Ingram (see Ref. 1 in the list at the end of this chapter).

References

1. T. M. Sugden and C. N. Kenney, *Microwave Spectroscopy of Gases*, Van Nostrand, London, 1965. See also D. J. E. Ingram, *Spectroscopy at Radio and Microwave Frequencies*, Butterworths, London, 1955, and *Free Radicals*, Butterworths, London, 1958.
2. T. S. Moss, "Modern Infrared Detectors," in *Advances in Spectroscopy*, Volume I, H. W. Thompson, Ed., Interscience, New York, 1959
3. *Applied Optics*, **4**, No. 6 (June 1965). (A major proportion of this issue is devoted to optical detectors, especially solid-state detectors.)
4. *RCA Phototubes and Photocells*, Technical Manual PT-60, Radio Corporation of America, Lancaster, Pennsylvania, 1963. Also similar publications or catalogs from other phototube manufacturers; for example, *EMI Photomultiplier Tubes*, available from the Whittaker Corporation, Gencom Division, Plainview, New York.
5. J. A. R. Samson, *Techniques of Vacuum Ultraviolet Spectroscopy*, Wiley, New York, 1967.
6. W. J. Price, *Nuclear Radiation Detection*. McGraw-Hill, New York, 1958. See also the article on solid-state detectors by G. Dearnaley in *Contemp. Phys.*, **8**, 607 (1967).
7. P. W. Bridgman, *The Physics of High Pressure*, Bell, London, 1949.
8. J. Yarwood, *High Vacuum Technique*, 4th ed., Chapman and Hall, London, 1967.
9. A. I. M. Keulemans, *Gas Chromatography*, 2nd ed., Rheinhold, New York, 1959.
10. A. H. Morrish, *The Physical Principles of Magnetism*. Wiley, New York, 1965.

Chapter **VII**

AUTOMATIC RECORDING

David R. Simonsen

1   INTRODUCTION

The rapid advance in recent years in electronics, particularly solid-state devices, has caused profound changes in methods of taking and recording measurement data. It is now possible to record automatically nearly any event that can be measured, whether it occurs in a fraction of a second or over a period of many days. So the question in essentially all recording applications is not whether the recording can be done but what method is most efficient.

A trend in physical science laboratories has been to incorporate automatic recordings in computer systems. The cost of such systems has been steadily decreasing, whereas their capabilities have been increasing; hence it has become practical to use computers with analytical instruments like gas chromatographs, electromechanical instruments, mass spectrometers, absorptive spectrometers, and nuclear magnetic resonance spectrometers. The type of recording selected will depend on whether a computer is involved and also whether the operation is routine or requires many changes during processing.

Generally, the results from a computer system are printed out in digital fashion. Even in an automated computer system, however, it is desirable to use trend recorders in setting up and trouble shooting the computer. Also, there are enough other uses for graphic recorders that a description of their important characteristics will be helpful in selecting a recorder for a given application.

2   GENERAL METHODS OF RECORDING

In recording the signal from a transducer or sensing element can be displayed directly in analog or digital form or it can be stored in a memory device and displayed later, either with or without computation. The analog or digital display can be produced by many kinds of writing technique. The use of memory devices permits taking data at high speed and processing them later at a much lower speed. The various types of memory device, including magnetic cores, drums, disks, and tapes, are described in the Chapter IX.

Graphic or analog recording is emphasized in this chapter. Digital recording, which is closely allied to computers, is also described in Chapter IX. For graphic recording a trace is produced on paper or film by ink, heated stylus, electric writing, scratching, optical beam, electrostatics, or electron beam. These types of recording are described in more detail in subsequent sections of this chapter.

The choice of a recorder for a given application will depend on its frequency response, input impedance, sensitivity, accuracy, the form of record desired, and cost. A number of journals in the field of instrumentation present tables periodically which summarize the characteristics of current commercial recorders.*

3   GENERAL CHARACTERISTICS OF RECORDERS

Frequency Response

Frequency response is a measure of the speed with which the recorder can respond to a changing signal. It is expressed in Hertz and usually indicates the maximum frequency at which the recorder can faithfully reproduce a full-scale sinusoidal signal. The speed with which a recorder can follow a signal is often expressed in terms of the time the recorder takes to give essentially 100% response to a full-scale signal. This is sometimes called "span-step response."

In every application there is an upper limit to the frequency response that is desired or is practical. For changes that occur at speeds above this limiting frequency it is advantageous that the recorder give an average value. Often a recorder is deliberately damped in response, and thus its high-frequency response is lowered. Some applications in which a high-frequency response might be used do not justify the cost in instrumentation, including the recording medium and the time needed to analyze the record. The frequency response of a given recorder is determined by its writing speed and damping characteristics. Damping not only controls the upper limit of the frequency response but is also necessary in many recorders to prevent "overshooting," a condition in which the recorder goes too far during a rapid measurement change.

Recorders fall into two general classes according to their frequency response: those whose frequency response is slower than approximately 4 Hz and those whose frequency response is faster than 4 Hz—up to several megaHertz. The former includes mechanical and electrical recorders, which record slowly changing processes such as temperature, pressure, and flow. The electric recorders in this class respond either to fluctuations in a dc signal or the rms value of an ac signal. Examples are the standard potentiometer and bridge balance recorders.

In the second class are recorders that have a higher frequency response; these are called "oscillographs." Three classes of oscillograph are direct-writing oscillographs, with frequency response to a few hundred Hertz, the photographic galvanometer type, with frequency response to 20 kHz, and the cathode-ray oscillographs, with frequency response to several

* For example, see *Ind. Res.*, 76–81 (November 1968); *Instr. Control Systems*, **37**, No. 7, 91 (1964).

megaHertz. All these classes of oscillograph, as well as some special types, are described in greater detail in Section 4.

Input Impedance

The input impedance of a recorder is the total amount of resistance (resistive, capacitive, or inductive) the recorder offers to an input signal; it determines the amount of power supplied to the recorder from a given signal. If the impedance of the recorder is higher or lower than that of the transducer producing the signal, the maximum transfer of power, or sensitivity, will not be obtained. In deflection instruments the impedance should usually be such that the recorder will receive maximum power without distorting the signal. A low-input impedance recorder will distort the signal, therefore it is generally advisable to have the input impedance as high as possible and still obtain sufficient sensitivity and speed of response. There are instances, however, in which it is advisable to keep the input impedance of the recorder relatively low; for example, when spurious signals are picked up in the leads running from the transducer or sensing element to the recorder. By keeping the input impedance relatively low the effect of the spurious signals is reduced to a minimum. In direct-reading instruments the input impedance should be at least 10 times the output impedance of the transducer. In null instruments the input impedance at unbalance should be of the same order of magnitude as, or higher than, the output impedance of the transducer; and the input impedance of the null instrument approaches infinity at balance.

The sensing elements or transducers that convert the measurements to signals to which recorders can respond have impedances that vary from a few ohms to a few thousand megohms. The sensing elements may be classified according to the type of electrical signal they produce. These types are potential, resistive, capacitive, and inductive.

Some examples of the potential type of sensing element are thermocouples, photovoltaic cells, pH electrodes, photoemissive tubes, and piezoelectric crystals. Thermocouples and photovoltaic cells have low impedance (below 3000 Ω) and the others have high impedances (above 3000 Ω). The resistive type of sensing element usually has low impedance. Examples are resistance thermometers, strain gages, photoconductive cells, and conductivity cells. Capacitive-type sensing elements have high impedance. These pickups are frequently used for determining liquid level and measuring sound or vibration levels and act as receivers in some nondispersive infrared analyzers. Inductive-type sensing elements usually have low impedance and are used in rotameters and other devices for measuring displacement, velocity, or acceleration. The impedance of the various devices is a function of the physical size of the devices. In order for capacitive-type elements to be of practical size they must have high impedance; resistive and inductive elements have low impedance.

Sensitivity, Span, and Accuracy

The sensitivity of a recorder is usually expressed in terms of the magnitude of the minimum signal required to produce a deflection in the recorder. More precisely, the sensitivity is equal to one-half the deadband when the deadband is the amount the signal can be varied without initiating recorder response. Span, as related to recorder sensitivity, is the magnitude of the signal (algebraic difference between end-of-scale values) which produces a full-scale deflection of the recorder. The sensitivity and span of a recorder are affected by such characteristics as input impedance, amplifier gain, and type of measuring circuit.

The accuracy of the recorder is given in terms of the uncertainty of the recorded value. It includes all possible errors* within the recorder but not of the sensing element and is often expressed in percentage of the full-scale response. The limitation in accuracy of graphic recorders is usually in the recording medium—paper, tape, or film—and this limiting accuracy is usually in the order of a few tenths of 1 %. Greater accuracy can be attained by using a recorder with an expanded scale or span together with zero suppression or by using digital recorders.

Cost

Not only the initial cost of the basic recorder must be considered but also the cost of the recording medium and the availability of added features. Recording paper for ink is less expensive than specially coated papers, such as temperature-, pressure-, or electric-sensitive papers or optically sensitive papers. Also, many possible extra features or options must be studied carefully in assessing the cost of a recorder, including multiple pens or channels, multiple chart speeds, adjustable range, adjustable zero, event markers, integrating devices, etc.

Deflection-Type Versus Null-Type Recorders

All analog graphic recorders can be classified as deflection- or null-type instruments. In the deflection-type recorders the indicator or recording pen is moved either directly by the input signal or, when the input signal is weak, after amplification. In the null-type instruments the input signal is compared to a reference signal. The difference between the two, the "error signal," is usually amplified. The amplified error signal is used to adjust the reference signal through a servosystem until the reference signal equals the

---

* A. Michael Honer, *Electronic Products*, 44 (October 1968).

input signal. The adjusted reference signal, then, is a measure of the input signal and consequently reflects the property or quantity being measured.

An example of a deflection-type instrument is a voltmeter, and the corresponding null instrument is a potentiometer. All the self-balancing null-type instruments and recorders require an auxiliary source of power in addition to the reference signal. The auxiliary power source is needed to drive the servomechanism which balances the recorder. The deflection-type recorder needs auxiliary power in the measuring circuit only if the signal requires amplification. All recorders with chart drives require power.

Deflection-type instruments have the advantage of greater simplicity, faster response, and, in general, lower cost. Oscillographs are deflection-type because they require high speed in response.

Null-type recorders usually are capable of higher accuracy, are more linear in response, have greater flexibility in zero adjustment, and are more adaptable for control purposes. The null-type instrument is usually more accurate because the error involved in comparing two quantities is smaller than that involved in measuring one quantity directly. The response of the null recorder is usually more linear because it is easier to control the linearity of a slide wire or variable capacitor than it is to control the movement of the deflection-measuring element. The zero reading of the null instrument usually can be changed readily by changing the reference point. This makes possible zero suppression with its advantage of reducing the span and thus obtaining greater accuracy. Amplified error signals in null instruments can be used to drive a valve or some other mechanism for controlling the process in which the measurement is made. Another advantage of the null-type instrument is that the amplifier used to amplify the error signal need be neither linear in response nor stable, since the balance point is determined by the reference signal. In fact, in some applications, particularly in those involving process control, a nonlinear response of the amplifier may be desirable.

4   TYPES OF RECORDER

Deflection-Type Recorders

Mechanical

Most mechanical and many galvanometer-type recorders belong to the class of deflection recorders that have no amplifier. Direct-reading, deflection-type mechanical recorders are probably the simplest and oldest type of automatic recording device. A recording thermometer* of this type is attributed to Renes in about the year 1663. In that instrument the expansion

---

* M. F. Behar, in *The Handbook of Measurement and Control Instruments*, Pittsburgh, 1951, p. 83.

of a liquid or gas was used to position a tablet along the temperature axis of the record and a clockwork mechanism drove the pencil along the time axis.

The deflection-type mechanical recorders in common use today may be classified according to the element used to drive the pen. These drive mechanisms can be a Bourdon tube, spiral, bellows, or diaphragm, each of which may receive the signal to be recorded from liquid-, vapor-, or gas-filled systems. The signals may denote temperature, pressure, or flow. The pen may also be driven by a bimetallic element for measurement of temperature, a membrane or fiber for measurement of humidity, or a float for measurement of liquid level, flow, or pressure.

The measuring element in the mechanical recorders usually produces a signal with sufficient power to drive the recording mechanism without amplification. Because of the inertia associated with the recording elements, however, the recording speed and frequency response are limited. The maximum speed of response of the mechanical recorders is of the order of full-scale deflection in 1 sec.

In pneumatic recorders power amplification of 300 can be obtained by a pneumatic servosystem in which the power is furnished by a compressed-air supply at 15 psi. The power amplification is useful for operation of all types of control devices like switches, valves, and relays. The Taylor Transcope, manufactured by the Taylor Instrument Company, Rochester, New York, is an example.

In the measurement of small displacements an optical lever can produce amplification. The recording may be photographic or the measurement may be converted to an electrical signal by means of a photocell pickup.

The over-all accuracy of mechanical recorders, as of deflection-type recorders in general, is seldom better than 1 %. The advantages of mechanical recorders are simplicity, lower cost, and greater safety in explosive atmospheres because they do not provide a source of ignition.

In addition to the limitations of recording speed and frequency response, mechanical recorders have a definite limitation in the distance that the mechanical signal can be transmitted. The signal, which is transmitted pneumatically, hydraulically, or by a mechanical linkage, has a substantial inertia and can be affected considerably by temperature. Temperature changes can cause nonlinear response and can also cause the system to freeze up. Furthermore, tubing or pipe lines between the sensing element and the recorder are not so adjustable as electrical lines.

Electrical Recorders

The measuring element in most deflection-type electrical recorders is a galvanometer. In simple direct-reading recorders a pen is attached to the

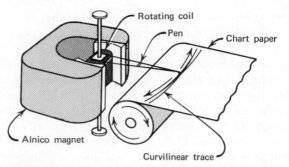

Fig. 7.1   Basic diagram of galvanometer recorder.

galvanometer coil suspension. As the signal through the coil changes, the suspension turns and causes the pen to move across the chart. A diagram of the principle of galvanometer recording is shown in Fig. 7.1.

Recorders without an amplifier have a relatively low input impedance that ranges from one to a few thousand ohms; their recording speed ranges from 0.1 to several seconds for full-scale deflection. Charts 50 to 120 mm wide are generally used. A 120-mm width is about the maximum chart size for a direct-reading deflection-type recorder. This is because the amount of force available at the pen of the moving coil is limited by the magnetic field and the power that the coil can dissipate. A sensitivity as great as 1 ma full scale is attainable with this type of recorder without an amplifier.

Most commercial recorders are provided with amplifiers which make possible higher input impedance, greater sensitivity, and greater writing speed. The advent of solid-state electronics has provided low-cost, high-gain amplifiers with relatively low power consumption. Because most amplifiers provide sufficient input impedance and sensitivity, the choice of a recorder is determined primarily by frequency response, resolution, number of channels, and form of record desired.

INK-PEN TYPE

The many kinds of deflection-type electrical recorder differ primarily in the way the record is produced. Those with a frequency response of about 100 Hz or higher belong to the general class of oscillographs. Recorders that use motors to drive inking pens or styli are limited in frequency response because of the mechanics of their respective pens or styli, which must be as long and as light as possible and yet be rigid and able to withstand large accelerating forces at high writing speeds. The tip of a 3-in. pen, with a signal of 0.5-in. amplitude, has an acceleration of approximately 510 G when writing at 100 cps. This demonstrates why there is a limit to the speed of the pen : light weight and sturdiness are opposing characteristics.

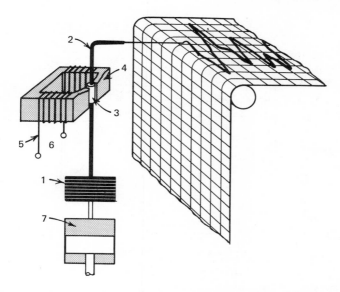

Fig. 7.2 Basic diagram of Siemens jet writing oscillograph taken from bulletin Ms7E entitled Siemens Oscillographs and Oscilloscopes. (Siemens America Inc. August 1967.)

The ink recorders continue to be popular because ink chart paper is the least expensive. Esterline Angus recorders pump the ink so that the pressure of the ink is a function of writing speed. This allows fast writing speeds without bleeding at slow writing speeds. The Siemens Oscillomink Oscillograph uses the liquid-jet direct-writing method shown diagrammatically in Fig. 7.2. Ink at relatively high pressure, 200 to 600 psi, is directed from a glass capillary jet with an opening of 0.0004 in. onto a recording paper. The direction of the jet is controlled by a galvanometer. This recorder has a maximum writing speed of 60 m/sec, which will produce an amplitude of ± 12.5 mm at 800 Hz.

INK JET

Another type of ink-jet recorder has been designed but is not too widely used commercially. It has an electrostatically charged jet or vapor that impinges on a recording material. The signal is applied to two plates (similar in principle to a cathode-ray oscilloscope) which direct the jet according to the value of the signal. A diagram of this recorder is shown in Fig. 7.3. Since the mass in the jet is small, the speed of response can be made very high—of the order of 1000 Hz. It is difficult, however, to maintain the extremely small jet nozzle and keep the deflection plates clear of fluid.

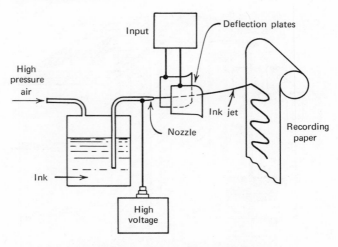

Fig. 7.3   Recorder using an electrically deflected ink jet.

FIXED-STYLUS RECORDER

One method of achieving relatively high writing speeds is to use a number of fixed styli located in a row across the width of the recording chart. In one recorder of this type the recording is accomplished by passing an electric current from the styli through current-sensitive paper to the roll supporting the chart paper. The recorder is therefore not limited by the inertia of a moving pen. The styli may be operated on an on-off basis if the information to the recorder is digitized or if the recorder has a means of converting an analog signal to digital form. This type of recorder is particularly suited to timing operations.

One particularly successful fixed stylus recorder is the Varian Statos* series of recorders in which electrostatic printing produces the record. A block diagram of these recorders is shown in Fig. 7.4. An electrostatic charge from a 600-V power supply is placed on the specially coated chart by means of 100 fixed styli on a bar in contact with the paper across its width. The charged paper then comes in contact with a liquid-dispersed toner that adheres to the charged portions of the chart. Grid and timing lines are printed on the chart paper at the same time as the recorded signals so that no loss in accuracy occurs because of errors in chart transport. The switching time of the digital signal in the recording process of the Statos recorder is 2 μsec. The time required for a full-scale deflection with 100 styli is 200 μsec, which represents the maximum rise time for a full-scale signal. The available chart

---

* Reginald T. Lamb, "Using Recorder Versatility for Better Information from Data," *Electronic Instrument Digest*, **4,** No. 12, 109 (1968).

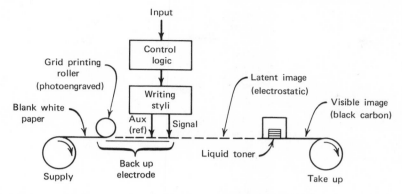

Fig. 7.4 Simplified block diagram of the Varian Statos Recorder.

speeds allow a maximum frequency response of approximately 1500 Hz. In addition to its high frequency response, the Statos recorder is especially suited for computer applications because it has a digital output available for each of its recorded signals.

MOVING STYLUS SWEEP-BALANCE RECORDER

A second type of direct-writing recorder capable of high response speeds is the moving-stylus, sweep-balance recorder. Keinath* designed a recorder in which the sliding contact is rapidly driven back and forth on the slide wire of a bridge circuit. As the sliding contact reaches the balance point, a relay is de-energized; the pen then receives an impulse from a charged condenser and produces a record on current-sensitive chart paper. When the contact on the slide wire moves past the balance point, the relay is again energized, which causes the pen circuit to open. Sweep rates of about 10/sec are available with this recorder.

HELIX RECORDER

The Helix type of recorder, for example, that made by the Alden Products Company, 117 North Main Street, Brockton, Massachusetts, also uses current-sensitive paper and is capable of high writing speeds. This recorder is shown diagrammatically in Fig. 7.5. The helix recorder has two electrodes, one on either side of the recording paper. A cylindrical drum with a single spiral of metal around its curved surface forms one electrode, which is the helix. The other electrode is a narrow-edged strip of metal located above the current-sensitive paper directly in line with the axis of the cylinder. As the drum is rotated, the point of intersection between the helix and the fixed

* G. Keinath, *Instruments*, **19**, 200 (1946).

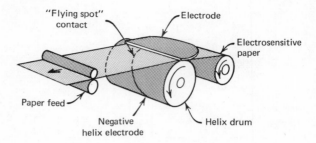

Fig. 7.5 Alden Helix Recorder.

metal strip moves across the chart paper. If a continuous dc signal is applied to the recorder and the helix is driven at a constant speed, a series of straight lines is produced on the chart. If, however, the signal consists of a series of pulses at the same frequency as the rotation of the helix, a straight longitudinal line is produced on the chart. Any deviation in the line is a measure of the difference in frequency of the signal and the rotation of the helix. The helix recorder is especially suited to recording information that can be converted to electrical signals with a definite repetition rate or sweep frequency. The Alfax Paper and Engineering Company claim writing speeds of 18,000 ipm. are possible with this method.

MICROFILM "SCRATCH" RECORDER

In the microfilm "scratch" recorder a diamond stylus etches lines 10 μ wide on a special 35 mm-wide, carbon-coated film. The data are enlarged and/or copied by standard microfilm reader-printers. The microfilm recorder is especially suited to relatively long continuous recording of measurements that require a frequency response of 30 to 90 Hz. The high density provides low cost, in addition to the long continuous recording. The YEW* "scratch" recorder has a feature that makes scratch recording more practical: the pen motor drive has a high-frequency bias—15,000 Hz—far higher than its natural frequency. This ac bias overcomes the friction of the pen and makes its movement much more stable.

OPTICAL OSCILLOGRAPH

For recording in the 200- to 20,000-Hz frequency range the optical oscillograph is most commonly used. It is shown diagrammatically in Fig. 7.6. A low-mass mirror galvanometer reflects the light from a fixed source onto a strip of light-sensitive film or paper. The sensitivity of the galvanometer varies considerably with its natural frequency. A typical high-frequency

---

* Yokogawa Electric Works, Inc., Larchmont, N.Y.

galvanometer with an undamped natural frequency of 8000 Hz has a sensitivity of 46 ma/in. with a resistance of 57 Ω, whereas a low-frequency galvanometer with an undamped natural frequency of 225 cps has a sensitivity of 10 μA/in. with a resistance of 86 Ω. These sensitivities are expressed in terms of an 11.5-in. optical arm. A galvanometer must be damped to prevent overshooting; 64% of critical damping is usually considered the optimum for rapid response with minimum overshooting. The optical oscillograph can record many channels simultaneously, superimposed on a single chart; for example, Model 5-133 of the Consolidated Electrodynamics Corp. can record as many as 52 channels on print-out paper 12 in. wide, with paper transport speeds of 0.1 to 160 ips.

Direct-writing oscillographs may use a variety of light sources such as high-pressure mercury or high-intensity tungsten lamps. Mercury lamps have the advantage of providing the high light output needed for extremely high writing-speed applications—writing speeds of more than 50,000 ips. Tungsten lamps, on the other hand, are used in recorders capable of recording up to 20,000 ips. These lamps require no special starting circuits and are simpler to replace when burned out, with a minimum of down time. A variety of photorecording papers is suited to each of these types of oscillograph (e.g., the Kodak Linagraph Direct Print Papers).

CATHODE-RAY-TUBE OSCILLOGRAPHY

The highest possible speed of response is given by the cathode-ray-tube oscillograph. This type of oscillograph consists of a cathode-ray tube and

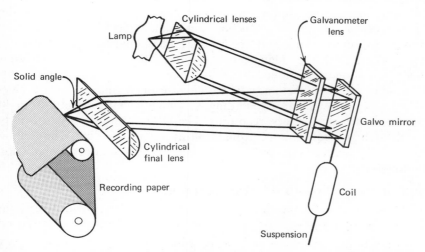

Fig. 7.6 Optical arrangement of a typical galvanometer light-beam oscillograph. Size of galvanometer lens, mirror, and coil has been exaggerated.

some kind of camera or other means of recording the traces on the screen of the CRT. Sensitive films like Kodak 2485 High Speed Recording Film and Polaroid Land Type 47 are used to obtain high writing speeds. The Kodak film is designed for CRT photography and has a relative CRT speed of 10,000 with recommended processing. The relative CRT speed is defined as the reciprocal of the tungsten exposure in meter-candle-seconds required to produce a density of 1.0 above gross fog when the exposure is 0.1 msec. The Polaroid Land Type 47 is rated at an ASA daylight exposure index of 3000 and can record with recommended processing at writing rates higher than 3250 cm/μsec on P.11 phosphor-coated tubes. The use of prefogged film, it is reported,* can increase the writing rate to 9000 cm/μsec.

The recently developed use of fiber optics in the face of the cathode-ray tube has increased the efficiency of recording the light from the screen phosphor, thereby giving improved resolution and writing speed. This feature is incorporated in the Honeywell Model 1806 CRT Visicorder. The Model 1806 Visicorder has other noteworthy features, including $XYY'Z$ axes recording and ability to record X-axis input versus time either longitudinally or transversely. The $XYY'Z$ feature is described in the section on X-Y recorders. In the transverse mode high-frequency data can be recorded without high paper speeds. The recorder automatically corrects for skew in the transverse mode, thus making it easier to interpret the record.

DIRECT ELECTRON RECORDING

Direct electron recording† is a special form of cathode-ray-tube oscillography in which the recording film is placed inside the evacuated cathode-ray tube and the electron beam exposes the film directly instead of by the fluorescence of a phosphor screen. Several Kodak Direct Electron Recording films have recently been introduced for this revolutionary method of photography. These DER-type films feature extremely fine grain emulsions on a conducting support developed expressly for electron recording applications. These films are available in negative or direct-positive image type. The chief advantage of direct electron recording is its high packing density, 10 to 30 times that of magnetic tape recording. The DER recording is particularly useful for high-frequency recording such as video recording. The writing speed of direct electron recording is equal to the fastest conventional CRT photography.

Null or Servo Potentiometer Recorder

The servo or self-balancing potentiometer recorder is widely used in chemical laboratories because almost every measurement can be converted

---

* William G. Hyzer, *Engineering and Scientific High-Speed Photography*, Macmillan, New York, 1962, p. 392.

† A. A. Tarnowski and C. H. Evans, *J. SMPTE*, **71**, 765 (1962).

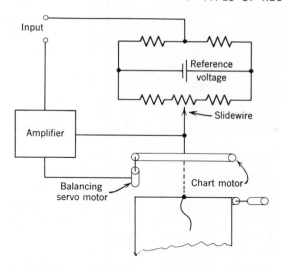

Fig. 7.7 Basic diagram of a potentiometer recorder.

to an electrical signal which this instrument can record. Furthermore, its output power is sufficient to produce the record in almost any form desired. The only serious limitation is the speed of response. The fastest full-scale response now available is approximately 0.2 sec.

All potentiometer recorders consist of a measuring circuit, differential signal amplifier, servo power amplifier, and servometer. These components are shown schematically in Fig. 7.7. The input signal is compared with a reference signal. The differential or error signal is amplified by the servo-amplifier whose output drives a servomotor, usually a two-phase induction motor that drives the sliding contact of the potentiometer bridge circuit until a balance is reached. The movement of the sliding contact is linked with the pen of the recorder to produce a record which is a measurement of the input signal.

Galvanometer-Type Potentiometer Recorder

The earliest self-balancing recording potentiometers used a galvanometer as the unbalance detector. The Leeds and Northrup Micromax is an example of this type; it was quite valuable even though it was limited in speed of response and input impedance. The Micromax recorder required about 30 sec to reach a balance.

The advent of electronic amplifiers made possible the electronic potentiometer and eliminated the galvanometer. Leeds and Northrup introduced the first instrument, the Speedomax A Recorder, in 1932. In this recorder the dc error signal from the measuring circuit was chopped or modulated by a carbon microphone in which the resistance was continually varied by the mechanical compression and relaxation of the carbon granules by the armature of an ac source. This modulated signal was amplified by an input transformer and an electron-tube amplifier. A split-phase dc servomotor was damped by a small tachometer generator attached to the motor shaft whose output was fed back into the measuring circuit. Its chief limitations were its relatively low input impedance and noisiness of the carbon microphone chopper.

The Brown ElectroniK potentiometer recorder, which appeared in 1942, was the first really successful and widely used electronic potentiometer recorder. A mechanical chopper, vibrating reed tape, converted a dc signal to ac. The resulting ac signal was amplified by an input transformer and electronic amplifier; the servomotor was a two-phase induction motor. Other makes of electronic potentiometer recorders became commercially available in the 1940's. They were similar to the Brown recorder and performed very well; many of them are still in use. Compared with present day recorders, they are limited in speed of response, input impedance, and versatility.

Nearly all of the potentiometer recorders currently available commercially use solid-state electronics. The advantages are compactness, lower consumption of power, and greater reliability. The new recorders also have many features, such as varying chart speeds, multichannels, event markers, and adjustable range, which formerly characterized direct-writing oscillographs. These features, many optional, are discussed in the following sections.

Measuring Circuits

The standard potentiometer recorder is usually set up to measure potential, and spans are available without preamplifier down to $100\ \mu V$. Input impedance at unbalance can be obtained from 10^4 to $10^9\ \Omega$.

Since the potentiometer recorder is a self-balancing servorecorder, it can be set up to measure resistance, capacitance, or inductance by the use of the proper input, measuring circuit, or bridge.

In resistance measurements the measuring circuit operates on the principle of the Wheatstone bridge. The measurement of the unknown resistance is independent of the voltage across the bridge, and no standardized voltage is required. Because the magnitude of the voltage determines the sensitivity of the bridge, a voltage, either ac or dc, is supplied to provide sufficient sensitivity. Since the amplifiers in the potentiometer recorder are ac amplifiers, the ac bridge circuit has the advantage of not requiring a chopper or inverter.

The bridge-balance recorder may be used for measuring capacitance or inductance by means of an impedance bridge similar to the bridge circuit used for measuring resistance. The impedance bridge has capacitors or inductors, instead of resistors, in at least two arms of the bridge and it must have a suitable ac supply. The Foxboro Dynalog Recorder is especially suited to the measurement of capacitance, since it uses a variable capacitor for rebalancing the bridge.

Capacitance can also be measured by incorporating the capacitor in a frequency-determining resonant tank circuit. The frequency is a function of capacitance and can be measured directly or by the heterodyne principle, which is used in the Foxboro recorder when high sensitivity or long transmission lines are required.

Many of the inductive pickups or transducers are of the linear-variable differential type. When they are used with a standard potentiometer recorder, the recorder is often equipped with a follower inductor that serves as the balancing unit. A diagram of the balancing circuit is shown in Fig. 7.8. In this recorder the follower inductor replaces the slide wire of the standard recorder. The slide wire can also be used for balancing the output of the differential inductor. Then the ratio of the reactances of the two windings of the inductor is balanced by the resistances in the other two arms of the bridge.

The Wien bridge can be used in a potentiometer recorder for measuring frequency. In the Wien bridge, shown in Fig. 7.9, one arm has a resistor and a capacitor in series and the adjacent arm has a resistor and a capacitor in parallel. With fixed resistors and capacitors the bridge is balanced at only one frequency. By placing the slide wire of the recorder in series with one arm of the bridge, the bridge can be balanced at different frequencies.

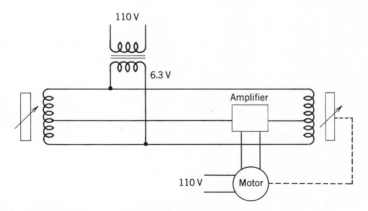

Fig. 7.8 Balancing circuit for inductance pickup.

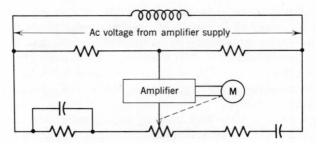

Fig. 7.9 Wien bridge for measuring frequency.

Converter

Most of the equipment used in potentiometer recorders to convert dc signal inputs to ac for amplification are the vibrating-reed type. The reed is usually driven by 60 Hz ac power, but some recorders use a different chopping frequency; for example, the Honeywell ElectroniK 194 uses a mechanical chopper which is driven at 400 Hz. The higher frequency makes possible higher response speeds. The contacts of the mechanical chopper are designed to give low thermal emf and minimum noise. Although the vibrating reed choppers usually have a satisfactorily long life (up to several years of continuous service), they eventually fail because the reed or the contacts wear out.

Converters with no moving parts are replacing the vibrating type. The Foxboro ERB Series Recorder uses a photoelectric converter in which an ac-driven neon bulb causes a modulation in the error signal circuit by shining on photoconductors.

Standardization

In the older potentiometer recorders a dry cell supplied the potentiometer or bridge current. Since this current was affected by temperature changes or aging of the dry cell, the current had to be standardized periodically by comparing the voltage drop across a resistor in the bridge circuit with the voltage of a standard cell. In most of the present recorders a temperature-compensated Zener diode-controlled power supply is used for the bridge circuit. These power supplies control the voltage within $\pm 0.2\%$ and provide a reliable, continuous supply.

Special Types

X-Y Recorders

The X-Y type of recorder has become available in many different makes and models and is useful for getting a direct plot of one variable as a function of another. The X-Y recorder has two complete and separate input and balancing systems and can usually be set up so that either the X or Y function can be a function of time, thus becoming an X-T or Y-T recorder. Most X-Y recorders operate with stationary chart paper and a mechanism for moving the pen in both the X- and Y-directions. The pen moves up and down along the Y-axis on an arm, which in turn moves along the X-axis in two tracks on the top and bottom of the chart. Some X-Y recorders, for example, the Houston Omnigraphic Model 6420, move the pen along the Y-axis in a manner similar to the pen movement of a standard potentiometer recorder and move the chart along the X-axis. With the latter design it is feasible to add a second pen for a second Y variable to produce a XYY' recorder. Also, a continuous chart can be used if desired.

The specifications of the X-Y recorders, in terms of speed of response, input impedance, span sensitivity, and accuracy, are similar to those of the standard potentiometer recorder.

A cathode-ray-tube oscillograph can serve as an X-Y recorder. The Honeywell Visicorder Model 1806, described in Section 4, is an example of an $XYY'Z$ recorder. The Z-axis is obtained by modulating the intensity of the cathode-ray beam.

Digital Plotting Recorders

Digital plotting recorders are direct ink-writing recorders. They accept and plot digital data directly by using bidirectional stepping motors to drive the pens; thus they can plot digital data without conversion to an analog signal. Some digital plotters can record both digital and analog signals (e.g., the Houston Omnigraphic Model 6710 Plotting System).

5 FORMS OF RECORDS

Charts

The two general forms of graphic records are round and the strip charts. In the first rotation provides one coordinate, usually the time scale; the distance from the center provides the other coordinate. Round chart recorders are generally used for monitoring processes, particularly on a day-by-day basis, in which the changes are slight or infrequent or in which high resolution of the record and calculations from it are not required.

Strip charts are preferred when high-speed recording, rectilinear co-ordinate, or high resolution is desired. Charts are available in a variety of widths up to 12 in. and continuous charts are supplied in roll or folded form. The roll format has been the standard strip format but it is being replaced by the folded chart because of a number of advantages of the folded format. The folded format has the advantage of continuous recording between supplies of chart paper by splicing a new supply onto the paper in the recorder without stopping the recorder. Also, any part of the record can be viewed by unfolding the paper without disturbing the rest of the chart paper. The folded format has been adopted particularly for the flat-bed writing method.

Writing Method*

Ink continues to be the commonest medium of writing because it is the least expensive and is capable of writing in a variety of colors at high contrast. A number of developments have improved the ink recorders, such as pressurized ink systems† to increase the speed of writing and remote ink supplies for increasing the recording time before refilling.

The heated stylus method of writing has the advantage over the ink method of never requiring refilling or pen maintenance. The heated stylus, however, has lower frequency response than the ink pen, all other things being equal, and presents a fire hazard. Under some conditions of chart stoppage the chart can ignite if the stylus is heated for high-speed writing.

The scratch or pressure type of stylus overcomes some of the objections of both the ink and heated stylus but the recording paper is more vulnerable to physical damage than the others. The relatively high mechanical power required on the stylus limits this type of writing to lower speed recording.

Electrostatic recording is being used in some special recorders like the Varian Statos series. It has the advantage of high speed and permanence but the entire system is expensive compared with the others.

Electric recording offers high reliability, permanent records, and a wide range of writing speeds from $\frac{1}{2}$ iph to more than 1000 ips. The recording is produced by passing an electric current through a special electrosensitive chart paper. The recorders are easily started up after long standby and the system can tolerate severe environmental conditions that involve temperature, altitude, and vibration. Its only important disadvantage is cost. Among the various electric writing systems that in which zinc oxide is reduced to zinc offers the advantages of wide range of writing speed, relatively low voltage, and excellent stability of recording paper.

Photographic recording offers the highest recording speeds and considerable flexibility in the superposition of multiple traces. It has the disadvantages of relatively high cost and lack of permanence unless the film or paper is processed.

* F. Clark Carnes, *ISA J.*, **13**, 55 (1966); D. R. Davis and C. K. Michener, *Hewlett-Packard J.*, 2 (October 1968).

† M. L. Felton, *Instr. Control Systems*, **39**, 83 (July 1966).

6   SPECIAL FEATURES

Zero and Span Adjustment

Most potentiometer recorders, including the X-Y type, have zero suppression and an adjustable span or range. These features not only allow use with a wider variety of transducers but also make possible greater accuracy in recording.

Event Markers

Event markers are offered as an optional feature in most recorders. These markers produce a short dashed line or a small displacement in a continuous line. The line or displacement indicates the closing or opening of a switch, which, in turn, indicates the start or end of an event.

Computing

The recorder may be used to make computations automatically on the input signal as well as to record the information. Computation may be based on a single input or on several inputs. With a single input the computation may involve reciprocal, power, or logarithmic function. With several inputs it can perform the arithmetic operations of addition, subtraction, multiplication, and division.

An application in which the reciprocal of the input might provide more usable information than the direct input is the case in which the direct signal indicates speed and the reciprocal indicates the length of time for a process to reach completion. If the speed is measured by a tachometer generator, a dc voltage that is proportional to the speed is produced. When this dc voltage is recorded in the normal way, a record is obtained of the speed of the process. If, however, the output of the tachometer generator is placed across the slide wire and the measuring circuit is balanced against a fixed voltage, the record obtained is a reciprocal of speed and can be made equivalent to the desired units of time. With the measuring circuit set up in this fashion, the sensitivity of the recorder is determined by the input signal. If the input signal varies in magnitude more than approximately two to one, the gain in the amplifier must be changed as the input signal changes. This can be accomplished automatically by having a sensitivity adjusting "pot" driven by the balancing servomotor.

A power-function computation can also be performed on a single input by the potentiometer recorder. This kind of computation is used in the determination of flow by measuring the pressure drop across an orifice. In this application the pressure is proportional to the square of the flow. Therefore, if the transducer used gives an output directly proportional to the pressure difference across the orifice, the square root of this signal is proportional to flow. The square root of a signal may be obtained by any of the following techniques.

1. A square root cam for driving the pen.

2. Nonlinear slide wire. A linear slide wire may be changed to a nonlinear by tapping it with resistors of the proper magnitude and at a sufficient number of points to produce the function desired—either the square root of the input signal or a logarithmic function.

3. A second slide wire. In addition to the usual slide wire that provides a dc voltage to balance the unknown dc signal, a second slide wire controls the voltage to the measuring circuit. The contacts on these slide wires are driven in parallel, so that as the signal increases and the servomotor drives the recorder upscale the voltage across the slide wire in the measuring circuit increases. This causes the recorder to require proportionally larger signals as it moves upscale. By a proper choice of resistors and slide wires the recorder can give the square root of the input signal.

Usually, when a logarithmic response is desired, a logarithmic amplifier is used in conjunction with a standard recorder. In some cases the logarithmic response is obtained by the same techniques as those used to obtain the square root of a signal.

Integration or differentiation of the signal may also be performed. Recorders are available with two pens; one for recording the original signal and the other for recording the time integral of that signal. This type of recording is useful for gas chromatography when it is desired to know both peak heights and the areas under the peaks. The differentiation of a signal can be accomplished simply by having a differentiating circuit in the input to the recorder.

Although multiple inputs, such as addition, subtraction, multiplication, and division can be employed, by proper design of the measuring circuit of a recorder analog computation is generally more satisfactorily done by the use of operational amplifiers as described in Chapter IX.

Analog-to-Digital Conversion

Analog-to-digital converters which can be added to the potentiometer recorder are available. The digital record can be printed directly on the strip chart or printed or punched on a card or tape.

References

1. H. H. Aronson, "Introduction to Recorders," *Instruments*, **31**, 830 (1958).
2. W. Gersch, "Recording Media, Techniques and Devices," *Automatic Control*, **7**, No. 6, 10 (1957); **8**, No. 1, 11 (1958); **8**, No. 2, 6 (1958).

3. *Electronic Products* (August 1966).
4. S. R. Gilford, "Direct-Indicating Recording Instruments," *Elec. Mfg.*, **52**, No. 5, 114; No. 6, 120 (1953).
5. *Instruments and Control Systems*, **37**, No. 7 (1964); **38**, No. 7 (1965).
6. *Instruments and Control Systems*, **41**, No. 7 (1968).
7. *Scientific American*, "On the Making of Recording Instruments," **193**, No. 5, 125 (1955).
8. *Scientific American*, "A Simple New Amplifying Device is Adapted to Driving a Pen Recorder," **222**, No. 5, 130 (1970).
9. "Strip Chart Recorders," *Indus. Res.*, **76**, (November 20, 1968).
10. J. E. Witherspoon, "Fundamentals of Electronic Recorders," *Instruments*, **25**, 900 (1952).

Chapter VIII

AUTOMATIC CONTROL

Donald E. Smith, Curtis E. Borchers, and Robert J. Loyd

5   A Sampling of Feedback Control Networks for Chemical Research

A Light Intensity Controller
An Automatic Balance
Current Controllers (Galvanostats)
A Dual Potential Controller
Reagent Concentration Controllers
Automatic Gain Control
Power-Line Conditioners

1   INTRODUCTION

Most laboratory operations are performed with some type of control. This control may be performed manually with relatively constant attention of the "operator" to maintain some desired result or it may be obtained "automatically" by the use of some mechanical or electrical mechanism. The growth in importance of automatic control systems to scientific endeavors probably has exceeded the most enthusiastic forecasts of the period in which the subject was first discussed in this series [1]. Growth of applications has been particularly noteworthy in the field of chemistry, in which it has at least paralleled the increased applications of electronic instrumentation. Approximately two decades ago the average research chemist encountered only a few common devices, such as constant temperature baths, automatic recorders, and fluid flow regulators, that employed automatic control. This rather simple situation has evolved to the present state in which the ubiquitous aspect of control systems in the tools of the average chemist is readily apparent. Magnetic-field stabilization systems in magnetic resonance spectrometers, radiation-source intensity-stabilization units in infrared, visible, and ultraviolet spectrophotometers, potentiostats and galvanostats in electrochemical instrumentation, pH-stats, power-line regulators, regulated dc power supplies, amplitude controllers in sinusoidal signal sources, automatic balances, automatic fraction collectors, and equipment for automated synthesis are among some of the common aids of the modern chemist in which automatic control is employed. A noteworthy fraction of these devices was designed not by electrical engineers but by chemists who were stimulated to master the subject of automatic control by the need for a particular control mechanism. In numerous examples in the realm of chemical measurements a substantial advance in the state of the art has depended primarily on the successful development by chemists of new or improved automatic control systems. Clearly, the foregoing remarks suggest the advisability of chemists' obtaining at least a moderate understanding of the basic principles underlying the operation of these systems. In a strictly pragmatic sense such knowledge permits more intelligent and effective use of many instruments at the chemist's disposal; it also allows more intelligent evaluation of commercial instrumentation whose purchase is contemplated and permits him to devise a control mechanism to solve a specific problem. In a broader, perhaps more philosophical, sense a basic understanding of control systems provides the chemist with deeper insights into certain aspects of the world in which he lives. The existence of naturally occurring automatic control mechanisms in biological and environmental systems has been recognized for hundreds of years. Recent developments in biology and ecology have expanded our appreciation of the vast profusion and subtle interactions of such systems. It is difficult to apply automatic control principles quantitatively in their present state of development to most natural control mechanisms. Nevertheless, qualitative application of these principles leads to rather profound implications regarding the response of the natural control mechanisms of our environment to man-made or natural perturbations. These implications, the most obvious of which will become apparent, should be recognized by chemists and other physical scientists whose activities often give birth to the man-made perturbations just mentioned.

For some time the subject of automatic control has been accorded treatment appropriate to a distinct, full-fledged scientific discipline. Numerous textbooks of impressive size have been devoted solely to this subject (e.g., [2–13]). Mathematical theoreticians have found the subject intriguing and have introduced some of the most sophisticated tools of applied mathematics into the theoretical framework of automatic control [9–10]. As implied in the preceding paragraphs, applications are numerous. The broad scope and high level of sophistication presently associated with the discipline of automatic control makes inappropriate any attempt to treat comprehensively the subject in this chapter. Instead, our efforts are directed toward relatively conservative goals. Consideration and application of theoretical principles are confined to the basic and most important, and the simplest mathematical tools consistent with reasonable accuracy are employed. Emphasis placed on the application of certain basic principles, rather than their derivation, gives the discussion a somewhat pragmatic or operational tone. The discussion of specific automatic control systems is confined to a small group of representative examples that should be of interest to chemists. It is our hope that the information presented here will be adequate to provide the reader with some capability of design and evaluation of control mechanisms in the class relevant to chemical instrumentation. Although the origins of some systems and their components are mentioned in the discussion of specific units, no attempt has been made to provide the reader with an over-all view of the appropriate vendors of such equipment. To list in a useful way the vastly diversified products of the many suppliers who deal in control systems and relevant components represents an overwhelming task (to us) whose results would not be particularly appropriate to a discussion primarily concerned with basic principles. The interested reader can quickly accumulate an extensive file on available equipment by examining advertisements in journals such as *Electronics, Electronic Products, Instruments and Control Systems, Control Engineering, Research/Development*, and *Analytical Chemistry* and availing himself of the Reader Service Card facility to obtain additional information from vendors of interest.

Additional objectives of this chapter are to furnish a sound basis on which to build further knowledge and to develop an appreciation of the usually impressive capabilities of modern control systems. Although the examples and discussion emphasize chemical instrumentation, it should be recognized that the basic principles presented are of general applicability.

Feedback

Automatic control networks may be operated with feedback (closed-loop) or without feedback (open-loop). Open-loop automatic control is usually time- or event-dependent or predictive. Time-dependent automatic control is obtained by causing an operation or series of operations to occur in predetermined time intervals. Event-dependent control involves a predetermined operation sequence whose progression is stimulated by certain related events. These types of automatic control are relatively simple and are not discussed here. Predictive control involves the determination of a condition change before it affects the system being controlled and is followed by compensation for the anticipated output (controlled variable) change. Predictive control requires a complicated network of devices, for it must measure any possible change in condition, know how that change will affect the output, and be able to take corrective action. This type of control is relatively complicated and is not discussed here [14].

Automatic control networks that utilize feedback are the type most encountered and applied by scientists and are primarily responsible for the advances attending the field of automatic control in recent years. In contrast to the open-loop controller, which acts in a preprogrammed manner without regard to the actual effects of its actions on the system being controlled, the closed-loop controller is continually receptive to the status of the system. In essence feedback control consists in maintaining a desired value of a quantity by measuring the existing value, comparing it with a desired value, and using the difference to cause some corrective action to decrease this difference. The difference signal may be changed by changing the desired (or input) value or by altering the existing value. The former change is employed in a servomechanism control system, the latter is associated with a regulating control system; that is, a servo system is designed to force the existing value to follow command changes, whereas a regulating system is designed to minimize effects of disturbances or load changes on the controlled variable. Servo systems are discussed in Chapter VII and we concern ourselves here primarily with regulating automatic control networks utilizing feedback.

The term "difference" employed repeatedly in the last paragraph is an implicit indication that the type of feedback employed in closed-loop control networks is negative. Positive feedback, by itself, is normally of little use in automatic control design. Therefore the ensuing discussion is confined primarily to the negative feedback case.

A Generalized Feedback Control Network

Clarification of some of the foregoing concepts, as well as those to follow, can be accomplished best by consulting the simple control network block diagram of Fig. 8.1. Consider a regulated-temperature water bath used to maintain the desired temperature for a distillation from a flask immersed in the bath. A resistance thermometer in a Wheatstone bridge measures the temperature and a variable resistor in the bridge is set to give a null signal (balanced bridge) at the desired temperature. The output from the bridge is amplified and used to regulate the amount of electrical current delivered to heater elements immersed in the bath. In this example the

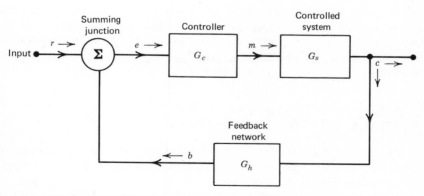

Fig. 8.1   Block diagram of generalized control system: r = input signal; e = error signal; m = manipulated variable; c = controlled variable; b = feedback signal; G_c = controller transfer function; G_s = controlled system transfer function; G_h = feedback network transfer function.

temperature is the controlled variable c; the resistance thermometer is the feedback element G_h; the variable resistor is the input or desired value r; the Wheatstone bridge is the summing junction Σ; the output of the bridge is the error signal e; the amplifier and regulator are the controller G_c; the current to the heater is the manipulated variable m; and the controlled system G_s consists of the heater, water bath, and distillation flask with its contents. Hopefully, this example of temperature control will suffice for the present to rationalize the basic configuration of the block diagram in Fig. 8.1 and give relevance to the four network components and five network variables. All specific automatic control networks discussed are also related to Fig. 8.1 so that eventually a more broad-based comparison to actual control networks will be developed.

As in most attempts to illustrate a generalized physical system, whenever an actual control network is related to the schematic of Fig. 8.1, a certain arbitrariness exists with regard to division of function of the various components; for example, in the case of the constant temperature bath we could have considered the heating element as part of the controller rather than as a controlled system component. In this case the manipulated variable m would have been the heat flux delivered by the heating element. Although the existence of such arbitrary choices may serve as a source of confusion to the beginner, it is irrelevant as far as analysis of system behavior is concerned. As long as one chooses a rational division and consistently analyzes the system within that framework, no difficulties will appear.

A representation of a general automatic control network could have included explicit representation of more components than indicated in Fig. 8.1; for example, it is sometimes useful to distinguish between a "controlled system" and a "load" (or "disturbance") [8, 15]. In this context the load is any input that influences the controlled variable other than the controller input (e.g., the flask and contents in the constant-temperature bath). Such distinctions, however, seem unnecessary for most control systems found in chemical instrumentation and are not employed here.

2   BASIC PRINCIPLES FOR ANALYSIS OF LINEAR FEEDBACK CONTROL NETWORKS

This section is devoted to developing definitions and mathematical principles of general applicability in the analysis of *linear* feedback control networks. Application to specific cases is undertaken in a following section.

Linear systems are described by ordinary linear differential equations in which the powerful superposition principle [5] is applicable. The mathematical techniques attending the solution of linear differential equations are relatively simple and are described in numerous texts. Chemists unfamiliar with the standard methods of solution usually can master them by self-teaching. On the other hand, treatment of nonlinear control systems demands a level of mathematical sophistication that seems inappropriate to an introductory discussion, particularly when the analysis fails to evolve simple, general design guidelines of the type found for linear systems. Strictly speaking, linear control networks are nonexistent when we consider the entire operating range, but most yield a linear response over a significant fraction of their range of operation and can be made to operate within this linear realm. Further, when deviations from linearity are not excessive, the assumption of linearity in the analysis is usually sufficiently accurate to provide valid design guidelines. These reasons and the fact that they are the norm in chemical applications dictated the emphasis on linear networks that characterizes this chapter. The reader is referred to appropriate texts for discussions of nonlinear networks (e.g., [5]).

Response Characteristics of Control Network Components

Basic Considerations—Transfer Functions

When considering the response of feedback control networks, it is convenient to apply the following definitions (see Fig. 8.1):

$$G_c = \frac{m}{e}, \tag{8.1}$$

$$G_s = \frac{c}{m}, \tag{8.2}$$

$$G_h = \frac{b}{c}, \tag{8.3}$$

$$e = r + b. \tag{8.4}$$

Equations 8.1 to 8.3 define the response of the controller, controlled system, and feedback network, respectively, in terms of the ratio of the associated input and output signals. It is conventional to refer to such signal ratios as *transfer functions*. The input and output signals are often referred to as the "excitation" and "response" functions, respectively. Thus (8.1) to (8.3) represent applications of a general formalism built around the relationship

$$\mathcal{R} = G \cdot E, \tag{8.5}$$

where $\mathcal{R}$ represents the generalized output or *response* function, and E, the generalized input or *excitation* function. It might seem that the commonly employed term "gain" is synonomous with "transfer function." A distinction, however, which assigns the term gain to the scalar magnitude of the input-output signal ratio observed within a particular frequency realm, is generally invoked, whereas the transfer function is a time or frequency-dependent quantity that usually possesses vectorial characteristics.

Equation 8.4 simply defines the operation of the summing junction of Fig. 8.1. An alternative sign convention is often employed in which the difference $r - b$ is used in place of the sum when representing the response of the summing junction [1]. Although the difference representation seems inconsistent with the almost universally applied designation "summing junction," it does indicate explicitly the negative character of the feedback signal b, which is only implicit in the convention of (8.4). We employ the sum representation of this equation because it is consistent with the terminology and because, in reality, the sign inversion that yields the negative feedback characteristic seldom is effected at the summing junction. The inversion operation generally originates in the controller. In rare cases the feedback network or the controlled system might perform this step.

The transfer functions defined by (8.1) to (8.3) are derivable from the differential equations that govern the response of the various components or they may be determined experimentally. In general the transfer functions are time-dependent, which implies a frequency-dependence when considering the response to periodic inputs. In the latter situation the transfer functions also assume vectorial characteristics because of the phase relationships implicit in periodic signals (see Chapter VI). The method of Laplace transformation [16] is a most convenient and powerful tool for solving the linear differential equations associated with the network responses under consideration. As a result usually the most efficient, useful, and common mathematical representation of transfer functions is in terms of the Laplace transform variable p (the symbol s is also used). Under zero initial conditions (no charge on network capacitances) p is equivalent to the operator d/dt [16]. In many situations the use of the Laplace transform method is analogous to the use of logarithms in numerical calculations. We consult tables of Laplace transform pairs that give the time-dependent function $G(t)$ and its corresponding Laplace transform $G(p)$ just as a logarithm table provides transform pairs; the number and its logarithm. A linear differential equation can usually be solved by first taking the Laplace transform of each term in the equation with the aid of a table of transform pairs. This operation yields an algebraic equation in transform space [16], which is solved for the unknown $G(p)$ by simple algebraic methods. The corresponding solution in "real" space, $G(t)$, is the *inverse transform* of $G(p)$, which is obtained from the table of transform pairs. The use of the Laplace transform of the transfer function allows us to calculate the network response function conveniently with the help of (8.5) in transform space,

$$\Re(p) = G(p) \cdot E(p), \tag{8.6}$$

even when the excitation function is relatively complex [e.g., when $E(t)$ is discontinuous (step or impulse)]. We simply multiply the transfer function in p notation by the Laplace transform of the excitation function to obtain the Laplace transform of the response $\Re(p)$. Inverse transformation of $\Re(p)$ gives the desired $\Re(t)$ function. In the special case of the steady-state response to sinusoidal inputs we need not perform the inverse Laplace transformation explicitly. It is readily shown [16] that with a sinusoidal input of unity amplitude and frequency ω, as far as the steady-state ac component is concerned, inverse Laplace transformation is equivalent to equating the response to the network transfer function, where p is replaced by $j\omega$ ($j = \sqrt{-1}$). The resulting response function in j-notation is analyzed by the usual procedures attending the use of j-notation for the periodic functions described in detail in Chapter III. Most questions regarding the accuracy and stability of feedback control systems can be answered by examining the system response to sinusoidal signals, and therefore the relation $p = j\omega$ is applied in most operations to follow. Only when we are interested in the quantitative aspects of the system transient response is it necessary to perform the inverse Laplace transformation in the explicit sense. For this reason further discussion of Laplace transformation properties is precluded and the reader is referred to relevant texts for additional information [16].

General Properties of Component Transfer Functions

All linear control system transfer functions fit the general formulation

$$G(p) = \frac{\sum_{n=0}^{k} K_n p^n}{\sum_{l=0}^{j} T_l p^l}, \qquad (8.7)$$

where K_n and T_l are constants. In other words, the numerator and denominator are polynomials of finite order in the Laplace transform variable p. In most cases the polynomials are of rather low order; for example, we often find controller and controlled system transfer functions of the form

$$G(p) = \frac{K_0}{1 + T_1 p}. \qquad (8.8)$$

The transfer functions (impedances) of common passive networks are also relatively simple, as illustrated in Table 8.1.

A network with a transfer function of the form shown in (8.8) is defined as a *first-order system*; that is, a first-order differential equation describes its response. One following a second-order differential equation (a *second-order system*) has an associated transfer function of the form

$$G(p) = \frac{K_0}{T_2 p^2 + T_1 p + 1}. \qquad (8.9)$$

Table 8.1   Transfer Functions for some Common Passive
Electrical Networks

	Network	Transfer Function (Impedance)
1.	R	R
2.	C	$(pC)^{-1}$
3.	L	pL
4.	R / C	$R(1 + pRC)^{-1}$
5.	R C	$(pC)^{-1}(1 + pRC)$
6.	L R	$R + pL$
7.	C / L	$pL(p^2 LC + 1)^{-1}$
8.	C C / R	$(1 + 2pRC)(p^2 RC^2)^{-1}$

It is appropriate at this point to examine the characteristics of first- and
second-order systems in some detail because they are frequently encountered
in automatic control networks and because higher order responses are
representable as a sum of first- and second-order responses [5].

The Laplace transform of a unit step function is p^{-1} [16]. Thus the response
transform of a first-order system with a unit step excitation is

$$R(p) = \frac{1}{p}\left(\frac{K_0}{1 + T_1 p}\right),$$ (8.10)

whose inverse Laplace transform has the form

$$R(t) = K_0(1 - e^{-t/T_1}).$$ (8.11)

The response curve is shown in Fig. 8.2. The basic parameter that describes
the time relationship between the system response and the step input is

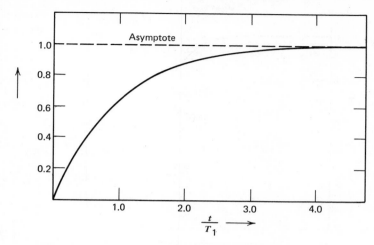

Fig. 8.2 Response of first-order system to step function input.

T_1, which is referred to as the *time constant* of the system; T_1 represents the time for the response to reach 63·2% of its final value. Characteristic times such as *rise time*, *dead time*, and *settling time*, also are sometimes used to describe transient responses [5]. All are related to the basic parameter T_1 and all are troubled by a lack of agreement regarding quantitative definitions; for example, the dead time (time for action to be initiated) is defined as the time required for the output to reach 10 or 50% of its final value, depending on the source of the definition. The 10% value is reached when $t = 0.105T_1$.

The steady-state ac response of a first-order system to a sinusoidal input is obtained by using the $p = j\omega$ transformation already outlined. We obtain

$$R(j\omega) = \frac{K_0}{1 + j\omega T_1},\qquad(8.12)$$

which implies (see Chapter III)

$$R(\omega t) = \frac{K_0}{\sqrt{1 + (T_1\omega)^2}} \sin(\omega t - \tan^{-1} T_1\omega).\qquad(8.13)$$

Figure 8.3 illustrates graphically the frequency-dependence of the first-order system response to sinusoidal excitations in terms of $\log[R(\omega t)/K_0]$ and ϕ versus $\log \omega$ plots. Log response-log frequency plots are known as *Bode plots* in honor of the individual who advocated their use in the analysis of control systems.

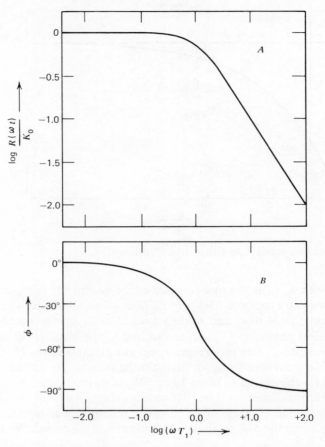

Fig. 8.3 Response of first-order system to sinusoidal input: (*a*) amplitude versus frequency response; (*b*) phase angle versus frequency response.

The response of second-order systems is best considered in terms of new parameters;

$$\zeta = \frac{T_1(T_2)^{-\frac{1}{2}}}{2},\tag{8.14}$$

$$\omega_0 = T_2^{-\frac{1}{2}},\tag{8.15}$$

where T_1 and T_2 are defined by (8.9). Rewriting (8.9) in terms of ζ and ω_0 gives

$$\frac{G(p)}{K_0} = \frac{\omega_0^2}{p^2 + 2\zeta\omega_0 p + \omega_0^2}.\tag{8.16}$$

The transform of a second-order system response to a unit step function is

$$\frac{R(p)}{K_0} = \frac{1}{p}\left[\frac{\omega_0^2}{p^2 + 2\zeta\omega_0 p + \omega_0^2}\right]. \tag{8.17}$$

Inverse transformation of (8.17) yields [17]

$$\frac{R(t)}{K_0} = 1 - \frac{e^{-\zeta\omega_0 t}}{(1 - \zeta^2)^{\frac{1}{2}}}\sin\left[\omega_0(1 - \zeta^2)^{\frac{1}{2}}t + \cot^{-1}\frac{\zeta}{(1 - \zeta^2)^{\frac{1}{2}}}\right]. \tag{8.18}$$

Plots of the response function of (8.18) for various values of ζ are given in Fig. 8.4. It is apparent from (8.18) and Fig. 8.4 that the characteristic time of the response (response speed) is determined by ω_0, whereas the exact form of the response varies widely, depending on the value of ζ. For obvious reasons ζ is referred to as the *damping factor*. As the value of ζ is varied, we can distinguish six distinct response forms; diverging, diverging oscillatory, steady-state oscillatory, converging oscillatory, critically damped, and overdamped. Table 8.2 defines the requirements for these six states and presents the form of $R(t)$ appropriate to each. It also notes one of several

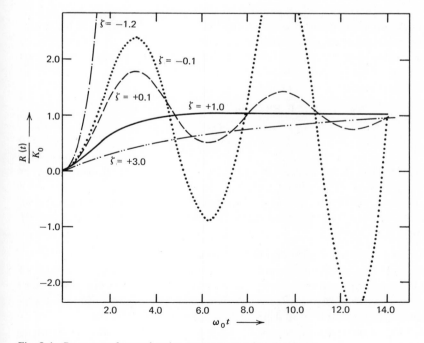

Fig. 8.4 Response of second-order system to step function input.

Table 8.2 Response Forms for Second-Order Systems

Type of Response	Condition	$R(t)/K_0$
1. Diverging	$\zeta \leq -1$	$1 - e^{\|\zeta\|\omega_0 t}\left\{\cosh\left[\omega_0(\|\zeta\|^2 - 1)^{\frac{1}{2}}t\right]\right.$ $\left. - \dfrac{\|\zeta\|}{(\|\zeta\|^2 - 1)^{\frac{1}{2}}} \sinh\left[\omega_0(\|\zeta\|^2 - 1)^{\frac{1}{2}}t\right]\right\}.$
2. Diverging oscillatory	$-1 < \zeta < 0$	Use (8.18).
3. Steady-state oscillatory	$\zeta = 0$	$1 - \cos\omega_0 t.$
4. Converging oscillatory	$0 < \zeta < 1$	Use (8.18)
5. Critically damped	$\zeta = 1$	$1 - (1 + \omega_0 t)e^{-\omega_0 t}.$
6. Overdamped	$\zeta > 1$	$1 - e^{-\|\zeta\|\omega_0 t}\left\{\cosh\left[\omega_0(\|\zeta\|^2 - 1)^{\frac{1}{2}}t\right]\right.$ $\left. + \dfrac{\|\zeta\|}{(\|\zeta\|^2 - 1)^{\frac{1}{2}}} \sinh\left[\omega_0(\|\zeta\|^2 - 1)^{\frac{1}{2}}t\right]\right\}.$

Note. For case 4, ζ and ω_0 can be calculated from experimental data by using the relationships $\omega_0(1 - \zeta^2)^{\frac{1}{2}} = 2\pi/$period of oscillation. Decay ratio (ratio of successive peak deviations from unity) $= \exp(-2\pi\zeta/\sqrt{1 - \zeta^2})$.

useful sets of mathematical expressions that allow calculation of ω_0 and ζ from experimental response behavior. The steady-state ac response of a second-order system to a pure sinusoidal excitation (no dc component) is given by

$$\frac{R(\omega t)}{K_0} = \frac{\omega_0 T^*}{2\zeta\sqrt{1 + (T^*\omega)^2}} \sin(\omega t - \tan^{-1} T^*\omega), \qquad (8.19)$$

where

$$T^* = \frac{2\zeta}{\omega_0[1 - (\omega/\omega_0)^2]}. \qquad (8.20)$$

Figure 8.5 depicts the frequency response defined by (8.19) and (8.20) for various values of ζ. As in the response to step functions, the reaction of second-order systems to sinusoidal inputs is markedly dependent on ζ. As ζ is varied, we encounter (a) free-running oscillations of frequency ω_0 ($\zeta = 0$), (b) tuned response ($-1 < \zeta < 1$), and (c) untuned response ($|\zeta| \geq 1$).

Controller Response—Special Characteristics

Although the foregoing remarks are applicable to all components of feedback control systems, each unit is characterized by certain special properties, typical response characteristics, or commonly employed terminology that should be noted. In the case of the controller the nature of its transfer function is often designated in a manner more familiar to chemists than that given above.

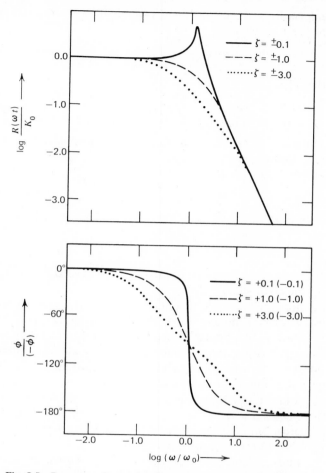

Fig. 8.5 Response of second-order system to sinusoidal input.

Proportional control refers to the case in which

$$G_c(p) = K_0,$$ (8.21)

which implies

$$R(t) = K_0 E(t);$$ (8.22)

that is, the response is directly proportional to the excitation signal. Thus proportional control is a special case of (8.7), where

$$K_{n>0} = T_l = 0.$$ (8.23)

With proportional control the control network's corrective action increases with increasing deviations of the controlled variable from the desired value.

Integral control results when

$$G_c(p) = \frac{1}{T_1 p},$$

(8.24)

which implies that [16]

$$R(t) = \frac{1}{T_1} \int E(t)\, dt.$$

(8.25)

Corrective action with integral control becomes increasingly larger as the error signal's period of existence increases.

Differential control exists when

$$G_c(p) = K_1 p,$$

(8.26)

which leads to the result

$$R(t) = K_1 \frac{dE(t)}{dt}.$$

(8.27)

The corrective action of a differential controller is enhanced by increasing rate of change of the error signal.

The foregoing three special types of control may be considered within the realm of *continuous* control modes in which the response is a continuous function of the excitation. In a rigorous sense we never encounter continuous controller actions that are purely proportional, integral, or differential. Such pure responses are neither obtainable over the entire frequency spectrum nor usually desirable; for example, many proportional controllers are amplifiers with first-order responses as in (8.8). It is apparent (see Fig. 8.3) that in such cases the control is proportional at low frequencies $[G_c(p) = K_0]$, whereas at high frequencies the control action is integral $[G_c(p) = 1/T_1 p]$. The response of such a controller to a step excitation is integral at short times and proportional at long times. However, the term proportional control is meaningful, despite the first-order character of the transfer function, provided that the controlled variable fluctuations are slow enough that the controller is required to respond at low frequencies only when $G(p) = K_0$. In a similar manner pure integral and pure differential control are obtainable only over a finite bandpass (bandpass is the frequency range over which the desired response is realized within tolerance limits). The integral and differential actions are usually obtained with the aid of amplifiers whose finite bandpass distorts the transfer functions at higher frequencies. Some examples of the exact transfer functions realized are given in Table 8.3. In many cases it is either desirable or essential to combine proportional, integral, and/or differential control. Careful consideration of the nature of these three control actions lead to the conclusion that they

Table 8.3 Response Characteristics of Selected Operational Amplifier Circuits

I. Open-Loop Operational Amplifier

1. *Circuit Schematic*

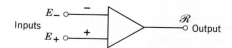

2. *Application in Control Systems*

(a) Fixed-gain proportional controller (usually with $E_+ = 0$).

3. *Transfer Functions*

(a) Standard unstabilized operational amplifier (Type I):

$$G_{\text{I}} = \frac{\mathscr{R}}{E_+ - E_-} = \frac{K_0}{1 + T_1 p}. \tag{Ia}$$

(b) Standard chopper-stabilized operational amplifier (Type II):

$$G_{\text{II}} = \frac{\mathscr{R}}{E_+ - E_-} = \frac{K_0 + K_1 p}{1 + T_1 p + T_2 p^2}. \tag{Ib}$$

(c) Chopper-stabilized operational amplifier with dual-slope high-frequency roll-off (Type III—see Fig. 8.6b):

$$G_{\text{III}} = \frac{\mathscr{R}}{E_+ - E_-} = \frac{K_0 + K_1 p + K_2 p^2}{1 + T_1 p + T_2 p^2 + T_3 p^3}. \tag{Ic}$$

(d) Ideal Transfer Function (low-frequency limit):

$$G = K_0 \quad \text{(all types)}. \tag{Id}$$

II. *n*-Input Adder with Gain (Inverting)

1. *Circuit Schematic*

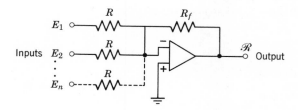

2. *Applications in Control Networks*

(a) Variable-gain proportional controller.
(b) Signal conditioning device.

(Continued overleaf)

Table 8.3 (*Continued*)

3. *Transfer Functions*

(a) Exact transfer function:

$$G = -\frac{G_i R_f}{[(1 + G_i)R + nR_f]} = \frac{\mathscr{R}}{\Sigma_{k=1}^n E_k},$$ (IIa)

where $G_i = G_I, G_{II}, G_{III}$, depending on the amplifier employed.

(b) Ideal transfer function (low-frequency limit):

$$G = \frac{\mathscr{R}}{\Sigma_{k=1}^n E_k} = -\frac{R_f}{R}.$$ (IIb)

III. *n*-Input Adder with Gain (Noninverting)

1. *Circuit Schematic*

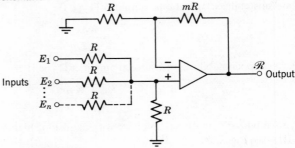

2. *Application in Control Systems*

(a) Signal conditioning devices.

(b) Component in two- or three-mode controller.

3. *Transfer Function*

(a) Exact transfer function.

$$G = \frac{\mathscr{R}}{\Sigma_{k=1}^n E_k} = \frac{G_i(1 + m)}{(1 + n)(1 + m + G_i)},$$ (IIIa)

where $G_i = G_I, G_{II},$ or $G_{III}.$

(b) Ideal transfer function (low-frequency limit):

$$G = \frac{\mathscr{R}}{\Sigma_{k=1}^n E_k} = \frac{(1 + m)}{(1 + n)}.$$ (IIIb)

IV. *n*-Input Integrator

1. *Circuit Schematic*

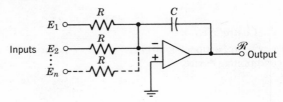

Table 8.3 (*Continued*)

2. *Application in Control Systems*

(a) Integral controller.

(b) Signal conditioning device.

3. *Transfer Function*

(a) Exact transfer function:

$$G = \frac{\mathcal{R}}{\Sigma_{k=1}^n E_k} = \frac{-G_i}{[(1 + G_i)RCp + n]}.$$ (IV*a*)

(b) Ideal transfer function (low-frequency limit):

$$G = \frac{\mathcal{R}}{\Sigma_{k=1}^n E_k} = -\frac{1}{RCp}.$$ (IV*b*)

V. *n*-Input Differentiator

1. *Circuit Schematic*

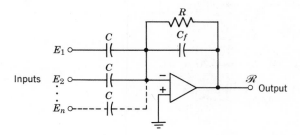

Note. Component C_f is required to stabilize and/or reduce noise levels in this circuit. Ideally it would not be required to effect derivative action.

2. *Applications in Control Systems*

(a) Differential controller.

(b) Signal conditioning device.

3. *Transfer Function*

(a) Exact transfer function:

$$G = \frac{\mathcal{R}}{\Sigma_{k=1}^n E_k} = \frac{-G_i RCp}{[(1 + G_i)(1 + RC_f p) + nRCp]},$$ (V*a*)

where $G_i = G_{\mathrm{I}}$, G_{II}, or G_{III}.

(b) Ideal transfer function (low-frequency limit):

$$G = \frac{\mathcal{R}}{\Sigma_{k=1}^n E_k} = -RCp.$$ (V*b*)

(*Continued overleaf*)

Table 8.3 (*Continued*)

VI. A Three-Mode Controller

1. *Circuit Schematic*

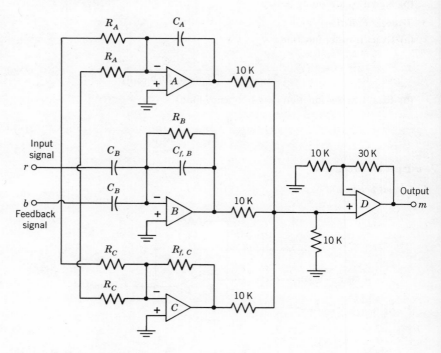

2. *Transfer Function*

   (a) Exact transfer function:

$$G = \frac{m}{r + b}$$

$$= -\left\{ \frac{G_{i,A}}{[(1 + G_{i,A})R_A C_A p + 2]} + \frac{G_{i,B}R_B C_B p}{[(1 + G_{i,B})(1 + R_B C_{f,B} p) + 2R_B C_B p]} \right.$$

$$\left. + \frac{G_{i,C}R_{f,C}}{[(1 + G_{i,C})R_C + 2R_{f,C}]} \right\}\left(\frac{G_{i,D}}{4 + G_{i,D}} \right), \tag{VIa}$$

where $G_{i,A}$, $G_{i,B}$, $G_{i,C}$, and $G_{i,D}$ represent Type I, II, or III transfer functions for amplifiers A, B, C, and D, respectively.

   (b) Ideal transfer function (low-frequency limit):

$$G = \frac{m}{r + b} = -\left[\frac{1}{R_A C_A p} + R_B C_B p + \frac{R_{f,C}}{R_C} \right]. \tag{VIb}$$

Table 8.3 (*Continued*)

VII. Unity-Gain Follower

  1. *Circuit Schematic*

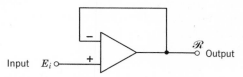

  2. *Application in Control Systems*

    (a) Impedance matching device (buffer amplifier).

  3. *Transfer Function*

    (a) Exact transfer function:

$$G = \frac{\mathscr{R}}{E_i} = \frac{G_i}{1 + G_i}. \tag{VIIa}$$

    (b) Ideal transfer function:

$$G = 1. \tag{VIIb}$$

---

are complementary. As a result we find many *three-mode controllers* whose ideal transfer function is of the form

$$G_c(p) = K_0 + \frac{1}{T_1 p} + K_1 p; \tag{8.28}$$

that is,

$$R(t) = K_0 E(t) + \frac{1}{T_1} \int E(t)\, dt + K_1 \frac{dE(t)}{dt}. \tag{8.29}$$

Three-mode controllers usually provide for variation of the coefficients K_0, K_1, and T_1^{-1} so that the relative amounts of proportional, integral, and differential control can be varied until optimum conditions are achieved for a particular application. *Two-mode control* arises in the special case in which one of the coefficients is effectively zero. Of course, for reasons already stated, the desired response of a three-mode controller (8.28) is realized only over a finite frequency range. Examples of exact transfer functions for the entire frequency spectrum that might be encountered with three-mode controllers are given in Table 8.3.

Although most modern high-performance control systems are based on continuous controller responses of the type just discussed, nevertheless controllers that respond to an excitation signal in a discontinuous manner are well known. Two main types of discontinuous controller are employed: on-off and digital. The former is perhaps the most familiar to chemists because of its appearance in many commonly encountered control systems such as home heating systems, laboratory constant-temperature baths, and refrigeration systems. Although less familiar at present, digital controllers are enjoying more attention from specialists and more increases in application than any other controller classification.

The response of on-off controllers may usually be described by the following set of relationships;

$$\mathcal{R}(t) = A_1 \quad \text{for} \quad E(t) < E_{ref}, \qquad (8.30)$$

$$\mathcal{R}(t) = A_2 \quad \text{for} \quad E(t) \geq E_{ref}, \qquad (8.31)$$

where A_1, A_2, and E_{ref} are constants. In other words, an on-off controller is a two-state device whose output state depends only on whether the excitation signal is above or below a reference value. Equations 8.30 and 8.31 imply that the change of state occurs instantaneously; that is, $\mathcal{R}(t)$ is either A_1 or A_2 and spends negligible time at intermediate values. This useful approximation is validated whenever the other components in the control system respond with characteristic times that are much longer than the "rise time" associated with the transition between states A_1 and A_2. In the vast majority of applications of on-off control such a situation exists. When this is not the case, the "time-delay" of the controller can be incorporated into (8.30) and (8.31). In some circles the definition of on-off control is restricted to the case in which either A_1 or A_2 (not both) is zero and the term *bang-bang* control is employed when both states correspond to nonzero response levels.

In *digital control* signal sensing, error calculations, and control action are all performed in an incremental and sequential manner. The continuous analog data is sampled periodically by a special sample-and-hold system (*sampled-data system* [18, 19]), which converts the continuous data into pulsed data. *Analog-to-digital conversion* is then performed on the sampled feedback (*b*) and desired value (*r*) signals. A digital computer calculates the error signal and generates a digital response which may be proportional, integral, differential, three-mode, or a more sophisticated type. The digital response is converted to an analog signal with the help of a *digital-to-analog* converter and applied to the controlled system. The incremental or step-functional nature of the data sampling, data analysis, and response operations, together with the many-level character of the discontinuous response (in contrast to the two-level on-off controller), introduces special problems in the mathematical analysis not encountered in the other types of control. Although digital control of process streams in the chemical industry is becoming increasingly important, digital control is not yet a ubiquitous commodity in the chemical laboratory. For this reason and because the rigorous mathematical analysis requires introduction of an additional mathematical tool (*z*-transforms [5]), we shall not attempt to discuss quantitatively the mathematical principles underlying digital control. We should recognize, however, that when the data sampling-calculation-response sequence involves a characteristic time that is much shorter than the response time of the controlled variable, the digital control operation may be approximated as continuous and we may apply at least semi-quantitatively the principles developed for continuous control systems.

Finally, we may also characterize any of these types of controller according to whether they are *bidirectional* or *unidirectional*. Bidirectional implies that the manipulated variable *m* may be positive or negative (constant temperature bath with heating and refrigerating elements). When the manipulated variable can assume only one polarity, the controller is unidirectional (constant temperature bath with heating element only).

Controlled System Response—Special Characteristics

Response characteristics of the controlled system for the most part are amply covered by the foregoing general discussion. The controlled system is usually described by a continuous transfer function of a first-, second-, or higher order type. Although rarely encountered by chemists, processes whose response properties may be considered discontinuous do exist; for example, machine tools in which tool "chatter" [20] and the like are sometimes best analyzed as a discontinuous phenomena. Most processes of interest to chemist are essentially *passive* rather than *active*; that is, they dissipate and/or store energy but do not serve as energy sources. Nevertheless, if encountered, active processes will fit the theoretical framework developed here.

Feedback Element Response—Special Characteristics

The feedback element generally consists of (a) a device to measure the controlled variable in the process, (b) associated signal-conditioning devices, and/or (c) passive networks designed to aid in optimizing the response of the over-all control system. There are no special characteristics or commonly employed definitions associated with the feedback element response that have not been covered here. The feedback element may be active or passive and its transfer function will fit into one of the previously discussed categories. Usually the feedback element response is continuous, but one notable exception develops when sampled-data systems are employed. Although the sampled-data procedure has been discussed in the context of digital control, its application is not confined to this type of operation. Sampled-data acquisition is occasionally performed in combination with continuous analog control [18, 19]. In such applications the data are maintained in analog form (no analog-to-digital conversion), but the pulse train character of the sampled-data often necessitates the type of mathematical analysis used with digital control.

Operational Amplifier Response—Special Characteristics

Although space limitations preclude any attempt to consider explicitly the vast array of specific devices that find application in control systems, the operational amplifier merits special consideration. The operational amplifier has enjoyed such growth of application in recent years that a generalized principle in low-frequency (≤ 100 KHz) analog electronics is rapidly evolving in which the operational amplifier together with the standard passive components (resistors, capacitors, diodes, etc.) represent the building blocks from which all analog functions are obtained. The combination of very high gain, high input impedance, low output impedance and wide

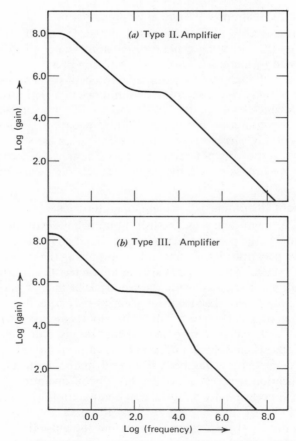

Fig. 8.6 Open-loop frequency response characteristics of chopper-stabilized operational amplifiers: (*a*) Type II Amplifier. (*b*) Type III Amplifier.

bandwidth represents the precise characteristics required for a versatile, high-performance electronic controller. A single operational amplifier constitutes a high-gain, wideband proportional controller. A single operational amplifier combined with one resistor and one or two capacitors will give an integral or differential control response, depending on the configuration (see Table 8.3). An operational amplifier can also be configured into an on-off controller [21]. These properties have led to frequent applications of operational amplifiers in modern control networks encountered by chemists as evidenced by their frequent appearance in the examples discussed later. Although the operational amplifier has been given detailed consideration in Chapter IV, it is desirable at this stage to indicate the general response characteristics of certain operational amplifier circuits that are useful in electronic control systems by using the transfer function notation of this chapter. This information is compiled in Table 8.3. The magnitudes of the various coefficients K_n and T_l, however, are not given, as they vary from one amplifier type to another. Methods by which these coefficients are determined, either experimentally or from the manufacturers' literature, are discussed in a later section. The classification of operational amplifiers as Types I, II, and III is strictly for purposes of this chapter and is not a standard designation. The frequency response of the open-loop gain for a Type I amplifier is given in Fig. 8.3. Figure 8.6 shows the corresponding plots for Types II and III. The transfer functions given in Table 8.3 are approximate in that they ignore small second-order effects arising from nonzero output and noninfinite input impedances. These effects, however, are negligible under most operating conditions.

General Response Characteristics of Feedback Control Networks

Basic Network Equations

Having considered the response characteristics inherent in the individual components of the feedback control network, it is now appropriate to deal with the properties of the complete control network. It is useful to consider first the control network response in terms of the transfer function which relates the existing signal c to the input signal r:

$$G_N = \frac{c}{r},$$
(8.32)

Algebraic combination of (8.1) to (8.4) shows that

$$G_N = \frac{c}{r} = \frac{G_s G_c}{1 - G_c G_s G_h}.$$
(8.33)

Although demonstration of its validity is almost trivial, (8.33) represents the master equation of feedback control networks from which all important operation criteria are readily deduced. When examining (8.33) we should keep in mind that the minus sign associated with the negative feedback operation is implicit in one of the component transfer functions (usually G_c).

Among the terms appearing in (8.33), the product $G_cG_sG_h$ is the most important, for its magnitude and phase response determine the quality of the control network operation. This product is usually referred to as the *open-loop gain* of the network G_{OL}. The reason for this terminology becomes readily apparent when we consider that

$$G_{OL} = G_cG_sG_h = \frac{b}{r + b}. \tag{8.34}$$

Equation 8.34 indicates that G_{OL} is the gain that would be observed by opening the control loop at the output of the feedback network and measuring the feedback network output signal b^* (in general, $b^* = b$ only under closed loop conditions) that would result from an input $r + b$ at the summing junction.

Control Network Accuracy

The importance of the control network open-loop gain becomes immediately evident when we consider accuracy; for example, we are often concerned with the error caused by fluctuations in the controller transfer function G_c. The active nature of the controller (amplifier, trigger circuit, etc.) often makes its fluctuations a main source of control network inaccuracy; that is, G_s and G_h usually are less susceptible to drift and the like. Differentiating (8.33) with respect to G_c yields

$$\frac{\partial G_N}{\partial G_c} = \frac{1}{(1 - G_{OL})^2}. \tag{8.35}$$

Dividing (8.35) by (8.33) gives

$$\frac{(\partial G_N/G_N)}{\partial G_c} = \frac{(\partial c/c)}{\partial G_c} = \frac{G_h}{G_{OL}(1 - G_{OL})}. \tag{8.36}$$

Equation 8.36 indicates that the relative error in the existing value of the controlled variable c, arising from variation in the controller response, is inversely proportional to the factor $G_{OL}(1 - G_{OL})$. Thus increasing G_{OL} (assuming $G_{OL} > 1$) tends to render the system less sensitive to variations in G_c.

The errors arising from fluctuations in the controlled system and feedback network transfer functions are readily obtained by the above approach.

We find

$$\frac{(\partial G_N/G_N)}{\partial G_s} = \frac{(\partial c/c)}{\partial G_s} = \frac{G_h}{G_{OL}(1 - G_{OL})} \tag{8.37}$$

and

$$\frac{(\partial G_N/G_N)}{\partial G_h} = \frac{(\partial c/c)}{\partial G_h} = \frac{G_{OL}}{G_h(1 - G_{OL})}. \tag{8.38}$$

The relative error arising from fluctuations of G_s follows the same relationship as G_c. On the other hand, the error associated with variations in G_h behaves differently, becoming insensitive to G_{OL} for large values of the latter.

In the extreme case in which

$$G_{OL} \gg 1, \tag{8.39}$$

(8.33) reduces to

$$G_N = (G_N)_I = -G_h^{-1}. \tag{8.40}$$

Thus, when (8.39) is obeyed, the correspondence between the controlled variable and the input is simply proportional to the reciprocal of the feedback network transfer function and is insensitive to the controller and controlled system characteristics. The validation of (8.40) is a highly desirable goal because (a) it allows simple calculation of the input value r appropriate to the desired controlled variable value c; and (b) errors arising from fluctuations in the controller and controlled system response are virtually eliminated. The realization of the condition of (8.39) usually depends on the controller. The transfer function G_s is subject to alteration by the designer, but one is usually limited to values less than unity. Gain can be introduced into the feedback network transfer function G_h, but this is usually inconvenient because large values of G_h demand correspondingly large values of the input variable to obtain a desired controlled variable value. This leaves the controller as the most convenient and available unit in which to obtain the high gain necessary to achieve the requirement of (8.39). In effect [from (8.34) and (8.39)] we demand that

$$G_c \gg \frac{1}{G_s G_h}. \tag{8.41}$$

Clearly, high gain is a desirable characteristic for a controller.

Frequently we can approach the design of a control network in an initial step of estimating the minimum G_c magnitude required to validate (8.40) within the desired accuracy. The relative error due to deviation of the *actual response* G_N from the *ideal response* $(G_N)_I$ may be written

$$\% \text{ error} = \left| \frac{G_N - (G_N)_I}{(G_N)_I} \right| \times 100. \tag{8.42}$$

Substituting (8.33) and (8.40) into (8.42) yields

$$\% \text{ error} = \left| \frac{100}{1 - G_{\text{OL}}} \right|. \tag{8.43}$$

For the actual response to fall within $\Delta\%$ of the ideal, we require that (except for large Δ)

$$|G_{\text{OL}}| \cong \frac{100}{\Delta} \tag{8.44}$$

or

$$|G_c| \cong \left| \frac{100}{G_s G_h \Delta} \right|. \tag{8.45}$$

Equation 8.45 may be applied to determine the minimum required G_c value for a particular tolerance (Δ), given the characteristics of G_s and G_h. A crude estimate may be obtained by using the smallest "gains"; that is, absolute magnitudes of G_s and G_h found within the frequency or time domains (bandwidth) over which accurate control is desired. Equation 8.43 then yields an estimate of the minimum $|G_c|$ required for the desired accuracy within the bandwidth of interest. This neglect of the vectorial character of the transfer functions is convenient in that it requires less detailed knowledge of the characteristics of G_s and G_h. The attendant error is often not serious, particularly with low-frequency control in which the frequency or time domain of interest primarily falls within the flat portion of the frequency response profiles for G_s, G_h, and G_c, where the imaginary components are small (see Figs. 8.3, 8.5, and 8.6 and relevant discussion). When this is not the case, it is best to obtain and utilize the G_s and G_h functions in the Laplace notation or frequency-dependent j notation to calculate rigorously the magnitude of the right side of (8.45) as a function of time or frequency. The largest value of this quantity within the bandwidth of interest corresponds to the minimum $|G_c|$ required.

In the simplest situations, for example, when a simple proportional control network is desired, we may actually terminate the control network design considerations with this initial evaluation of the minimum required $|G_c|$ and proceed with acquisition of an appropriate controller. In not infrequent cases this approach will yield a well-behaved, sufficiently accurate control system. However, just as often we will observe uncontrolled, sustained oscillation of the control network on closure of the feedback loop. Such an observation is a rather impressive demonstration of a well-known fact of control theory (and experiment): an open-loop gain characteristic sufficient to yield accurate response over the frequency or time domain of interest is no guarantee of a successful control network. The tendency toward unstable, oscillatory behavior characterizes all high-gain feedback networks, including those designed for control applications, and the study of requirements for control network stability is one of the most important and active areas in this field.

Control Network Stability

The tendency of control networks toward instability can be ascertained from (8.33). The key is to recognize that although the relevant transfer functions may have essentially ideal properties within the bandwidth in which control is desired the inescapable roll-off (decrease in gain with increasing frequency) in transfer function magnitude and phase at high frequencies (Figs. 8.3, 8.5, and 8.6) implies that they will exhibit decidedly nonideal properties at appropriately high frequencies. Thus, for example, it is possible that at some point in the frequency or Laplace domain

$$G_{OL} = G_c G_s G_h = 1. \qquad (8.46)$$

The condition of (8.46) corresponds to the singular point of (8.33), and the various expressions for accuracy (8.36–8.38 and 8.43). The implication is that if (8.46) is realized at a particular frequency, the closed-loop network will undergo sustained constant amplitude oscillations at that frequency [1–8]. Equation 8.46 represents a sufficient but not a necessary condition for instability. It represents a special case of positive or regenerative feedback [5, 22] that develops whenever the phase relations of the transfer functions deviate sufficiently from the ideal of negative feedback (G_{OL} real and negative) so that G_{OL} becomes a positive quantity. Positive feedback causes the error signal to be enhanced by the feedback signal which, under certain conditions, will lead to instability in the form of oscillations or a "limited controller" (controller continually emitting its maximum dc output). Consequently it is not sufficient to fulfill these criteria for accuracy to obtain a useful control network. We must take measures to ensure that the singularity of (8.46) and other unstable states associated with regenerative feedback are avoided throughout the frequency spectrum. A more detailed discussion of the precise conditions for instability is beyond the scope of this chapter but can be obtained from a variety of sources [2–12, 15, 22]. The remainder of this discussion is confined to presenting, without proof, the requirements for stable operation.

A number of stability criteria have been proposed for linear networks. All are essentially equivalent and differ only in the way the relevant information is presented. The most popular involve graphical representation of G_{OL} in the frequency domain (i.e., use $p = j\omega$ in all transfer functions). The approach of Nyquist [23] which involves frequency response plots in the imaginary plane [3, 5, 6] and that of Bode [2] which is based on Bode plots (Figs. 8.3, 8.5, and 8.6) are the best known. We present the latter approach here, since it has some advantages with regard to convenience and simplicity.

The Bode criteria for stability relates to the Bode plot of log $|G_{OL}|$ versus log ω. Bode has shown that the stability of the network can be ascertained from the slope of this Bode plot at the *unity gain cross-over frequency* (frequency at which $|G_{OL}| = 1$). A statement of the Bode criteria is the following:

The closed-loop network will be stable if the slope of the Bode plot of open-loop gain versus frequency is greater (less negative) than -2 *at unity gain.*

More frequently the slope is given in units of decibels per decade of frequency (dB $= 20 \log G$). A slope of -2 is equivalent to -40 dB per decade. The term octave is also used in reference to frequency (1 octave change equals a factor of 2 change in frequency). Thus the term -12 dB per octave is also used in reference to the Bode plot slope at the transition between stable and unstable operation.

An incomplete rationale of the Bode criteria is obtained by recognizing that the slope of the log $|G_{OL}|$ versus log ω plot is intimately related to the phase shift of the open-loop gain. This interrelationship is implicit in Figs. 8.3 and 8.5 and Eqs. 8.13 and 8.19 which deal with the frequency-response of first and second-order systems. A slope of -40 dB per decade of frequency in the Bode plot corresponds to a 180° phase shift (relative to the pure negative feedback case) of G_{OL}, which is the transition point between positive and negative feedback. A 40-dB-per-decade slope at unity gain thus implies that $G_{OL} = 1$. A second-order response with a zero damping factor (ζ) is an example in which such a state exists. More negative slopes correspond to phase shifts in excess of 180° which also fall in the positive feedback realm. Less negative slopes imply phase shifts of less than 180° (negative feedback); for example, a -20-dB-per-decade roll-off means a 90° phase shift. A first-order response corresponds to this situation and, as seen earlier, represents a stable configuration. The -20-dB-per-decade case is said to have a 90° *phase margin* (the difference between 180° and the actual phase shift).

Operationally, the use of the Bode criteria is quite simple. We assess the open-loop gain as a function of frequency, either by direct measurement or by calculations with the aid of transfer functions (see later for further details) and then construct the Bode plot. From the behavior of the slope at unity gain as a function of network parameters we can determine conditions for stable operation. It is important to note [see (8.34)] that

$$\log |G_{OL}| = \log |G_c| + \log |G_s| + \log |G_H|. \tag{8.47}$$

Equation 8.47 indicates that the Bode plot of the control network open-loop gain is simply the sum of the individual Bode plots of the controller, controlled system, and feedback network transfer functions. This fact proves useful in many situations and represents one of the main conveniences of the Bode criteria.

Although the use of Bode plots in design of control networks has been introduced in the context of stability analysis, they are also directly applicable to accuracy evaluation, since they contain the essential data on G_{OL}. Thus the two key aspects of control network behavior, stability and accuracy, are manifested in the Bode plot.

Simple Relationships Between Time and Frequency Domain Response

Because of the importance of the frequency domain response to stability evaluation, it is evident that this aspect of control network behavior will always be examined in any careful analysis. We might ask whether, on completion of the frequency domain examination, we must carry out explicitly the inverse Laplace transformation of the transfer function G_N in order to obtain the transient response characteristics. The answer to such an inquiry depends on the amount of detail and precision we require with regard to the transient response. If precise knowledge of the transient shape and rise time properties are essential, then we must effect the rigorous analysis. However, frequently our interest in the transient response is only semiquantitative. In the latter situation we can obtain the desired information directly from the open-loop gain Bode plot [15]. From inspection of the correlations between the frequency and time domain behavior the following approximate guidelines are evolved [15]:

1. The control-network closed-loop response time (time constant) to a step excitation is roughly the reciprocal of the unity-gain cross-over frequency (in Hertz) on the open-loop gain Bode plot.

2. High gains at low frequencies on the Bode plot indicate a control network with high long-term accuracy in response to a step input, that is, use zero-frequency gain and (8.36 to 8.38 and 8.43).

3. A Bode plot unity gain slope of approximately -20 dB/decade is indicative of a near critically damped network; more negative slopes imply a ringing system; less negative slopes indicate an overdamped system.

3   THE ACQUISITION OF TRANSFER FUNCTION DATA

Appropriate Variables and Parameters

In order to apply the foregoing concepts to the analysis and design of automatic control systems it is essential to obtain first the relevant transfer function data. Whether these data entail direct experimental measurement or transformation of manufacturers specifications into mathematical or graphical representation of transfer functions (manufacturers often do not give transfer functions explicitly), we must know precisely what system variables and parameters relate to the transfer function. In addressing ourselves to this problem for the first time, we may find the preceding section of little help, since only generalized signals were considered. Although many chemists may readily recognize the significance of the signals r, b, m, and c in the context of electronic devices, the situation may be somewhat clouded when other types of physical process are involved (e.g., mechanical or hydrodynamic). Clarification of the nature of the signals and transfer functions for control network components involving various types of physical process is worthwhile before proceeding further.

All dynamic physical processes include the transport of a *generalized quantity* under the influence of a *generalized potential gradient* (force field). The associated *energy change* is the product of the quantity transported times the potential gradient. Usually the energy transport is given in terms of an energy flux (energy transport per unit time) which is the product of the potential gradient times the quantity flux (*generalized current*); for example, in electrical processes the potential gradient is the electrical potential gradient (voltage drop), the quantity is the electrical charge (coulombs), and the quantity flux is the electrical current (amperes). In a thermal process the potential gradient is the temperature gradient (degrees per centimeter), the quantity is heat (calories) and the current is the heat flux (calories per second). The characteristic times and other properties of these transport processes are determined by the system parameters that, for linear systems, are independent of the magnitudes of the input and output levels (potentials and quantities). Linear system parameters are of three types; generalized resistance, generalized capacitance, and generalized inductance. Resistances dissipate energy (more correctly, they convert energy to a nonuseful form for the process in question). Resistances include electrical and thermal conductors, and mechanical and fluid friction sources. Capacitances (electronic capacitance, mechanical springs) are devices that store potential energy. Inductances (electronic inductors, mechanical mass) "store" kinetic energy; that is, they are forms of inertia. The fact that analogs of electrical potential, charge, current, resistance, capacitance, and inductance can be recognized for all physical processes is the basis of the use of the electronic analog computer as a method of modeling and computing the properties for a wide range of dynamic processes. These analogies validate and give broad utility to the use of the generalized notation of the preceding section. The mathematical relationships between generalized currents, voltages, and impedances for any physical process are the same as those for the more familiar (to chemists) electrical process. Thus, in applying the equations of the preceding section to a nonelectrical system, we are required only to recognize parameters and variables that are the analogs of the electrical resistance, capacitance, etc. These analogies are readily clarified by recalling that all linear transport processes are described by the generalized equation of motion

$$A \frac{d^2 Q(t)}{dt^2} + \frac{B \, dQ(t)}{dt} + C^{-1} Q(t) = E(t), \tag{8.48}$$

which in transform space may be written

$$\frac{Q(p)}{E(p)} = \frac{C}{1 + BCp + ACp^2}. \tag{8.49}$$

The parameters A, B, and C are the generalized inductance, resistance, and capacitance, respectively. The function $E(t)$, often referred to as the "force function," is the generalized potential gradient; $Q(t)$ normally represents the quantity transported. Table 8.4 provides a compilation of the analogous variables and parameters for physical processes most frequently encountered in automatic control. In employing conventional representations of the dependent variable $Q(t)$ for the mechanical systems in Table 8.4, the identity of $Q(t)$ as a "quantity" is lost. Conventional usage identifies $Q(t)$ as a position variable whose representation as a quantity transported requires an over-extension of the imagination. This conceptual difficulty, however, is inconsequential as far as mathematical treatment of mechanical systems is concerned.

In addition to its applicability to all classes of physical processes, the generality of the preceding section's notation accommodates another type of degree of freedom. Within the framework of a particular physical process classification, we can define and employ several types of transfer function: (a) potential ratios (potential transfer functions), (b) current ratios (current transfer functions), (c) potentials divided by currents (impedance transfer functions), (d) currents divided by potentials (admittance transfer functions). All four types are accommodated by the foregoing treatment. Of course, we must follow certain obvious rules of dimensional analysis when using these various transfer function types; for example, it is apparent that G_{OL} must be dimensionless [see (8.33)]. Thus, if G_c is a voltage ratio transfer function and G_s is represented as an impedance transfer function, we must necessarily employ an admittance transfer function for G_h.

Experimental Measurement—Basic Considerations

The chemist will frequently be confronted with the necessity of obtaining transfer functions by direct experimental measurements. Fortunately this operation is relatively simple in most cases. The obvious approach is to measure the response of the components of interest to an excitation signal

Table 8.4 Analogous Variables and Parameters of Physical Processes

Type of Process	$E(t)$	$Q(t)$	A	B	C
1. Electrical	Electrical potential drop = E (V)	Electrical charge = q (C)	Electrical inductance = L (H)	Electrical resistance = R (Ω)	Electrical capacitance = C (F)
2. Thermal	Temperature drop = ΔT (deg)	Heat = q (cal)	None	Reciprocal of heat conductivity coefficient = K^{-1} (deg-sec-cal^{-1})	Heat capacity = C (cal-deg^{-1})
3. Fluid	Pressure drop = ΔP (atm)	Volume = V (cm^3)	Unsteady flow coefficient = K (atm-sec^2-cm^{-3})	Viscous friction coefficient = B (atm-sec-cm^{-3})	Static head = C_h (cm^3)
4. Mechanical (linear)	Force = F (dyn)	Linear position = x (cm)	Mass = M (g)	Frictional damping coefficient = D (dyn-sec-cm^{-1})	Reciprocal of spring gradient (Hooke's law constant, K) = K^{-1} (cm dyn^{-1})
5. Mechanical (rotary)	Torque = T (dyn-cm)	Angular position = θ (rad)	Moment of inertia = J (dyn-cm-sec^2-rad^{-1})	Frictional damping coefficient = F (dyn-sec-rad^{-1}-cm)	Reciprocal of torque gradient (shaft stiffness coefficient K_t) = K_t^{-1} (rad dyn^{-1}-cm^{-1})
6. Chemical	Concentration difference = ΔC (moles-cm^{-3})	Moles = N (moles)	None	Reciprocal of diffusion coefficient = D^{-1} (sec-cm^{-2})	Volume = V (cm^3)

of known character. The basic requirements are a signal source and a device to readout the response signal (e.g., recorder or oscilloscope). Both are common commodities in the modern laboratory. Usually a step or sinusoidal excitation waveform is employed. Because in most cases the final objective is to obtain a Bode plot of log gain versus log frequency, the use of a sinusoidal excitation represents the most direct approach. One simply plots the raw data of response amplitude versus frequency on log-log paper to obtain the desired Bode plot. For many types of process rapid automatic readout of the Bode plot is possible. By providing the Bode plot directly the sinusoidal response measurement eliminates the need to fit the observed response to any particular theoretical response formula, that is, it is not necessary to determine explicitly whether the response is first-order, second-order, and so on. This represents a noteworthy advantage over transient response measurements.

Although the readout provided is several steps removed from the desired Bode plot, step-function excitations are frequently employed. In some situations, such as very slowly responding systems in which sinusoidal inputs of appropriately low frequency are either unavailable or time consuming to employ, they represent the only rational possibility. Measurement of the response to a step function has the general advantages of requiring considerably less measurement time than the sinusoidal approach and usually a much less expensive signal source. The primary disadvantage attending the use of step functions, or any other transient excitation, is that a nontrivial data-analysis step is required before the Bode plot is obtained, in contrast to the situation with the sinusoidal signals. In order to obtain a Bode plot from the response to a step function, we must fit the observed response curve to one of the theoretical response formulations such as the first-order equation. The curve-fitting operation yields the response parameters (K_n's and T_i's) from which the sinusoidal response can be calculated. In the case of a first-order response this operation is relatively simple. The time required for the response to reach 63.2 % of its final value is identified as T_1. The final value is K_0 [see (8.8)]. These parameter values then allow us to calculate the sinusoidal response amplitude from (8.13) and complete the transformation from the time to the frequency domain. If second-order or more complex responses are encountered, this procedure becomes somewhat tedious (see Section 2), but the required parameters are definitely obtainable. Of course, if we wish, digital computer aids may be applied to this operation.

In addition to having a choice in our approach to measuring transfer functions, we must also decide the level at which transfer function data will be obtained; that is, we can measure (a) the open-loop gain G_{OL} directly, (b) transfer functions of the controller, controlled system, and feedback network individually, and/or (c) transfer functions of subunits of the controller, controlled system, and feedback network. Measuring G_{OL} directly provides the essential information on the control network stability and accuracy without requiring subsequent calculations or graphical data manipulation. The importance of G_{OL} data, however, usually does not preclude the need to examine other transfer functions. If we find that the open-loop gain characteristics are undesirable from the point of view of stability or accuracy, modification of the control network is indicated. In this situation knowledge of G_{OL} alone is often inadequate, since it fails to isolate the source or sources of the undesirable properties. Knowledge of the individual component transfer functions, G_c, G_s, and G_h provides these insights as well as guidelines on how to modify the troublesome component(s) to obtain the desired response (see next section). Occasionally it is either desirable or convenient to proceed one step further and obtain response characteristics of subunits of either the controller, controlled system, or feedback network. Such information provides even deeper insights into the origins of the control network response properties; for example, we may approach the experimental evaluation of G_c for the three-mode controller of Table 8.3 (Part VI) by measuring the transfer functions of the individual operational amplifiers (G_i's) and the passive circuit elements (we often accept the manufacturers data for the latter); G_c is then calculated from these data with the help of (VIa) in Table 8.3. In this case obvious advantages are realized by explicitly considering G_c in terms of the properties of the individual subunits because the mathematical relationship which must be developed (VIa) provides the basis on which to adjust the properties of G_c (relative amounts of proportional, differential, and integral control) intelligently to optimize the G_{OL} characteristics. A strictly empirical approach would be considerably less efficient. These ideas are further illustrated below.

As we survey the discussion to follow, it becomes apparent that transfer function measurements usually involve signal sources and measuring devices that are not ultimately part of the control network. Like the control network components under test, these extraneous testing devices involve physical processes with finite response characteristics. When used in measuring the response of a control network component, we must be certain that they do not contribute to the transfer function measured; that is, the testing devices should respond much more rapidly than the system under investigation or, when this cannot be achieved, appropriate corrections must be introduced. In some cases this may be a decidedly nontrivial problem.

Experimental Measurements—Specific Examples

To clarify the foregoing concepts, particularly with regard to the use of Table 8.4 and the special measurement situations encountered in various types of physical system, some specific examples are considered at this point. More comprehensive treatments of the measurement problems are available [5, 6, 13, 24].

Electrical Systems

If measurement of the transfer function of an electronic system is desired, the main problem confronting the chemist is his choice among the vast proliferation of possible approaches. The scope and sophistication of the electronic art is such that we are usually faced with a variety of techniques that will give the desired information with speed and accuracy, regardless of whether we are concerned with current or voltage signals. Voltage ratio, current ratio, and impedance and admittance transfer functions can be measured with reasonable ease in most situations. Automated measurement is feasible with the aid of components which are readily acquired by purchase or loan. Figure 8.7 is a schematic of a system that will record Bode plots automatically for any of the four conceivable transfer-function types. The frequency sweep oscillator provides a sinusoidal output (voltage or current) of constant amplitude whose frequency varies with time (usually linearly). Such devices often provide a frequency-proportional dc output which, on logarithmic conversion, provides the abscissa (log frequency) for the x-y plotter. The sinusoidal response (voltage or current) of the system under test is converted to an amplitude-proportional dc signal by full-wave rectification and filtering. The resulting output undergoes logarithmic conversion (log gain) and is applied to the ordinate of the x-y plotter. The resulting x-y plot provides only the relative gain as a function of frequency and may be converted to absolute units simply by locating manually the unity gain point (log $G = 0$). Absolute gain can be recorded directly with an electronic divider [25, 26] that will divide the output amplitude level by the input magnitude, but the added convenience seldom justifies the added expense.

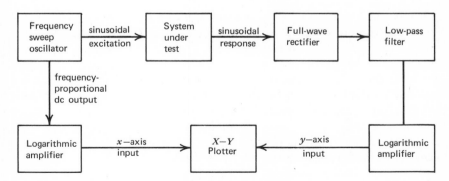

Fig. 8.7   System for automatic Bode plot measurement with electronic devices.

The schematic of Fig. 8.7 can also be used to represent the essential features of an apparatus for point-by-point measurement of the frequency response (replace the frequency-sweep oscillator with a manual frequency-selection device and the x-y recorder with a digital or analog dc voltmeter).

Chemical Systems

Measurements of chemical system transfer functions involve measurement hardware quite familiar to those at whom this chapter is directed. Accordingly, detailed consideration of the rather specialized and sophisticated chemical measuring devices will be avoided.

When encountered, chemical systems almost invariably appear as the controlled system in man-made control networks. They seldom act as controllers or feedback networks, although this is not unusual in naturally occurring control networks [27]. Variables we wish to control with chemical systems usually involve the concentration (or activity) of one or more species or an electrical property such as an electrochemical cell potential or current. On rare occasions some less familiar variable such as particle size in a dispersion might be involved. Regardless of which case is relevant, the state of the art is such that measurement of the controlled variable by the feedback network usually yields an electronic signal as the output. When concentrations are monitored by some concentration-related readout such as cell potential (e.g., pH measurement), spectral transmittance or conductivity, modern instrumentation invariably yields an electronic readout. Control of electrochemical properties of necessity involves an electronic readout. As a result, aside from the chemical system itself, most of the equipment supporting the transfer-function measurement can be drawn from the offerings of the highly developed electronic art. It should be mentioned that this state of affairs is not a property of chemical systems alone. Transducing nonelectronic signals into electronic and vice versa is an art of rather broad scope as the ensuing discussion illustrates.

When the operation involves control of a concentration or activity, the apparatus usually includes (a) an electronically activated reagent delivery system, such as a motor-driven buret or an electrochemical cell for *in situ* or external electrolytic reagent generation, (b) a chemical system (reactor), and (c) a measuring device such as an electrochemical cell with an appropriate signal conditioning device or an optical window in the system container coupled to a spectrophotometer. Items (a) and (b) may be considered as the controlled system [(a) is categorized in this manner for convenience—it could also be considered part of the controller]. Item (c) represents the feedback network. It is probably evident that sinusoidal signals usually are not well suited to such equipment, particularly when a motor-driven buret or other type of liquid-flow delivery system is encountered. A step input is more appropriate. We may measure the $G_s G_h$ product transfer function simply by stepping the electrical input to the reagent delivery system and following the electrical response at the measuring system output with the aid of an oscilloscope or recorder. The "rise time" we observe will, in principle, include contributions from the finite response of the reagent delivery system from the time delay associated with mixing and chemical reaction rates in the reactor and from the response time of the measuring system. If desired, the individual transfer functions G_s and G_h can be obtained by measuring G_h independently, from which G_s is calculable by using the $G_s G_h$ value (independent measurement of G_s is less convenient). Measurement of G_h might involve operations such as the artificial introduction of a sudden change in apparent absorptivity (inserting filter in front of detector, switching light intensity, suddenly changing the solution in contact with an electrochemical measuring system, etc.). Also, the subsidiary transfer functions in G_s, which are associated with the delivery system and reactor, may be obtained individually. This could be accomplished by separate measurement of the delivery-system response; for example, measurement of the delivery flow-rate in grams per second (see under fluid systems). Clearly, detailed transfer-function measurements of this type often require some planning, ingenuity, and special equipment. Such reasons often lead us to confine measurement to the readily obtained $G_s G_h$ transfer function unless more extended insights are absolutely necessary.

Whenever an electrochemical variable such as a cell potential or current is the controlled quantity, the control-system designer is usually justified in subverting the chemical aspect of the system to the point at which it is considered just another electronic circuit element. Transfer-function measurements then involve the same operations of any electronic device. Sinusoidal test signals are perfectly acceptable and a setup of the type illustrated in Fig. 8.7 might be used; for example, a two-electrode cell response to ac signals is often approximately that of an ohmic resistance (bulk solution resistance) and pure capacitance (electrode-solution interfacial capacitance) in series or parallel. Ignoring the chemistry is most justified when essentially nondestructive electrolysis is envisioned as in dc polarography or conductivity measurements in which the amount of electrolysis is negligible during the measurement period. In such cases, even though the impedance properties may be notably more complex than the simple RC-type just mentioned, the system nevertheless behaves as an electrical circuit element characterized by a relatively constant, measurable transfer function. As any loyal chemist would expect, however, failure to give due recognition to the chemistry will occasionally lead to difficulties. We must keep in mind that the chemical and electrical properties of the electrochemical cell are intimately coupled. Whenever an operation leads to a change in the chemical make-up (e.g., large-scale electrolysis), the electrical properties (transfer function) will vary accordingly. Failure to concern ourselves with this principle may lead to serious design errors. The implications are explored in greater detail in Section 4.

Thermal Systems

Most thermal systems consist of a heating and/or cooling element and bulk material whose temperature or rate of temperature change is maintained constant. Heating elements usually involve electrical heaters or a fluid heat source-heat exchanger system. Cooling elements are generally of the fluid coolant-heat exchanger type. The input to the thermal system may be a voltage (current) from an electrical or electronic controller or pressure from a pneumatic controller, expansion-bulb thermometer, or electronic controller which incorporates a current-to-pressure transducer. The latter is used when the control loop contains an electronic controller, but the manipulated variable is the flow of a fluid heater (e.g., steam) or coolant.

The transfer function most frequently utilized to characterize thermal systems is the output/input ratio of change in temperature per unit change in controller signal. The "thermometer" always associated with a thermal system is not normally considered part of the thermal system. It is more properly identified as the feedback element.

Experimental determination of transfer functions for thermal systems is most readily achieved by making a step change in the input (electrical current, pressure applied to a valve, etc.) and recording the thermometer output. If an electrical heater is used, a step change is effected by increasing or decreasing the amount of current to the heater instantaneously. If a fluid heat source (e.g., steam) or coolant is employed, the step change can be made by abruptly opening or closing (by a small amount) the value controlling the fluid flow rate to the heating element. If the thermometer and recording device are chosen properly, the observed response will be a true representation of the thermal system response because most thermal systems are characterized by a large thermal capacitance and respond relatively slowly. As a result, most thermometers and recorders are more than adequate in response speed to indicate the true response of the thermal system; that is, the measurement-system transfer function may be taken as unity. Occasionally a system of small thermal capacity is encountered (faster response), and some care must be exercised in choosing the thermometer to ensure that this simple situation exists (any modern recording device will still be adequate). A thermometer with a small time constant without a well or shield must be used. Typical examples are unshielded thermocouples (useful only if the thermal system material does not affect the thermocouple junction) or small expansion-bulb thermometers. Because the output of thermistors is exponential with temperature, these devices should be avoided unless a linearizing circuit (logarithmic amplifier) is provided. To ensure that the observed response reflects only the thermal-system transfer function, the time constant of the thermometer and recorder must be at least an order of magnitude smaller than that of the system. In situations in which a thermometer that meets these standards is unavailable, the recorder readout must be taken as the product of the thermal system and thermometer transfer functions; that is, the measurement yields $G_s G_h$. To obtain G_s we must measure the thermometer transfer function G_h independently. This also is accomplished best by a step-function input. The step change can be made by rapidly removing the thermometer from an environment at one temperature (determined by a "standard thermometer") and plunging it into an environment at another. If this environment is a fluid, care must be taken to use a fluid with similar heat-transfer properties to that of the controlled system. This care is necessary, since the fluid-film heat-transfer coefficient plays a dominant role in the thermometer transfer function [28, 29].

The observed transfer functions of most thermal systems are overdamped second- or third-order types; that is, transfer functions with two or more separable time constants. Occasionally the transfer function may be higher than third-order. These separable time constants may be obtained from the time-versus-temperature response to a step change by easily applied graphical techniques [5, 13].

Fluid Systems

When considering a fluid system as part of a control system, it must be considered from one of two different viewpoints, depending on whether the controlled fluid system is a fluid-flow system (flow control) or a pressure or liquid-level system (pressure or liquid-level control). To obtain flow control it is necessary to manipulate pressure or level; to obtain pressure or level control it is necessary to manipulate flow. Of course, such a statement has an analog in all nonfluid systems; that is, in electrical networks we control potential by manipulating current and vice versa. Just as we normally cannot control electrical current and potential simultaneously, in fluid systems simultaneous control of flow and pressure (or level) is not possible.

Although perhaps less familiar to chemists than the analogous electronic devices, the hardware available for control-network synthesis and transfer-function measurement with fluid systems (pressure, fluid-flow rate and liquid-level measuring devices) is nevertheless readily available, versatile, and sophisticated. Indeed, the science of "fluidics" has shown signs of particularly rapid growth, and we now find numerous fluidic analogs of the more complex electronic circuits such as operational amplifiers. The reader is referred to the appropriate literature for descriptions of available hardware [6].

To determine transfer functions for the fluid pressure or level systems experimentally it is preferable to include the control valve and any associated current-to-pressure converters as part of the controlled system. This element often plays a major role in determining the system controllability. The latter statement also applies to most feedback elements whose transfer function is invariably nonunity under normal operating conditions. Since the feedback element must be used to observe the controlled-system response in transfer-function measurements, the observed response must be recognized as manifesting the product transfer function $G_s G_h$. As in previous examples, the controlled-system transfer function G_s is calculable, provided G_h is known or independently measurable. Complications such as nonlinearity of fluid flow through restrictions, differences between laminar and turbulent flow, differences between adiabatic and isothermal flow in gases, and whether exact level (or pressure) control or averaging control is desired abound in fluid systems. As a result it is particularly important that the experimental determination of the transfer function be made under operating conditions close to the desired value of the controlled variable. The transfer function may be obtained by making a small step change in the input to the control-valve mechanism and measuring or recording the output of the feedback element. The feedback element may have an output signal of pressure, current or voltage, position, depending on the type of element (pressure gage, float, etc.). Of course, any signal converter necessary to make the feedback signal compatible with the controller should be included as part of the feedback element in such measurements. Fluid systems sometimes respond rapidly enough that transfer-function determination with sinusoidal inputs may be used with the aid of "low-frequency" sine-wave generators.

Fluid-flow controlled systems differ from most other types in that the time constant of the process itself is often negligible, that is, after the value moves to a new position the final flow rate for that position is reached in a time period that is short compared with other events in the control operation. Thus the response of the control network (G_{OL}) depends primarily on the controller, the feedback element, and control valve. Because of the non-linearities of actual fluid flow relations, a change in flow rate is accompanied by apparent changes in controlled-system gain and/or time constant (it may be possible to insert a static nonlinearity into the system to get constant gain and time constant; for example, a control value which has the proper characteristics to achieve constant gain and time constant with various flow rates is often chosen). Another consideration of flow systems is that the feedback signal is often noisy. Part of the noise is due to actual changes in flow which are too fast to be corrected by the control system. These may come from fluctuations in the differential pressure which is the flow driving force or from random changes in the flow pattern in different parts of the system. In addition, many types of flow meter have inherent noise patterns, especially those that are based on pressure or force measurements. Because of these problems, it is also necessary in flow systems, as in pressure or level systems, to determine the transfer function of the controlled system under conditions close to the desired set-point. Step inputs may be used for flow-system transfer-function measurements. Flow systems also respond sufficiently rapidly, however, to make feasible the use of sinusoidal inputs and frequency-response techniques that yield more precise data.

Flow-rate changes are obtained by changing the differential pressure across the system. This is achieved either by changing the high-pressure value, the low-pressure value, or the pressure drop across some element in the system. Usually it is most convenient to manipulate the input to the control valve.

The "circuit" elements of fluid systems (Table 8.4) consist of resistance, capacitance, and inductance or inertance. In most systems of concern to chemists flow, pressure, and level usually have finite average values and the deviations from these values are the parameters considered; for example, fluid capacitance usually is defined as $\Delta V/\Delta P$ (V = volume, P = pressure), and in the case of liquids it is usually defined by the container cross-sectional area. Fluid resistance is defined as $R = \Delta P/\Delta F$ (F = flow rate). The one common exception to this is pneumatic instrument and controller air lines, the consideration of which requires more attention than can be given here [8, 13, 30, 31].

Mechanical Systems

Mechanical systems are generally composed of various masses connected by elements that provide damping and spring effects. As a result, most mechanical systems may be reduced to second-order systems and are characterized by the damping ratio ζ and characteristic frequency ω_0, as discussed in Section 2. Because of the possibility of the oscillatory nature of mechanical systems, experimental determination of transfer functions is best performed by using sinusoidal inputs and frequency-response techniques for analysis. When the mechanical system is overdamped, step input response may be used with graphical techniques to obtain the ζ and ω_0 parameters [5, 13]. A step response can be used with underdamped systems to determine ζ and ω_0, as described in Section 2, but these results are often not so satisfactory as those derived from frequency response analysis.

The commonest mechanical systems of interest to the chemist are the manometer and the servo-driven recorder. The latter is discussed at length in Chapter VII, which provides enough information to conclude the present discussion at this point.

Calculations from Available Data

Although properly performed experimental measurements of transfer functions give the most reliable data, this task is often avoidable. In most mathematical analyses of control networks extreme precision is not required to reach valid conclusions on accuracy and stability; therefore data from manufacturers' specifications and certain other sources often suffice. Many times the available information is not in the desired transfer-function formulation and data transformation is required. Some brief remarks on recognizing the appropriate data and on their manipulation are given at this point.

Many individual *active* components (e.g., amplifiers) characterized by first-order transfer functions will be encountered. For such elements one common and completely adequate form of performance specification gives the unity-gain crossover frequency and the dc gain. These two simple data points enable expression of the transfer function in mathematical or graphical form. By consulting (8.13) we can recognize that the dc gain is K_0 and T_1 is obtainable from the unity-gain crossover frequency (f_1), using the relationship

$$T_1 = \frac{K_0}{2\pi f_1}. \tag{8.50}$$

Having obtained the K_0 and T_1 values, we may construct the Bode plot from calculations based on (8.13). Alternatively, the approximate Bode plot can be obtained simply by extending two straight lines to their points of intersection, one being the line of zero slope at the ordinate value of log K_0 and the other, the line of -1 slope which passes through the unity-gain frequency. This yields a Bode plot with an abrupt change in slope from zero to -1 at the point of intersection, whereas the actual roll-off ensues with a smooth, continuous transition in slope (see Fig. 8.3). However, the approximation is of little consequence in most applications of Bode plots. An example of an electronic component of first-order response whose unity-gain crossover frequency and dc gain are invariably quoted in the manufacturers specifications is the Type I operational amplifier. Electronic and nonelectronic proportional controllers also are often characterized in this manner.

When we consider active components whose responses are more complex than first-order, the possibilities expand so enormously that any complete discussion is precluded. Therefore only a few brief examples are considered here. Fortunately, most devices we might purchase for control-network controllers and feedback elements are designed so that their transfer functions are not overly complex. Otherwise the user would require the insights of an experienced electrical engineer which does not favor sales performance. One type of second-order transfer function occasionally encountered is characterized by a roll-off slope of -2 (40 dB/decade) at *all* frequencies in the roll-off region. This response corresponds to a critically damped second-order system ($\zeta = 1$) in which [see (8.16)]

$$G(p) = \frac{K_0}{(p/\omega_0 + 1)^2}. \tag{8.51}$$

The magnitude of this transfer function is given by

$$|G(\omega t)| = \frac{K_0}{[1 + (\omega/\omega_0)^2]}. \tag{8.52}$$

From (8.52) we see that ω_0 is related to the unity-gain frequency f_1 by

$$\omega_0 = \frac{2\pi f_1}{K_0^{\frac{1}{2}}}. \tag{8.53}$$

Consequently, as in the first-order case, statement of the dc gain and the unity-gain crossover frequency implicitly defines K_0 and ω_0. Approximate Bode plots are constructed as in the first-order case except that the line through the unity-gain frequency is of -2 slope.

Occasionally we encounter a transfer function characterized by a Bode plot with two 20 dB/decade roll-off regions separated by an intermediate frequency region of constant gain. An example is the Type II operational amplifier (Fig. 8.6a). In this case four data points must be known: (a) the dc gain, (b) the gain after the first roll-off (intermediate frequency gain), (c) the frequency at which the first roll-off ensues (or ends), (d) the unity-gain crossover frequency. Conversion of these data into a mathematical transfer function formulation is best accomplished by considering the appropriate transfer function [(IB), Table 8.3]:

$$G(p) = \frac{K_0(1 + A_1 p)}{(1 + A_2 p)(1 + A_3 p)}. \tag{8.54}$$

Evaluation of the parameters from the data points is aided by recognizing that at frequencies beyond the first roll-off (8.54) reduces to

$$G(p) = \frac{K_0 A_1/A_2}{1 + A_3 p}. \tag{8.55}$$

Thus the intermediate frequency gain G_{INT} is given by

$$G_{\text{INT}} = \frac{K_0 A_1}{A_2}, \tag{8.56}$$

and the unity-gain crossover frequency is given by a modification of (8.50), where $K_0 A_1 / A_2$ replaces K_0; that is,

$$f_1 = \frac{K_0 A_1}{2\pi A_2 A_3}. \tag{8.57}$$

It can also be shown that the approximate frequency at which a first-order roll-off ensues (the break-frequency of f_b) is given by [refer to (8.13)]

$$f_b = \frac{1}{2\pi T_1}. \tag{8.58}$$

Thus K_0 is obtained as usual from the dc gain, A_2 is evaluated from (8.58), where A_2 is identified as T_1. These results then permit calculation of A_1 from (8.56), followed by application of (8.57) to give A_3.

In many cases manufacturer's literature actually provides transfer functions in the form of Bode plots. These are, of course, directly applicable to graphical analysis of the control network. Occasionally, however, we wish to perform an extensive analysis of the control-network response as a function of various controllable parameters. For such endeavors we may wish to avoid the tedium of repeated plotting by developing a computer program so that a digital computer can perform extensive numerical calculations and, if desired, produce the Bode plots via a computer-controlled plotter. Consequently, we wish to transform the graphical Bode plot data into mathematical transfer-function expressions. We approach this task in the same manner, since all of the required data points just described are explicitly given in the Bode plots.

The foregoing remarks on transforming data into transfer functions are most relevant to items we purchase to serve as the controller or feedback network or subunits thereof. On the other hand, the origin and nature of the controlled system is often determined by the individual chemist so that the foregoing types of specifications on the performance of the controlled system usually are not available in the direct sense. Occasionally the same situation will concern the feedback network (measuring device). In such situations, however, more basic data forms are often available on the system subunits which may be synthesized into a calculated total system response. Most frequently the controlled system and/or feedback element is *passive* in nature and the data required for transfer-function calculation are the impedance magnitudes (generalized) considered in Table 8.4. Because it defines the nature of the physical parameters corresponding to the various impedances, Table 8.4 may be viewed as a compilation of the data forms we must find in manufacturers specifications or other sources for all relevant types of physical systems. We need only combine these impedance data with the appropriate laws governing impedance combinations (see Table 8.2 or more extensive tabulations [32]) to obtain calculated transfer functions.

Application of these ideas is usually straightforward and is considered here for the case of thermal systems only. Some specific aspects of the transfer-function calculation problem for electrochemical systems may be found in the next section. A general discussion of unique problems or guidelines for all special types of physical process is well beyond the scope of this chapter and may be found in the literature [1–13, 24, 28–31, 33].

Estimation of transfer functions for well-defined thermal systems is readily accomplished with the assistance of certain approximations. One of the commonest approximations is found in the assumption that all fluids are at thermal equilibrium; that is, the fluids are well-stirred or flowing at high velocities. This assumption is incorporated in the discussion to follow with certain other approximations that are noted when appropriate. Results of such idealized calculations, although inexact, are often adequate as guidelines for stability and accuracy estimates of temperature control systems under consideration. The problems associated with calculating and utilizing exact transfer functions are discussed in more detailed treatments [28, 29, 34].

A simple example of a thermal system is an electrical resistance wire heater immersed in a liquid fluid bath. The transfer function of this system consists of two parts: the transform of current or voltage from the controller into heat output of the heater and the transform of heat flow into bath-fluid temperature. The transfer function of current or voltage into heat output is simply a magnitude factor; that is, $\dot{q}/i = G'$, where $\dot{q} = $ cal/sec, $i = $ amps, and G' is determined by a linear approximation of the power dissipation law for ohmic elements [29]. The transfer of heat output into bath temperature involves the dynamics of heat flow from the wire across a thermal resistance usually consisting of the wire-heater sheath insulator into a capacitance consisting of the heat capacity of the fluid bulk. Also involved are the heat losses from the bath to the surroundings in which heat flows across the thermal resistance of the bath container. In general, thermal resistances are given by

$$\text{resistance} = \frac{\text{insulator thickness}}{(\text{insulator thermal conductivity} \times \text{insulator area})}, \quad (8.59)$$

where the units are deg-sec/cal.

Strictly speaking, three time constants are associated with the heat-transfer process under consideration, $R_s C_w$, $R_s C_b$, and $R_w C_b$, where R_s is the insulator-sheath thermal resistance, R_w is the bath-wall thermal resistance, C_w is the heater wire-heat capacity, and C_b is the bath-fluid heat capacity. The wire-heat capacity is relatively small and normally the transient associated with the $R_s C_w$ time constant is not observed and its contribution may be neglected. In effect, this means that the wire temperature quickly reaches its steady-state value in which the heat flow from the wire to the bath equals the heat generation rate $\dot{q}$. If, in addition, the bath is well-insulated so that heat losses to the surroundings may be ignored, the transfer function for heat output into temperature $G'' = T/\dot{q}$ is simply that of a pure capacitance; that is, $G'' = (pC_b)^{-1}$. Thus the total system transfer function is

$$G_s = Ti^{-1} = G'(pC_b)^{-1}. \tag{8.60}$$

If heat losses to the surroundings must be considered, the system transfer function becomes first-order with a time constant equal to R_wC_b [34].

A more relevant example to chemists involves the control of the temperature of the contents of a beaker suspended in a water bath. The system is illustrated in Fig. 8.8. If we ignore the heat capacity of the beaker, which is usually small compared with that of the bath and beaker contents, we may write from simple heat balance considerations

$$q_{in} - \frac{1}{R_T}(\theta_b - \theta_f) = C_bp\theta_b, \tag{8.61}$$

$$\frac{1}{R_T}(\theta_b - \theta_f) = C_fp\theta_f, \tag{8.62}$$

$$R_T = \frac{1}{k_o} + \frac{1}{k_i} + \frac{1}{k_g}. \tag{8.63}$$

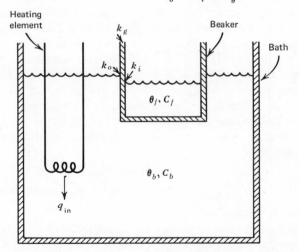

Fig. 8.8 Thermal system: beaker in constant temperature bath: q_{in} = heat input (cal/sec.); θ_b = bath temperature; θ_f = beaker contents temperature; C_b = total heat capacity of bath fluid (specific heat times mass); C_f = total heat capacity of beaker contents; k_g = reciprocal of beaker wall thermal resistance (8.59). k_o = thermal transmission coefficient of film of bath material times outside area of beaker; k_i = thermal transmission coefficient of film of beaker contents times inside area of beaker.

The various parameters are defined in the legend of Fig. 8.8. Equation 8.61 states essentially that the difference in heat input (q_{in}) and output $[(1/R_T)(\theta_b - \theta_g)]$ to the bath equals the bath heat capacity times the rate of temperature change (remember: $p = d/dt$). Equation 8.62 is a similar heat-balance relationship for the beaker contents. Both expressions ignore heat losses to the surroundings (which are often significant). A combination of (8.61) and (8.62) yields

$$\frac{\theta_f}{q_{in}} = \frac{R_T}{(T_1 p + 1)(T_2 p + 1) - 1},$$ (8.64)

where

$$T_1 = R_T C_f,$$ (8.65)
$$T_2 = R_T C_b,$$ (8.66)

Thus a pseudo-second-order response is expected. In situations in which the beaker heat capacity is important and/or heat losses to surroundings must be considered even higher order transfer functions are obtained. All of the factors in the transfer function of (8.64) may be calculated from available data. The heat capacities are obtained from standard chemical references. The thermal transmission coefficients may be obtained from treatises on heat transmission [8, 29]. Because we know the weight of the materials and beaker surface area, all constants are calculable.

Transfer functions for thermometers may be calculated in a manner similar to the preceding example. A heat balance is made between the temperature of the measured fluid and the temperature indicated by the thermometer. Different forms of the transfer function, that is, first-, second-, or third-order, may be obtained, depending on the relative size of the capacitances and resistances involved, whether thermometer wells are used, and so on. This problem is extensively treated elsewhere [8, 13].

4   APPLICATION OF BASIC PRINCIPLES TO SPECIFIC SYSTEMS

This section is devoted to illustrating how the foregoing ideas can be applied to specific automatic control systems. The examples selected begin with a rather simple all-electronic system, progress through standard thermal (temperature controller) and mechanical servo systems to a relatively complex dual-feedback loop system found in modern electrochemical potentiostats.

An Electrical Potential Control Network

Figure 8.9 illustrates a system for control of electrical potential. It is useful whenever a precision signal source (r) is unable to furnish adequate current

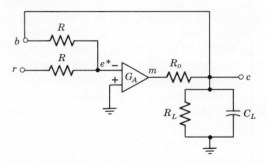

Fig. 8.9 Electrical potential control network: G_A = control amplifier open-loop gain = $-K_o/(1 + T_1p)$; e = voltage at negative (inverting) input of control amplifier; r = input signal (volts); b = feedback signal (volts); m = manipulated variable (volts); c = controlled variable (volts); R = summing network resistors; R_o = output resistance of control amplifier and/or output conductor resistance; R_L, C_L = load resistance and capacitance.

levels. The amplifier designated by G_A together with its input resistors (R's) is the controller. The inputs of the controller resistors represent the summing junction. Components R_o, R_L, and C_L constitute the controlled system and the connection (simple wire) between points b and c is the feedback network.

The controller amplifier may be an operational amplifier or an appropriate type of power supply (e.g., an operational power supply [35]), depending on the current levels demanded. Summing the input and feedback signals through two resistors represents one type of practical summing junction, the resistive mixing approach. In effect, we are summing the currents through the input resistors. We must recognize that a factor of 2 is introduced because of the voltage division action of the summing resistors. Therefore the amplifier input voltage signal e^* is given by

$$e^* = \frac{r + b}{2} = \frac{e}{2} ; \tag{8.67}$$

that is, e^* differs by a factor of 2 from the error signal, as defined earlier. This means that the controller transfer function is one-half the transfer function of the controller amplifier.

The system components are represented as two parallel elements across which potential control is desired, R_L and C_L, and one "extraneous" element, R_o. R_L and C_L may actually be an electronic resistor and capacitor in parallel. Their possible identity, however, should be considered in a broader sense; for example, R_L and C_L may represent the cumulative resistance and capacitance of a large array of electronic components in a major instrument. Alternatively, R_L and C_L could represent the impedance of a two-electrode electrolytic cell in a controlled-potential electrolysis setup. The component

R_o may be considered as representing the resistance in a connecting lead between the controller and the components R_L, C_L and/or the output impedance of the controller amplifier. In cases in which remote-sensing is employed (the controller and R_L, C_L are physically well separated) the conductor resistance may be significant. In many cases the amplifier output impedance is nontrivial (50 to 100 Ω). We might think it more appropriate to consider R_0 as part of the controller, particularly when it originates in the controller output impedance. This approach would represent a reasonable alternative that necessarily could not influence the final results. The previously mentioned arbitrary choices we encounter in identifying the role of certain control network components is manifested in the choice we have in assigning R_o.

We now consider the network of Fig. 8.9 for the case in which the controller amplifier is characterized by a first-order response:

$$\frac{m}{e} = \frac{m}{r + b} = G_c = \frac{-K_o/2}{1 + T_1 p} \; ; \tag{8.68}$$

K_o is the dc gain of the amplifier. The factor of 2 arises for reasons given in (8.67). The minus sign indicates that in the configuration shown the controller amplifies at normal frequencies with inversion of sign, thus providing the negative feedback characteristic. This sign relationship would occur for any operational power supply. If we assume that the amplifier input resistors (R's) are large enough that the current through the feedback loop is negligible compared with the current through R_L and C_L (easily realized and logically the only relevant conditions to consider, since we do not wish to load the input source r), then G_s may be written

$$G_s = \frac{c}{m} = \frac{1}{(1 + R_o/R_L) + R_o C_L p} . \tag{8.69}$$

Ignoring the resistance of the feedback wire, we may write

$$G_h = 1. \tag{8.70}$$

By substituting (8.68) to (8.70) in (8.34), we obtain

$$G_{\text{OL}} = \left(\frac{-K_o/2}{1 + T_1 p}\right)\left(\frac{1}{(1 + R_o/R_L) + R_o C_L p}\right). \tag{8.71}$$

Equation 8.71 may be rearranged in the more useful form

$$G_{\text{OL}} = \frac{-K_o}{2(1 + R_o/R_L)}\left(\frac{1}{1 + T_1 p}\right)\left(\frac{1}{1 + T_1^* p}\right). \tag{8.72}$$

where

$$T_1{}^* = \frac{R_oC_L}{(1 + R_o/R_L)}.$$

(8.73)

At the outset it should be recognized that at low frequencies G_{OL} reduces to

$$\lim (G_{OL})_{\omega \to 0} = \frac{-K_o}{2(1 + R_o/R_L)}.$$

(8.74)

If the amplifier dc gain K_o is large enough that

$$\left| \frac{K_o}{2(1 + R_o/R_L)} \right| \gg 1,$$

(8.75)

then the low-frequency closed-loop transfer function G_N (8.33) will equal -1 within the error given by (8.43). Thus, if a high-gain amplifier is used, the desired signal c will equal the input signal r; that is, the ideal response is consistent with the objective of potential control.

It should be apparent, on brief inspection of (8.72) and application of previously stated concepts; that the open-loop gain is the product of two first-order responses, that is, a second-order system, which can be characterized by a unity gain slope of -40 dB/decade (see Fig. 8.5) under many conditions. Therefore unstable operating conditions exist for this circuit. It is also evident that the source of the possible instability is in the coupling of the elements R_o and C_L. If either were zero ($R_oC_L = 0$), a simple, stable first-order response would characterize G_{OL}.

Additional insights into the accuracy and stability characteristics of the control network in question are obtained by examining the Bode plots of G_{OL} as a function of the system parameters. Some typical examples are shown in Figs. 8.10 to 8.12. Figure 8.10 shows the effect on the Bode plot of changing the controller amplifier time constant, using typical values of the other parameters. With the slowest amplifier response considered ($T_1 = 1.6$) the Bode plot is characterized by a steady 20 dB/decade roll-off to frequencies well beyond the unity-gain value. Thus a well-behaved, stable system is obtained. The response of the network in this case, however, is relatively slow. Although the dc accuracy in the context of (8.43) is excellent (0.004% error), the accuracy degrades rapidly with frequency (11% error at 250 Hz). Of course, some applications will find such a response speed more than adequate and the network with $T_1 = 1.6$ sec will perform in excellent style. When $T_1 = 1.6 \times 10^{-1}$ sec (Fig. 8.10), the threshold between stable and unstable operation has been reached. The break from -20 to -40 dB/decade slope is occurring at the unity-gain frequency. Strictly speaking, the system should be stable, but any slight change in a network parameter (e.g., a slight increase in K_o) may cause the system to go unstable. The two

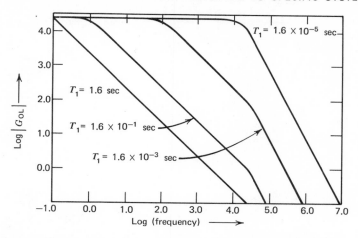

Fig. 8.10   Bode plots of potential control network open-loop gain showing effect of T_1 $K_o = 1.00 \times 10^5$, $R_o = 100\ \Omega$, $R_L = 100\ \Omega$, $C_L = 1.00 \times 10^{-7}$ F.

highest T_1 values of Fig. 8.10 yield -40 dB/decade unity-gain slopes and thus unstable systems. It is apparent that for the conditions considered in Fig. 8.10, attempts to increase high-frequency accuracy by using a faster amplifier will be attended by a decrease in the stability margin. A slight qualification of the last statement is in order, for if T_1 were made sufficiently small a reverse trend would begin (faster amplifier, greater stability). However, this would require amplifier response rates that greatly exceed the present state of the art. Indeed, the combination of $T_1 = 1.6 \times 10^{-5}$ sec and $K_o = 10^5$ used in Fig. 8.10 slightly exceeds what is now available.

Figure 8.11 shows the effect of R_o on the Bode plot for a case involving a relatively fast controller amplifier. Increasing R_o not only decreases stability but also reduces the dc accuracy; R_o is clearly an undesirable element. With the exception of $R_o = 0.1$ ohm, the Bode plots of Fig. 8.11 correspond to unstable conditions. Thus, in order actually to realize the benefits of the fast amplifier considered in Fig. 8.11, that is, to achieve a fast, yet stable control network, R_o must be reduced to nearly 0.1 Ω.

Figure 8.12 shows the effects of the C_L value. Unlike R_o, C_L has no effect on the dc accuracy. Like R_o, C_L markedly influences stability. The Bode plot of Fig. 8.12 with $C_L = 10^{-9}$ barely falls in the stable realm. Larger values of C_L correspond to an unstable system and vice versa. Figures 8.11 and 8.12 show that there is an upper limit on the R_oC_L time constant for a given amplifier. Either one maintains a small capacitance or takes pains to reduce the output resistance of the amplifier and the output conductor resistance. Such principles have been stated repeatedly by manufacturers of high-gain

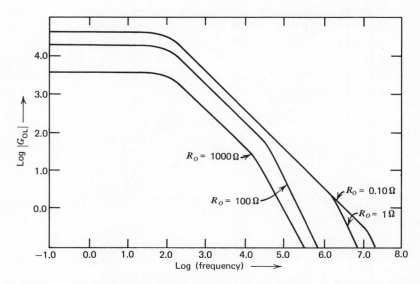

Fig. 8.11 Bode plots of potential control network open-loop gain showing effect of R_o. $K_o = 1.00 \times 10^5$, $R_L = 100\ \Omega$, $C_L = 1.00 \times 10^{-7}$ F, $T_1 = 1.60 \times 10^{-3}$ sec.

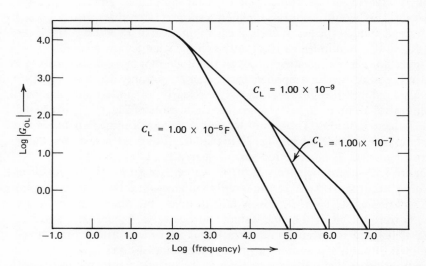

Fig. 8.12 Bode plots of potential control network open-loop gain showing effect of C_L: $K_o = 1.00 \times 10^5$, $R_o = 100\ \Omega$, $R_L = 100\ \Omega$, $T_1 = 1.60 \times 10^{-3}$ sec.

fast-response operational amplifiers [36–38]. A generalization of this idea is that the system in question will be stable only if the time constants T_1 and T_1^* are sufficiently different that the *unity-gain crossover frequency* associated with one time constant is equal to or less than the *break frequency* associated with the other. In other words [adapting (8.50) and (8.58) to the present case], for stable operation we must have either

$$\frac{1}{2\pi T_1} \geq \frac{K_o}{4\pi T_1^*(1 + R_o/R_L)} \tag{8.76}$$

or

$$\frac{1}{2\pi T_1^*} \geq \frac{K_o}{4\pi T_1(1 + R_o/R_L)}. \tag{8.77}$$

If we define ξ as the ratio of the largest of the two time constants over the smallest, this criteria for stable operation may be given in the more compact form

$$\xi \geq \frac{K_o}{2(1 + R_o/R_L)}. \tag{8.78}$$

Certain basic principles are made eminently apparent by these results. First of all, most attempts to improve accuracy such as raising the gain term K_o (or improving high-frequency accuracy) are accompanied by a decrease in the stability margin. In other words, accuracy and stability are mutually incompatible requirements and we must seek a compromise to achieve both to a reasonable degree with any given network. This principle applies to control mechanisms in general. The second important concept is that relatively subtle, seemingly harmless alterations in a control network can sometimes cause a change from seemingly ideal operation to disaster or vice versa. For example, the conductor from the controller amplifier to the components R_L, C_L might be changed from an unshielded to a shielded cable. The added capacitive load (the conductor-shield capacitance adds to C_L) may be sufficient to cause an otherwise stable system to become unstable. Figure 8.10 with $T_1 = 1.6 \times 10^{-1}$ sec, Fig. 8.11 with $R_o = 0.10\ \Omega$, or Fig. 8.12 with $C_L = 10^{-9}$ represent conditions in which this could readily occur.

A Temperature Control Network

The majority of thermal control loops that the chemist encounters are simple on-off control systems. They depend on large thermal capacitances to smooth out the discontinuities of the manipulated variable and the cyclic variation of the controlled system heat load. Many systems, however, are encountered in which more sophisticated control modes are necessary to achieve thermal stability with adequate precision. In general, the smaller the capacitances, the larger their number, and the larger the coupled thermal resistances (unless they completely overwhelm the effect of capacitance), the more complex the controller must be to obtain the desired control precision.

The thermal control problems of chemists largely fall into the classification of heat exchanger problems. The dynamics of heat exchangers are widely varying, depending on the type of exchanger and physical state of the two fluids. We limit the following discussion to one specific type of heat exchanger and refer the reader to more detailed treatments given elsewhere [8, 22, 28, 29, 39, 40].

We now consider a system in which temperature control of a liquid flowing into a spectrophotometer is desired. The liquid is normally at a varying temperature somewhat below the desired temperature. To achieve control the liquid is pumped through a heat exchanger at a constant velocity. The heat exchanger is of the dead-end type in which all the steam (heat source) condenses on the tube coil; thus constant temperature is maintained over the outside length of the coil (a cooling coil in an agitated bath is also this type of exchanger). A control valve in the steam feed line regulates the steam pressure and thus the steam temperature, as the condensing temperature, θ_s, is directly related to the steam pressure. The temperature of the liquid is measured by a thermocouple in a well immersed in the immediate exit flow from the exchanger, perpendicular to the flow. The voltage from the thermocouple (feedback signal) is fed directly to an electronic controller. The output of the controller is converted to a 3- to 15-psi air signal by an electropneumatic positioner which operates the control valve in the steam line.

A block diagram of the control network is shown in Fig. 8.13 in which the relevant transfer functions are defined. Figure 8.14 is a more descriptive

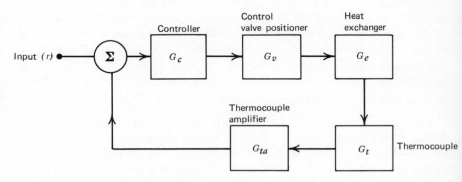

Fig. 8.13 Block diagram of temperature control network: G_c = controller transfer function; G_v = valve positioner transfer function; G_e = heat exchanger transfer function; G_{ta} = thermocouple amplifier transfer function; G_t = thermocouple transfer function; $G_s = G_v G_e$ = controlled system transfer function; $G_h = G_t G_{ta}$ = feedback network transfer function.

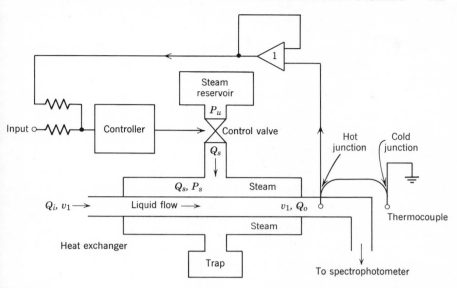

Fig. 8.14 Temperature controller based on heat exchanger. Amplifier 1. Operational amplifier in unity-gain follower configuration: P_u = steam reservoir pressure; P_s = steam pressure in heat exchanger; Q_s = steam flow rate; θ_s = steam temperature in heat exchanger; θ_i = liquid temperature at input to heat exchanger; θ_o = liquid temperature at output of heat exchanger; v_1 = liquid flow rate.

schematic of the network. Unlike the preceding example, we shall not consider in detail the effects of varying controlled-system properties on the control network behavior. Rather a fixed-configuration controlled system is assumed and emphasis is placed on modeling the controller response to fit the particular controlled system best. One frequently faces this type of situation.

The transfer function of the valve positioner G_v, which we are considering for this example was obtained from published manufacturers data [41]. The mathematical formulation best fitting this data is

$$G_v = \frac{0.14 \text{ in./mA}}{(1 + 0.98 \times 10^{-3}p)^3}, \tag{8.79}$$

where the time constant (0.98×10^{-3}) is in units of minutes rather than seconds. Minutes are used as the dimension for all time constants in this example. The frequency scales in the Bode plots (e.g., Fig. 8.15) are in units of cycles per minute (cpm). The dc gain of the value positioner is 0.14 in./mA because an input of 1 mA from the controller positions the valve stem at

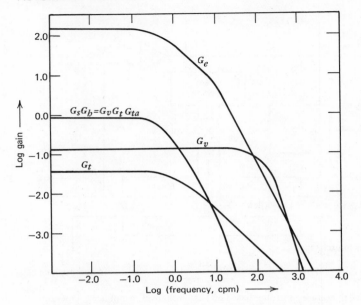

Fig. 8.15 Bode plots of temperature-control network components.

minimum travel or zero inches, whereas a controller output of 5 mA positions the stem at maximum travel of $\frac{9}{16}$ in.

The heat exchanger considered in this example has the following characteristics:

$$P_u = 25 \text{ psi}$$
$$P_s = 7 \text{ psi}$$
$$\theta_s = 111°C \text{ for 7 psi}$$
$$Q_s = 0\text{–}270 \text{ lb/hr}$$
$$\theta_i = 16°C$$
$$\theta_o = 45°C \text{ control point}$$
$$v_l = 2.25 \text{ ft/sec}$$

exchanger shell length = 5.7 ft
exchanger shell O.D. = 0.292 ft
exchanger shell I.D. = 0.256 ft
exchanger material = wrought iron (C_p = 0.1 cal/g°C)
exchanger tube length = 5.7 ft
exchanger tube O.D. = 0.070 ft
exchanger tube I.D. = 0.052 ft
exchanger tube material = brass (C_p = 0.092 cal/g°C)

By using the flow characteristics of the valve obtained from manufacturers literature for a 1-in. linear valve [6] and a heat balance calculation as in Section 3, the transfer function of the heat exchanger system is found to be

$$G_e = \frac{154°C/in.}{(1 + 0.0166p)(1 + 0.432p)}. \tag{8.80}$$

A thermocouple in intimate contact with the well may be represented as a single time constant made up of the liquid film resistance and the well heat capacity. The time constant is dependent on the fluid flow rate, since it determines the film thickness. For a well of stainless steel with a $\frac{1}{2}$-in. diameter and a weight of 4 oz at the flow rate of the system in question we may calculate by standard film coefficient formulas [13] that the time constant of the thermocouple and well is 0.18 min. If we use a chromel-alumel thermocouple with the reference junction at 0°C for the temperature range 0 to 100°C, the output will be 0–4.1 mV. Over this temperature range the dc gain is 0.041 mV/°C. Therefore

$$G_t = \frac{0.041 \text{ mV/°C}}{1 + 0.18p}. \tag{8.81}$$

The transfer function of the thermocouple amplifier has the form

$$G_{ta} = \frac{G_i}{1 + G_i}, \tag{8.82}$$

where G_i is the open-loop gain transfer function of the operational amplifier employed for this purpose (Part VII, Table 8.3). Ideally, this amplifier provides a low-impedance output equal to the thermocouple emf without drawing current through the thermocouple. Because even the slowest operational amplifiers are characterized by time constants that are much smaller than those of the thermal system and control valves, the roll-off in G_i will not ensue and G_i will greatly exceed unity throughout the frequency range of interest in this analysis. Consequently, to a very high degree of accuracy we may assume that the ideal response given by

$$G_{ta} = 1 \tag{8.83}$$

is operative.

The combined transfer function of the valve positioner, the heat exchanger, the thermocouple, and the thermocouple amplifier represents the controlled system-feedback network transfer function (see notation definitions in Fig. 8.13), and is given by

$$G_s G_h = G_v G_e G_t G_{ta}$$

$$= \frac{0.885}{(1 + 0.18p)(1 + 0.0166p)(1 + 0.432p)(1 + 0.98 \times 10^{-3}p)^3}, \tag{8.84}$$

where the dimensions of G_sG_h are millivolts per milliamperes. Figure 8.15 shows Bode plots of the G_v, G_e, G_t, and G_sG_h transfer functions. Note that in the frequency range in which the G_sG_h response is shown, the roll-off contributed by the valve positioner G_v is not yet operative so that this unit is affecting only the dc gain of the G_sG_h function.

The transfer function of primary interest, G_{OL}, is obtained by multiplying the transfer function of (8.84) by the controller transfer function G_c. In this example we consider a more versatile controller in which various combinations of proportional, integral, and differential control are possible (i.e., single-mode, two-mode, and three-mode control are considered). The controller may be represented by the circuit diagram in Part VI of Table 8.3 where, in some examples to follow, one or two of the possible control modes may be left inoperative. Two items with regard to the controller transfer function should be clarified before proceeding. First, as in the case of the thermocouple amplifier, the operational amplifiers of the controller respond so rapidly relative to the controlled system that the ideal transfer function of the controller given by (VIb) of Table 8.3 may be considered sufficiently accurate. Second, the transfer function of (VIb) is a voltage-ratio transfer function. The appropriate transfer function in the present case must have dimensions of milliampere per millivolt; that is, it must be an admittance transfer function. This is obtained by multiplying the controller voltage-ratio transfer function by the reciprocal of the valve-positioner input impedance, which is 2200 Ω for the unit under consideration [42]. Thus

$$G_c = (2200)^{-1}G_{VIb},\tag{8.85}$$

where G_{VIb} is the voltage-ratio transfer function of (VIb).

Careful inspection of the G_sG_h Bode plot (Fig. 8.15), double checked by a calculation of the phase shift, shows that the 180° phase shift (roll-off slope of -2) is reached when log (frequency) $= 0.54$. At this point log $G_sG_h = -1.6$. Thus, in principle, a pure proportional controller (which introduces no phase shift) characterized by log $G_c < 1.6$ ($G_c < 40$) would yield a stable system. A proportional gain close to 40, however, would not allow sufficient margin for changes in the heat exchanger load which might occur (e.g., through a variation in the temperature of the liquid entering the exchanger). Control network designers often allow approximately a 40° phase margin (140° phase shift) at unity gain to accommodate such anticipated fluctuations in the controlled system. The 140° phase shift in G_sG_h occurs when log (frequency) $= 0.12$ and log $G_sG_h = 0.90$. We conclude that the maximum pure proportional gain consistent with a reasonable stability margin is $G_c \cong 8$. The Bode plot of G_{OL} for $G_c = 8$ is shown in Fig. 8.16 with results for other control modes. We see that the dc magnitude of G_{OL} is only 7.1. In the context of (8.43) this corresponds to a dc error (usually referred to as *offset*)

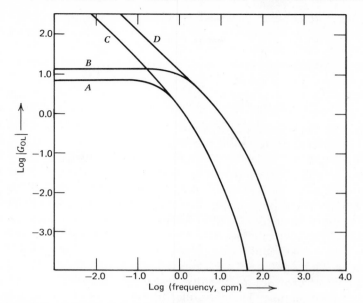

Fig. 8.16 Open-loop gain bode plots for temperature control network. $A: G_c = 8$; $B: G_c = 16(1 + 0.432p)$; $C: G_c = 8[1 + (0.432p)^{-1}]$; $D: G_c = 16[1 + 0.432p][1 + (0.18p)^{-1}]$.

of 12 %. Even if we operated with a very small phase margin, the offset would still be significant. This is seen from the fact that the Bode plot with a proportional gain of 40 (zero phase margin) has a G_{OL} dc gain of just 35 which corresponds to an offset of $\simeq 3\%$. In addition to the substantial offset, a relatively slow response will be observed (note that the unity-gain crossover frequency is only 1.3 cpm for $G_c = 8$).

It is apparent that for most applications a network based on simple proportional control will not perform adequately. Improvement can be effected by adding derivative or integral control or both. A two-mode proportional-derivative controller transfer function may be written

$$G_c = K(1 + T_d p). \tag{8.86}$$

It is apparent from inspection of (8.86) that the derivative action has no direct effect on the dc error ($T_d p = 0$ at dc). If T_d is chosen properly, however, the roll-off in the G_{OL} Bode plot will be reduced in the relevant frequency region, thus allowing us to employ a larger proportional gain, yet maintain the same stability margin. Consequently, offset will be reduced and the response speed improved. A reasonably simple and effective rule sets T_d equal to the largest time constant in the denominator of the $G_s G_h$ transfer function. In the present case we would use $T_d = 0.432$ min, that is,

$$G_c = K(1 + 0.432p), \qquad (8.87)$$

so that the G_{OL} transfer function would be given by

$$G_{OL} = \frac{0.885K}{(1 + 0.18p)(1 + 0.0166p)(1 + 0.98 \times 10^{-3}p)^3}. \qquad (8.88)$$

We then deduce the appropriate K value for a particular phase margin as in the above discussion for pure proportional control. For the transfer function of (8.88), $K \cong 16$ yields a 40° phase margin at unity gain. A K-value of approximately 63 corresponds to the zero phase margin case (-2 roll-off slope at unity gain). The Bode plot of G_{OL} in which $K = 16$ is shown in Fig. 8.16. Compared to pure proportional control, the G_{OL} magnitude and frequency response is definitely enhanced by combining proportional and derivative control. Nevertheless, the dc offset is still significant, as for $K \cong 16$ and $T_d = 0.432$, and the dc value of G_{OL} is 14, corresponding to an offset of about 7%.

Integral control provides an effective answer to the offset problem encountered in this example. The controller transfer function for two-mode proportional-integral control may be written

$$G_c = K\left(1 + \frac{1}{T_i p}\right). \qquad (8.89)$$

The fact that $G_c \rightarrow \infty$ as $p \rightarrow 0$ illustrates that integral control yields high gains at dc or low frequencies, thus effectively eliminating offset. The integral action, however, provides another source of roll-off which tends to destabilize the system. The optimum choice of T_i corresponds to the smallest T_i-value (largest T_i^{-1}), which still does not significantly enhance the roll-off at unity gain for the G_{OL} Bode plot, as this would reduce the stability margin. To a reasonable approximation, the optimum choice is obtained by making T_i approximately equal to the largest time constant in the denominator of $G_s G_h$; that is, we apply the same rule as in choosing the derivative time constant T_d. By applying this rule to the system in question we make $T_i = 0.432$ min. Assuming that this choice of T_i does not influence the Bode plot in the region in which the roll-off originating in $G_s G_h$ arises, we obtain a 40° phase margin at unity gain for a proportional gain of 8 ($K = 8$), as in the case of pure proportional control. Figure 8.16 provides a comparison of the Bode plots for $G_c = 8$ and $G_c = 8[1 + (0.432p)^{-1}]$ that shows the effects of this near-optimum choice of proportional-integral control. Enhancement of the low-frequency gain and the resulting elimination of offset is the essential contribution of integral control. A careful calculation of the phase margin at unity gain for the conditions considered in Fig. 8.16

indicates that the actual phase margin has been reduced to about 30°. This indicates that the foregoing rule for selecting T_i is only approximately correct in that a slight stability margin reduction will result which is usually not serious.

Although introduction of either integral or differential control alone may realize improvement over pure proportional control, the best results are frequently obtained by combining differential, integral, and proportional control. The transfer function for an ideal three-mode controller (VIb, Table 8.3) may be written in the alternative form

$$G_c = K(1 + T_d p)\left(1 + \frac{1}{T_i p}\right), \qquad (8.90)$$

which is more useful for determining the appropriate combinations of K, T_d, and T_i. The approximate optimum choice of T_d and T_i for three-mode control corresponds to setting T_d equal to the largest time constant in the denominator of the $G_s G_h$ transfer function and T_i equal to the second largest. The proportional gain K is then the largest possible value consistent with a reasonable phase margin at unity gain; that is, approximately the value that we would employ with two-mode proportional-derivative control. For the system under consideration application of these guidelines yields

$$G_c = 16(1 + 0.432p)\left(1 + \frac{1}{0.18p}\right). \qquad (8.91)$$

Figure 8.16 also shows the G_{OL} Bode plot for a controller characterized by the transfer function of (8.91). We can see that among the possibilities considered this three-mode controller yields the best over-all results. The phase margin at unity gain for this case is about 30°.

The foregoing example illustrates the key features of integral and derivative control. Derivative control tends to reduce the roll-off of the G_{OL} transfer function, thus stabilizing the system, enhancing the network response rate, and allowing the system to accept larger proportional gains. Integral control eliminates offset, but if used indiscriminantly it will increase roll-off in the critical frequency region around unity gain and destabilize the system.

Although illustrative of these features, the present example should not be considered typical. The actual benefits to be gained by addition of derivative or integral control can vary widely, depending on the nature of the various elements in the control network; for example, consider a $G_s G_h$ transfer function of the form

$$G_s G_h = \frac{1}{(1 + T_1 p)^3}. \qquad (8.92)$$

This third-order transfer function is one whose Bode plot is characterized by a roll-off slope of -3. A controller with even the slightest amount of proportional gain will raise this -3 slope to the unity gain point. Furthermore, addition of derivative control where $G_c = K(1 + T_1 p)$ does not help much because the resulting G_{OL} transfer function given by

$$G_{OL} = \frac{K}{(1 + T_1 p)^2} \qquad (8.93)$$

will have a unity gain slope of -2 which is still characteristic of an unstable system. Although it reduces the roll-off slope, simple derivative control in this case is still ineffectual in providing a stable network of adequate proportional gain. In effect, the roll-off associated with $G_s G_h$ is too steep to begin with and simple derivative control does not compensate sufficiently. Thus the advantages of derivative control in enhancing the response of the thermal system considered here are not always realized. On the other hand, enormously greater gains can be obtained through derivative control in certain cases. In particular, if

$$G_s G_h = \frac{1}{(1 + T_1 p)(1 + T_2 p)}, \qquad (8.94)$$

the use of derivative action with T_d equal to either of the time constants in (8.94) will yield a simple, first-order G_{OL} function characterized by a stable roll-off of -1 slope. In such a situation we could, in principle, increase the proportional gain term until the unity-gain frequency reached the point at which the controller itself became nonideal; that is, (8.86) no longer applies and transfer functions such as (VIa) of Table 8.3 must be used. In any event, when $G_s G_h$ is a simple second-order transfer function, derivative control may reap considerably larger benefits than obtained in the above example of the thermal system.

In a similar manner we can envision situations in which integral control may be of greater or lesser (usually the latter) utility than in the example considered here. The next example to deal with a mechanical system will serve to represent a case in which integral control is of little use.

Another nontypical aspect of the thermal system lies in the fact that we were able to assume ideal integral and differential action in the controller. This assumption was validated because the network was based on the use of relatively fast electronic controllers in combination with a relatively slow thermal system. Had we considered, for example, the slower pure pneumatic controller, ideal differential and integral control could not have been assumed. In such cases the problem of "tuning" the controller (selecting the optimum time constants and gain) becomes more complicated and usually poorer results are obtained than in the example considered. Of course, similar difficulties would arise if the "fast" electronic controller of this example had been combined with a rapidly responding system (such as the resistive-capacitive load in the earlier example of an electronic potential control network).

A Mechanical Servomechanism

The situations in which control of mechanical parameters is used in chemical applications are fairly well known and the most important examples are discussed at some length in other chapters of this volume. Thus it appears unnecessary to preface the present analysis with the usual background material designed to bring relevancy to the control network considered.

The example we have selected is a mechanical servosystem of the type used in automatic recorders. A schematic of the system is shown in Fig. 8.17. It is based on a controller-driven two-phase ac motor [43, 44]. The controller output is an ac signal whose magnitude is determined by the difference between the input signal r and the feedback signal b. The motor drives a gear train that adjusts the position of the recorder pen (controlled variable) and the slidewire potentiometer. The latter controls the feedback signal magnitude. For present purposes we consider the two-phase ac motor, together with the gear train stages and pulley leading to the pen, as the controlled system. The feedback network will be taken as including the pulley and gears leading from the pen to the output of the slidewire potentiometer. We should recognize that this example could easily represent

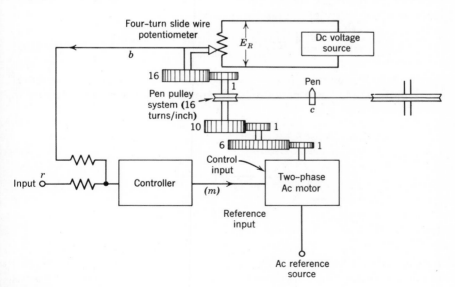

Fig. 8.17 Mechanical servomechanism.

mechanical servosystems other than automatic recorders; for example, by connecting the pulley system to an antenna shaft we have an antenna position controller. This alteration would have no effect on the stability-accuracy analysis at the level of rigor considered here.

Several simplifying assumptions are appropriate for this example. Two phase ac motors are high-speed devices with low efficiencies. They are generally coupled to a "load" through a gear train of high gear ratio as shown in Fig. 8.17. As a result, little of the load inertia is reflected back to the motor shaft and most of the developed torque is applied to the motor's own inertia. As a reasonable approximation we can ignore the load of the gear train, slide-wire potentiometer, etc., in evaluating the system performance. This approximation is invoked in the present case. It is also assumed that the output impedance of the control amplifier is negligible. Since the controller is coupled to the relatively low impedance of the motor control windings, a high-quality power amplifier is required at the controller output to validate this assumption. Finally, friction and backlash in the gear train are neglected.

The controller required to activate the ac motor must deliver an ac output. This requirement is readily accommodated even within the framework of a complex control action. Any type of control action can be achieved by applying the output of a normal electronic controller (e.g., Part VI, Table 8.3) to a modulator based on an electronic multiplier followed by a power amplifier output stage whose circuit is shown in Fig. 8.18. The transfer function of the modulator, given by

$$G_M = \frac{\text{modulator ac output amplitude}}{\text{dc input}}, \tag{8.95}$$

may be taken as unity, provided the controller is not called on to respond too rapidly. Under such conditions the controller transfer function will be

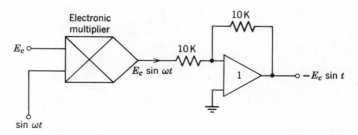

Fig. 8.18 Modulator for mechanical servomechanism controller: E_c = signal from normal electronic controller; $\sin \omega t$ = signal derived from ac reference source (must be 90° out of phase with signal applied to ac motor reference windings).

that of the conventional electronic controller which drives the modulator. Assumptions of ideality in controller action can easily be validated for the network under consideration because, as in the preceding example, a relatively slow controlled system is involved.

Next we consider a type of ac motor whose transfer function has been shown to be [45]

$$G_{acm} = \frac{\theta}{E} = \frac{6.93 \ (rad/V)}{p(1 + 0.213p)(1 + 0.00219p)}, \tag{8.96}$$

where θ is the motor shaft position in radians, E is the amplitude of the ac voltage on the motor control windings, and the time constants are in dimensions of seconds. The controlled system transfer function G_s is obtained by multiplying G_{acm} by the transfer function that converts motor-shaft position to pen position which we designate as G_x. If we ignore friction and backlash in the gear train, we have (see Fig. 8.17)

$$G_x = (960)^{-1} \ in./rad. \tag{8.97}$$

G_s is given by

$$G_s = G_{acm}G_x = \frac{7.20 \times 10^{-3} \ (in./V)}{p(1 + 0.213p)(1 + 0.00219p)}. \tag{8.98}$$

The feedback network involves all components from the pen to the potentiometer output. The gear train-pulley contribution to the feedback network transfer function is unity (pen movement of 1 in. corresponds to one turn on the slide-wire potentiometer drive gear). The potentiometer contribution is $E_R/4$, so that

$$G_h = \frac{E_R}{4} \ (V/in.). \tag{8.99}$$

Thus the G_sG_h transfer function is

$$G_sG_h = \frac{1.80 \times 10^{-3}E_R}{p(1 + 0.213p)(1 + 0.00219p)} \tag{8.100}$$

and a dimensionless quantity. For the remainder of the discussion we shall consider the case in which $E_R = 1$ V. A Bode plot of G_sG_h for this case is shown in Fig. 8.19.

One aspect of the G_sG_h transfer function in Fig. 8.19 that should be recognized immediately is the -1 slope at low frequencies which manifests the fact that the low-frequency limit of (8.100) is ($E_R = 1$)

$$G_sG_h = \frac{1.80 \times 10^{-3}}{p}. \tag{8.101}$$

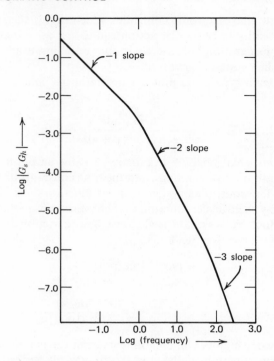

Fig. 8.19 Bode plot of $G_s G_h$ transfer function for mechanical servomechanism.

In other words, integral action is built into the system transfer function by the use of a motor. The motor responds to a step input by passing through a transient during which the motor "speeds up" and eventually reaches a constant speed. In the latter state the output variable θ increases at a constant rate. Such behavior is precisely that associated with integral action. Clearly, the addition of integral control with such a controlled system is both unnecessary and self-defeating. An integral term in the controller transfer function would raise the low frequency slope of the open-loop gain to -2, making the system unstable for all values of proportional gain.

The $140°$ phase point for the transfer function of (8.100) occurs at 0.91 Hz, where $|G_s G_h| = 2.5 \times 10^{-4}$. Thus a simple proportional controller with a gain of 4×10^3 will give a $40°$ phase margin at unity gain. The open-loop gain Bode plot for this case is shown in Fig. 8.20. A controller with derivative action could be very beneficial with this servo system. The optimum derivative time constant is 0.213 sec so that G_c is given by

$$G_c = K(1 + 0.213p) \qquad (8.102)$$

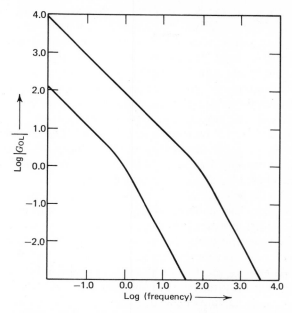

Fig. 8.20 Open-loop gain bode plot for mechanical servomechanism.

and G_{OL} has the form

$$G_{OL} = \frac{1.80 \times 10^{-3} K}{p(1 + 0.00219p)}. \tag{8.103}$$

The $140°$ phase shift for the latter transfer function occurs at 90 Hz. This frequency is made the unity-gain frequency if $K = 3.2 \times 10^5$. Figure 8.20 also depicts the open-loop gain Bode plot for this two-mode proportional-derivative control action. It is apparent that derivative action enhances both the frequency response and the open-loop gain magnitude by approximately two orders of magnitude. With a controller characterized by (8.102) with $K = 3.2 \times 10^5$, the open-loop gain magnitude is nearly 100 at 1 Hz, which indicates an accuracy approaching 1% at this frequency. Errors due to the assumption of perfect gear train behavior, etc., may make the actual network performance somewhat poorer. Nevertheless the network is expected to be reasonably fast by mechanical system standards.

A Potentiostat for Three-Electrode Cell Configurations

The field of experimental electrochemistry has undergone a profound revolution in the last decade by virtue of applications of automatic-control principles to electrochemical instrumentation. In the late 1950's pioneering workers such as Booman [46], DeFord [47], Gerischer and Staubach [48], and Kelley, et al. [49, 50], designed practical instruments by which rapid, automatic control of potential or current could be effected with a three-electrode cell configuration. Numerous variations and improvements on these original circuits have been described [50–60]. The devices in question are referred to as *potentiostats* (potential control) and *galvanostats* (current control). Later, when the demand arose, automatic control of the electrical charge (via a "coulostat") was achieved [61]. The analysis of one recent version of the potentiostat three-electrode cell network is considered here. The principles underlying the three-electrode cell concept and the stability-accuracy analysis are treated rather briefly. Numerous detailed works on these subjects are available in the literature [46–59].

The three-electrode cell originated as an attempt to alleviate a basic measurement problem encountered whenever an electrochemical cell is operated under nonequilibrium conditions (net current flow). Under such circumstances the potential difference between the two electrodes involved in the current flow is not the rational potential to control or measure from either a thermodynamic or kinetic viewpoint. The problem lies in the ohmic resistance of the bulk solution between the electrodes. A potential drop is developed across this resistance whenever current flows. This ohmic potential drop (or iR *drop*) is not accommodated by most equations of electrochemical thermodynamics and kinetics. Incorporation of this effect into the mathematical theory or correction of data for its influences is possible, but the operations add notably to the tedium of the measurement and data interpretation. Often the raw data is distorted sufficiently by the iR drop that the measurements are deemed useless (e.g., two-electrode dc polarography in high-resistance solvent-supporting electrolyte systems). The rational potential, which we should like to control or measure, is that across the working electrode (electrode in which processes of interest occur)-solution interface. It is well known that such potentials cannot be measured or controlled in an absolute sense. However, we can envision control or measurement of the potential *changes* across this electrical double-layer with reasonable precision. Indeed, with a properly operating reference electrode, negligible iR drop and boundary potential changes this is accomplished. Thus the goal of automatic control applications in electrochemistry is the control and measurement of variations in the potential across the electrical double layer at the working electrode. The three-electrode cell represents a major advance in approaching this goal. The reasons underlying its applicability may be revealed in terms of the electrical analog depicted in Fig. 8.21. The electrodes are designated as auxiliary, working, and reference electrodes. The bulk-solution ohmic resistance in the electrolysis solution (external solution) is represented by resistor R_s. A similar resistance in the reference electrode

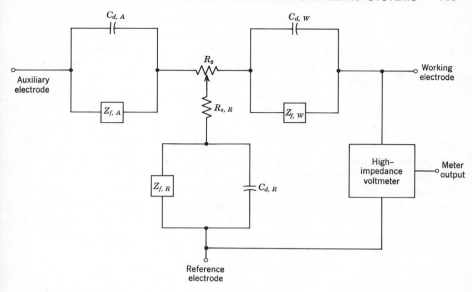

Fig. 8.21   Electrical analog of three-electrode cell: $C_{d,A}$, $C_{d,W}$, $C_{d,R}$ = electrical double layer capacities of auxiliary, working and reference electrodes, respectively; $Z_{f,A}$, $Z_{f,W}$, $Z_{f,R}$ = faradaic impedances of auxiliary, working and reference electrodes, respectively; R_s = bulk ohmic resistance of solution between auxiliary and working electrodes; $R_{s,R}$ = bulk ohmic resistance of reference electrode compartment.

compartment (including the resistance of the frit or asbestos plug to prevent solution mixing) is designated as $R_{s,R}$. The interfacial impedance of each electrode is represented as a parallel combination of a double-layer capacity (C_d's) and a faradaic impedance (Z_f's). The former is the nearly ideal capacitance associated with the electrical double layer. The latter constitutes contributions to the interfacial impedances associated with the electrolysis process. Its magnitude may be controlled by rate processes, such as diffusion, the heterogeneous charge transfer step, homogeneous and heterogeneous chemical reactions coupled to the charge transfer step and adsorption processes. The rather complicated properties associated with the faradaic impedance [55, 62, 63] need not be considered in the present study. Regardless of the variable controlled, operation of the three-electrode cell involves passage of current between the auxiliary and working electrode, whereas the potential between the working and reference electrodes is monitored by a high-impedance voltmeter (draws negligible current through the reference electrode). In a potential-control application such as that considered below a controller induces the current flow and the resulting voltmeter output is the feedback signal. With a well-mannered automatic control network, the current level sought by the controller will be that which is sufficient to effect the desired working electrode-reference electrode potential difference. In current control the desired current levels are forced between the auxiliary and working electrodes, whereas the resulting reference-working electrode potential difference is the read-out signal. In either case many normal sources of iR drop are eliminated. The reference electrode acts essentially as a high impedance probe that actually senses the potential difference between the point in the external-solution corresponding to the tip of the reference electrode probe (junction between reference electrode solution and external solution) and the working electrode. This statement is validated by the fact that, with a high-impedance voltmeter, the negligible current flowing through the reference electrode negates contributions of the internal impedances of the reference electrode, $R_{s,R}$, $C_{d,R}$, and $Z_{f,R}$. Thus, if the tip of the reference electrode probe is placed close to the working electrode, only a fraction of the external solution ohmic resistance and none of the auxiliary electrode interfacial impedance is sensed (the latter is usually small because of the customary use of large auxiliary electrodes). This elimination of ohmic resistance effects associated with frits, asbestos plugs, etc., at solution boundaries, together with a significant portion of the external solution resistance results in a considerable improvement over the situation faced with a two-electrode cell. Nevertheless not all of the solution ohmic resistance effects are eliminated from the measurements, since the reference electrode probe must remain a safe distance from the working electrode. Also ohmic potential drops associated with the working electrode itself, which are sometimes significant (e.g., resistance in dropping mercury electrode capillary), are not eliminated. Consequently, the three-electrode cell affords marked improvement in many cases, but it is not the complete answer, particularly with high-resistance solutions in which these *residual iR drops* may still be undesirably large. In effect, the designer of electrochemical control systems is faced with the unusual problem of being unable to sense directly the variable he wishes to control, the potential across $C_{d,w}$ relative to a reference electrode. Instead, he must be satisfied with a signal that differs from the desired signal by the residual iR drop.

The control network shown in Fig. 8.22 represents a recent version of an operational amplifier potentiostat for three electrode cells in which compensation for the residual iR drop is provided. The measured cell current exhibits virtually no iR drop effects if the device is properly employed. Figure 8.22 is taken from a literature source [60] that employed slightly different notation than this chapter. The signals designated as e_{in}, e_o, and e_f of Fig. 8.22 may be identified as r, m, and c, respectively (Fig. 8.1). Adaptation of the single-loop system considered above to the two-loop network of Fig. 8.22 amounts to identifying the feedback signal b as the sum of the two feedback

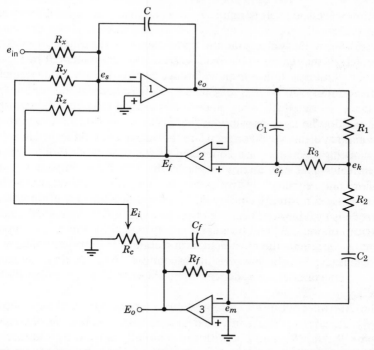

Fig. 8.22 Potentiostat-cell system: amplifier 1—control amplifier: Analog Devices Model 210 in this work; amplifier 2—voltage follower amplifier: Philbrick/Nexus Model Q25AH; amplifier 3—current measuring amplifier: Analog Devices Model 210; C = feedback capacitor of control amplifier; C_f = feedback capacitor of current-measuring amplifier; C_1 = by-pass capacitor between auxiliary and reference electrodes; C_2 = electrical double-layer capacitance of working electrode; R_x, R_y, R_z = control amplifier summing network resistors (in this work $R_x = R_y = R_z = R$); R_f = feedback resistor of current-measuring amplifier; R_c = potentiometer controlling % iR compensation; R_1 = solution resistance between auxiliary electrode and tip of reference electrode probe; R_2 = cell ohmic resistance to be compensated by positive feedback signal; R_3 = reference electrode resistance; e_{in} = input voltage to potentiostat-cell system; e_s = voltage at minus input of control amplifier; e_o = output voltage of control amplifier; e_f = input voltage to voltage follower amplifier (= reference electrode voltage); e_k = solution voltage at tip of reference electrode probe; E_f = output voltage of voltage follower amplifier (= input voltage to summing network resistor R_z with closed loop); e_m = voltage at minus input of current-measuring amplifier; E_o = output voltage of current-measuring amplifier; E_i = voltage at center tap of positive feedback control potentiometer (= positive feedback voltage = input to summing network resistor R_y with closed loop). Permission to reprint was granted by the American Chemical Society.

signals E_f and E_i, that is,

$$b = E_f + E_i. \tag{8.104}$$

In this case the open-loop gain is represented as

$$G_c = \frac{b}{r+b} = \frac{E_f + E_i}{E_f + E_i + e_{in}}. \tag{8.105}$$

The three-electrode cell is represented as an electrical analog comprised of components R_1, R_2, R_3, and C_2: R_1 represents the solution resistance between the auxiliary electrode and tip of reference electrode probe (resistance to the left of the reference electrode contact on component R in Fig. 8.21); R_3 is the ohmic resistance in the reference electrode compartment, including frit at boundary ($R_3 = R_{s,R}$ of Fig. 8.21); R_2 represents the residual ohmic resistance whose effects must be compensated by the control network; and C_2 is the double-layer capacity at the working electrode-solution interface. The auxiliary electrode is connected to the output of amplifier 1. The reference and working electrodes are connected to the inputs of amplifiers 2 and 3, respectively. The cell analog neglects the interfacial impedances of the auxiliary and reference electrodes because they are relatively small with the electrode sizes normally employed. The faradaic impedance of the working electrode is also ignored because of the complexity of a reasonably accurate electrical analog [63] and because a purely capacitive interfacial impedance normally represents the most demanding condition for potentiostat stability and accuracy. With a few possible exceptions [60], the analysis based on neglect of the faradaic impedance can be considered as examining the "worst case."

The controller of Fig. 8.22 is represented by amplifier 1 and the components R_x, R_y, R_z, and C. The controlled system may be taken as the cell components R_1, R_2, R_3, and C_2, with the externally applied *bypass capacitance* C_1. The feedback network contains amplifiers 2 and 3 and the components R_c, R_f, and C_f. The capacitances C, C_f, and C_1 represent *possible* stabilizing elements; C and C_f alter the characteristics of the associated amplifier responses. Capacitance C_1 represents an external control on the system response. Hopefully one or more of these capacitances will influence the response at frequencies near the unity-gain point in a favorable manner, that is, reduce the Bode plot slope, without greatly altering the system response at frequencies in which potential control is desired.

The *idealized* operation of the network of Fig. 8.22 (the low-frequency limit) can be considered as follows:

The response of amplifier 1 to an input e_{in} yields an output e_o which induces current flow between the auxiliary and reference electrode. Amplifier 3 responds by emitting an output E_o equal to the cell current, i_{cell}, times R_f ($E_o = i_{cell}R_f$) while holding the working electrode at a virtual ground (ideally the impedance of C_f is infinite and $e_m = E_o/G_3 \simeq 0$ at frequencies of interest). In other words, amplifier 3 simultaneously maintains the working electrode at a well-defined potential and provides an output proportional to the cell current which serves as the instrument readout as well as the means for compensation of residual ohmic potential losses. Amplifier 2 is an operational amplifier with a particularly high input impedance in a voltage follower configuration. It senses the potential of the reference electrode versus ground, that is, versus the working electrode, and delivers an output voltage equal to this value at a low output impedance. The feedback path constituting the reference electrode and amplifier 2 is the negative feedback path. This is the only feedback path employed in most three-electrode potentiostats. The circuit of Fig. 8.22 represents a recent modification in which a second feedback path is provided by amplifier 3 and the components R_c, R_f, and C_f. This *positive* feedback path is designed to compensate for the residual ohmic potential drop ($i_{cell} \times R_2$). The positive feedback voltage E_i is made equal to ($i_{cell} \times R_2$) by adjusting R_c appropriately. This operation requires knowledge of R_2, which is readily obtained [60]. In effect, this operation causes the ideal working-reference electrode potential difference to correspond to ($e_{in} + i_{cell}R_2$) so that the actual potential across the double-layer capacity of the working electrode (relative to the reference electrode-solution potential) equals e_{in}. Although the ideal operating conditions are correct, the foregoing results for simpler control networks strongly suggest that one as complicated as that of Fig. 8.22 will be characterized by a generous realm of unstable operating conditions. The need for a careful stability analysis of this network is apparent.

Examination of Fig. 8.22 indicates that the potentiostat-cell network involves eight unknown voltages, which makes the deduction of appropriate voltage ratio transfer functions somewhat difficult if the rather informal algebraic approach of the earlier examples is used. Also, once the appropriate formulations are developed, numerical calculations are cumbersome. Complex, multiloop control systems are handled best by adopting a more formalized algebraic approach involving determinants. Representation of transfer functions in terms of determinants is readily accomplished, even for complex systems, and proves ideal for subsequent computer calculations. The network in question was analyzed in this manner [60]. Representation of the unknown network voltages in determinental form is accomplished with the assistance of the eight independent network equations which assume $R_x = R_y = R_z = R$:

$$e_o + G_1 e_s = 0, \tag{8.106}$$

$$e_f - G_2^* E_f = 0, \tag{8.107}$$

$$E_o + G_3 e_m = 0, \tag{8.108}$$

$$E_i - \beta^* E_o = 0, \tag{8.109}$$

$$a_1 e_s - a e_o - E_i - E_f = e_{in}, \tag{8.110}$$

$$a_2 e_o + e_k - a_3 e_f = 0, \tag{8.111}$$

$$a_4 e_k + a_5 E_o - a_6 e_m = 0, \tag{8.112}$$

$$a_7 e_k - a_8 e_o - a_9 e_m = 0, \tag{8.113}$$

where

$$G_2^* = \frac{G_2 + 1}{G_2}, \tag{8.114}$$

$$a = RCp, \tag{8.115}$$

$$a_1 = RCp + 3, \tag{8.116}$$

$$a_2 = R_3 C_1 p, \tag{8.117}$$

$$a_3 = R_3 C_1 p + 1, \tag{8.118}$$

$$a_4 = R_f C_2 p, \tag{8.119}$$

$$a_5 = (R_2 C_2 p + 1)(R_f C_f p + 1), \tag{8.120}$$

$$a_6 = R_f C_2 p + (R_2 C_2 p + 1)(R_f C_f p + 1), \tag{8.121}$$

$$a_7 = (R_2 C_2 p + 1)[(R_1 + R_3)C_1 p + 1] + R_1 C_2 p(R_3 C_1 p + 1), \tag{8.122}$$

$$a_8 = (R_2 C_2 p + 1)[(R_1 + R_3)C_1 p + 1], \tag{8.123}$$

$$a_9 = R_1 C_2 p(R_3 C_1 p + 1), \tag{8.124}$$

$$\beta^* = \frac{\beta R_2}{R_f}, \tag{8.125}$$

Equations 8.106 to 8.108 are the defining equations for the operational amplifier open-loop gains, G_1, G_2, and G_3. Equation 8.107 is specialized for the case of the voltage follower [(VIIa), Table 8.3]. Equation 8.109 and its subsidiary (8.125) define the positive feedback fraction β, the idealized (low-frequency) fraction of the residual iR drop which is compensated. For the present work we may take β as unity (100% iR compensation). Equations 8.110 to 8.113 relate various voltages and intervening impedance through generalized ohms-law considerations. The feedback network-controlled system transfer function $G_s G_h$ is expressible as

$$G_s G_h = \frac{E_f + E_i}{e_o} = \frac{D_{E_f} + D_{E_i}}{D_{e_o}}, \tag{8.126}$$

where D_{E_f}, D_{E_i}, and D_{e_o} are the determinants

$$D_{E_f} = \begin{vmatrix} 1 & 0 & 0 & 0 & 0 & 0 & 0 & G_1 \\ 0 & 1 & 0 & 0 & 0 & 0 & 0 & 0 \\ 0 & 0 & 0 & G_3 & 1 & 0 & 0 & 0 \\ 0 & 0 & 0 & 0 & -\beta^* & 1 & 0 & 0 \\ -a & 0 & 0 & 0 & 0 & -1 & e_{in} & a_1 \\ a_2 & -a_3 & 1 & 0 & 0 & 0 & 0 & 0 \\ 0 & 0 & a_4 & -a_6 & a_5 & 0 & 0 & 0 \\ -a_8 & 0 & a_7 & -a_9 & 0 & 0 & 0 & 0 \end{vmatrix} \tag{8.127}$$

$$
D_{e_o} = \begin{vmatrix}
0 & 0 & 0 & 0 & 0 & 0 & 0 & G_1 \\
0 & 1 & 0 & 0 & 0 & 0 & -G_2^* & 0 \\
0 & 0 & 0 & G_3 & 1 & 0 & 0 & 0 \\
0 & 0 & 0 & 0 & -\beta^* & 1 & 0 & 0 \\
e_{\text{in}} & 0 & 0 & 0 & 0 & -1 & -1 & a_1 \\
0 & -a_3 & 1 & 0 & 0 & 0 & 0 & 0 \\
0 & 0 & a_4 & -a_6 & a_5 & 0 & 0 & 0 \\
0 & 0 & a_7 & -a_9 & 0 & 0 & 0 & 0
\end{vmatrix}, \quad (8.128)
$$

$$
D_{E_i} = \begin{vmatrix}
1 & 0 & 0 & 0 & 0 & 0 & 0 & G_1 \\
0 & 1 & 0 & 0 & 0 & 0 & -G_2^* & 0 \\
0 & 0 & 0 & G_3 & 1 & 0 & 0 & 0 \\
0 & 0 & 0 & 0 & -\beta^* & 0 & 0 & 0 \\
-a & 0 & 0 & 0 & 0 & e_{\text{in}} & -1 & a_1 \\
a_2 & -a_3 & 1 & 0 & 0 & 0 & 0 & 0 \\
0 & 0 & a_4 & -a_6 & a_5 & 0 & 0 & 0 \\
-a_8 & 0 & a_7 & -a_7 & 0 & 0 & 0 & 0
\end{vmatrix}. \quad (8.129)
$$

The controller transfer function may be written [see (IVa), Table 8.3]

$$
G_c = \frac{e_o}{e_{\text{in}} + E_i + E_f} = \frac{-G_1}{[(1 + G_1)RCp + 3]}. \quad (8.130)
$$

Thus the open-loop gain may be written

$$
G_{\text{OL}} = G_c G_s G_h = \left\{ \frac{-G_1}{[(1 + G_1)RCp + 3]} \right\} \left\{ \frac{D_{E_f} + D_{E_i}}{D_{e_o}} \right\}. \quad (8.131)
$$

Bode plots of the open-loop gain defined by (8.131) have been calculated for the case in which amplifiers 1 and 3 are Analog Devices Model 210 operational amplifiers (Type III) and amplifier 2 is a Philbrick Model Q25AH operational amplifier (Type I). For this case

$$
G_1 = G_3 = \frac{K(1 + A_2 p)(1 + A_4 p)}{(1 + A_1 p)(1 + A_3 p)(1 + A_5 p)}, \quad (8.132)
$$

where

$$K = 1.0 \times 10^8 \tag{8.133}$$

$$T_1 = 3.98 \text{ sec,} \tag{8.134}$$

$$T_2 = 5.32 \times 10^{-3} \text{ sec,} \tag{8.135}$$

$$T_3 = 5.33 \times 10^{-5} \text{ sec,} \tag{8.136}$$

$$T_4 = 5.00 \times 10^{-6} \text{ sec,} \tag{8.137}$$

$$T_5 = 6.25 \times 10^{-5} \text{ sec,} \tag{8.138}$$

and

$$G_2 = \frac{K_2}{1 + A_6 p}, \tag{8.139}$$

where

$$K_2 = 3.0 \times 10^4, \tag{8.140}$$

$$A_6 = 1.6 \times 10^{-4} \text{ sec.} \tag{8.141}$$

Results of some of these calculations are shown in Figures 8.23 to 8.26 [60]. All refer to the case in which 100% iR compensation is in effect. All figures show only expanded segments of the Bode plots in the vicinity of the unity-gain frequency. Figure 8.23 illustrates the effect of the bypass capacitance C_1 in terms of the $R_3 C_1$ time constant. Other stabilizing capacitors are

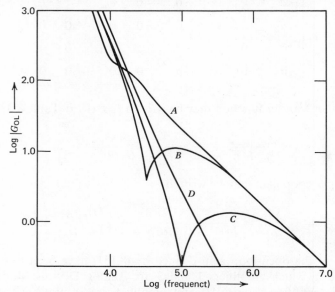

Fig. 8.23 Bode plot for potentiostat-cell system open-loop gain for various values of $R_3 C_1$. $R_1 = 25.0 \ \Omega$; $R_2 = 100 \ \Omega$; $C_2 = 1.00 \ \mu\text{F}$; $C = C_f = 0$. A: $R_3 C_1 = 1.00 \times 10^{-5} \text{ sec}$; B: $-R_3 C_1 = 1.00 \times 10^{-6} \text{ sec}$; C: $-R_3 C_1 = 1.00 \times 10^{-7} \text{ sec}$; D: $-R_3 C_1 = 0$. Permission to reprint was granted by the American Chemical Society.

considered absent. Cell-parameter values are characteristic of aqueous media. We find a decidedly unstable response in absence of C_1 (curve D). However, if C_1 is made large enough (Curves A and B), the Bode plot is transformed into one characterized by a much higher unity-gain frequency with an attendant slope corresponding to stable behavior. Capacitance C_1 tends to increase the gain at higher frequencies and thus stabilizes the system. At the same time it decreases somewhat the open-loop gain at lower frequencies and reduces accuracy at the frequencies of interest. The net result often leads to a minimum in the Bode plot (Curves B and C). A key to stable operation suggested by the results of Fig. 8.23 is maintaining conditions in which the minimum does not drop below unity-gain so that the steep roll-off on the low frequency side of the minimum does not cross the unity-gain value. For the conditions in Fig. 8.23 a good compromise between stability and accuracy is found with R_3C_1 between 10^{-5} and 10^{-6} sec.

Careful examination of the G_{OL} transfer function makes apparent that the major destabilizing component in the control network is the working electrode double-layer capacitance. Although it is an unavoidable aspect of an electrochemical experiment, the double-layer capacity can be minimized by employing the smallest electrodes possible (C_2 is directly proportional to electrode surface area). Figure 8.24 shows that much can be gained by this technique. Reducing the magnitude of C_2 is seen to decrease the depth of the minimum of the Bode plot, thereby increasing the stability margin. This is accompanied by a notable increase in G_{OL} on the low frequency side of the minimum, thus increasing accuracy.

Figures 8.25 and 8.26 show the effects of the capacitors across amplifiers 1 and 3. The capacitor (C) across amplifier 1 is found to yield disastrous results. Increasing the magnitude of this capacitance reduces the open-loop gain at all frequencies. This will decrease accuracy and reduce the stability margin. If the minimum on the Bode plot drops below unity gain (Curve C, Fig. 8.25), an unstable system will result. Continued increase in the capacitance C beyond the values considered in Fig. 8.25 decreases the slope of the Bode plot at unity gain (which now appears below the minimum frequency— see Curve C) and will eventually lead to a new stable configuration but at considerable loss in bandpass (frequency limit for acceptable accuracy). Thus, as capacitance C is increased, it first exerts a destabilizing influence but eventually the effect reverses. The effect on bandpass attending an increase in C is monotonically negative. Figure 8.26 indicates that the capacitance C_f across amplifier 3 exerts an effect similar to that of the bypass capacitance C_1. Increasing C_f notably enhances stability (increases G_{OL} value at minimum) at the cost of only moderate losses in accuracy. This desirable effect of C_f is realized only in concert with the capacitance C_1.

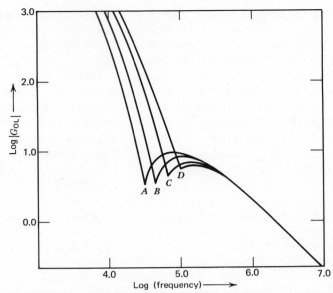

Fig. 8.24 Bode plot of potentiostat-cell system open-loop gain for various double-layer capacitance values. $R_1 = 25.0\ \Omega$; $R_2 = 100\ \Omega$; $C = C_f = 0$; $R_3 C_1 = 1.00 \times 10^{-6}$ sec; $A: -C_2 = 1.00\ \mu\text{F}$; $B: -C_2 = 0.50\ \mu\text{F}$; $C: -C_2 = 0.20\ \mu\text{F}$; $D: -C_2 = 0.10\ \mu\text{F}$. Permission to reprint was granted by the American Chemical Society.

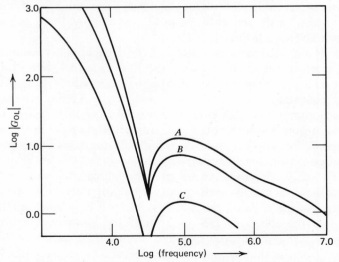

Fig. 8.25 Bode plots of potentiostat-cell system open-loop gain showing effects of control amplifier damping capacitance. $R_1 = 25.0\ \Omega$; $R_2 = 100\ \Omega$; $C_f = 0$; $C_2 = 1.00\ \mu\text{F}$; $R_3 C_1 = 1.00 \times 10^{-6}$ sec; $A: -C = 0\ \mu\text{F}$; $B: -C = 1.00 \times 10^{-5}\ \mu\text{F}$; $C: -C = 1.00 \times 10^{-4}\ \mu\text{F}$. Permission to reprint was granted by the American Chemical Society.

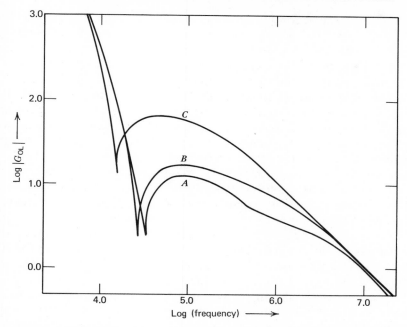

Fig. 8.26 Bode plots of potentiostat-cell system open-loop gain showing effects of current measuring amplifier damping capacitance. $R_1 = 25.0\,\Omega$; $R_2 = 100\,\Omega$; $C = 0$; $C_2 = 1.00\,\mu F$; $R_3 C_1 = 1.00 \times 10^{-6}$ sec; $A: -C_f = 1.00 \times 10^{-5}\,\mu F$; $B: -C_f = 1.00 \times 10^{-4}\,\mu F$; $C: -C_f = 1.00 \times 10^{-3}\,\mu F$. Permission to reprint was granted by the American Chemical Society.

In absence of C_1 a much less desirable result is obtained in which stabilization by C_f alone is effected only at considerable cost in bandpass. We conclude that the best approach to stabilization requires the use of capacitance C_1.

The effects of other parameters such as cell resistance (R_1-, R_2-values) have been studied [60]. Basically it is found that increased cell resistance leads to decreased bandpass (decreased G_{OL}).

The implications of the results of Figs. 8.23 to 8.26 with regard to stability are rather interesting if we consider the relationship of the various cell parameters to the chemical make-up of the electrochemical cell. As in the preceding examples, if the potentiostat-cell system in Fig. 8.22 is "critically tuned" for maximum response (maximize bandpass, minimize stability margin) for a particular set of controlled system (cell) parameters, a change in any one of these might lead to instability. One might realize ideal performance with a particular cell, but a change in electrode or electrolyte composition might be met with grossly unstable behavior. Most often such transitions from stable to unstable operation can be related to changes in the double-layer capacity C_2 whose magnitude depends not only on solution and electrode composition but also on electrode area and the applied dc potential. An operator using a dropping mercury electrode might observe a transition from stable to unstable behavior as the mercury drop grows. A befuddled polarographer may observe with chagrin that his potentiostat is stable over only part of the dc potential range of interest. All such operations—changing solutions, allowing the dropping mercury electrode to grow, changing working electrodes, and scanning the dc potential—are seemingly quite innocent, yet the critically tuned potentiostat can suggest otherwise. Clearly, a knowledge of automatic control principles, if only qualitative, will go a long way toward preserving the sanity of the electrochemist who is interested in high-speed experimentation. Fortunately for most, a critically tuned potentiostat-cell system is not a requirement for most electrochemical measurements so that one may employ large stability margins in which such "weird" behavior is not observed.

The accuracy of the potentiostat-cell network of Fig. 8.22 was evaluated as a function of frequency in a manner that differs from the general approach given above [60]. The approach used is more relevant for the network in question than the general one. Network accuracy was related to the transfer function E_o/e_{in} which ideally should equal the double-layer admittance times R_f; that is, if e_{in}, a sinusoidal voltage of frequency ω, is maintained across the double-layer capacity C_2,

$$\left|\frac{E_o}{e_{in}}\right|_{ideal} = R_f C_2 \omega. \tag{8.142}$$

The actual value of the transfer function is

$$\left|\frac{E_o}{e_{in}}\right| = \left|\frac{B^*}{G_1^{-1}[(1 + G_1)RCp + 3] - A - B}\right|, \tag{8.143}$$

where

$$B^* = \frac{E_o}{e_o} = \frac{D_{E_o}}{D_{e_o}}. \tag{8.144}$$

D_{e_o} is given by (8.128) and

$$
D_{E_o} = \begin{vmatrix}
1 & 0 & 0 & 0 & 0 & 0 & 0 & G_1 \\
0 & 1 & 0 & 0 & 0 & 0 & -G_2^* & 0 \\
0 & 0 & 0 & G_3 & 0 & 0 & 0 & 0 \\
0 & 0 & 0 & 0 & 0 & 1 & 0 & 0 \\
-a & 0 & 0 & 0 & e_{in} & -1 & -1 & a_1 \\
a_2 & -a_3 & 1 & 0 & 0 & 0 & 0 & 0 \\
0 & 0 & a_4 & -a_6 & 0 & 0 & 0 & 0 \\
-a_8 & 0 & a_7 & -a_9 & 0 & 0 & 0 & 0
\end{vmatrix}. \tag{8.145}
$$

Table 8.5 Summary of Upper Frequency Limits for Stable, Accurate Potentiostat Response with Various Double-Layer Capacitance and Cell Resistance

Cell and potentiostat parameters: $R = 1.00 \times 10^3 \, \Omega, R_f = 1.00 \times 10^3 \, \Omega; C = 20 \, \text{pF}$,
$C_f = 0.00 \, \text{pF}, \beta = 1.00, R_3 C_1 = 1.00 \times 10^{-6} \, \text{sec}$,
$R_1 = R_2$

Double layer capacitance $(\mu F) \rightarrow$	2×10^{-6}	1×10^{-6}	5×10^{-7}	2×10^{-7}	1×10^{-7}
Cell resistance $R_2 (\Omega)$			*Frequency* (Hz)		
25	1900	3200	5000	10000	15000
100	1400	2000	3200	4500	7000
200	1200	1500	2100	3300	5000
500	800	950	1300	2100	3200
1000	500	650	1000	1300	2100
2000	350	500	650	1000	1600

With the help of the results of the stability analysis and calculations of the relative percent difference between the actual response (8.143) and the ideal response (8.142) it was possible to compile a summary of the bandpass for 2% or better accuracy as a function of the cell parameters. These data, which are shown in Table 8.5, provide useful guidelines for application of the control network in question.

5   A SAMPLING OF FEEDBACK CONTROL NETWORKS FOR CHEMICAL RESEARCH

A Light Intensity Controller

The double-beam spectrophotometer which automatically compares light transmitted through a sample cell to that transmitted through a reference cell with light-chopping equipment has been effective in reducing problems associated with light source intensity variation. However, many situations exist in which such procedures are inappropriate. Often the simplicity of the single-beam instrument is extremely desirable, as, for example, in spectrophotometric monitoring of chemical plant process streams. Here relatively trouble-free operation and simplicity of maintenance are crucial requirements. In other cases the light-chopping procedure attending the conventional dual-beam operation is inappropriate, as in kinetic spectrophotometers in which transient changes in absorbance must be monitored. Applications such as these often demand a light source with ultrahigh long-term stability. This performance is obtainable with the help of feedback control.

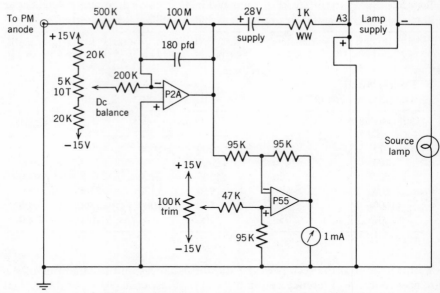

Fig. 8.27 Lamp intensity controller. Permission to reprint was granted by the American Chemical Society.

An example of a light intensity feedback control network is shown in Fig. 8.27. This unit was employed in a kinetic spectrophotometer in which detection of small changes in absorbance (10^{-4}–10^{-5} absorbance units) was demanded [64]. This required averaging of repetitive transient signals over a significant time period during which a constant source lamp intensity was essential. The control system of Fig. 8.27 effectively stabilized the lamp against intensity changes of more than 3-msec duration and improved the instrument sensitivity nearly an order of magnitude.

The feedback network of this control system, which is not explicitly indicated in Fig. 8.27, involves photoelectric coupling of the source lamp and a reference photomultiplier (PM) tube; 15% of the source lamp output is deflected from the spectrophotometer detecting beam to the reference photomultiplier with a precision ground quartz plate [64]. The output of the photomultiplier tube (the feedback signal) is delivered to the proportional controller which consists of the P2A amplifier (Philbrick/Nexus Research Model P2A Solid-State Operational Amplifier) with its attendant dc balance supply and passive components, the 28-V supply (Electronics Researches Model SP 28P5), the 1-K resistor and the lamp supply (Hewlett-Packard Model 6367A programmable power supply operated essentially as a power amplifier with proportional response). The controlled system is, of course, the source lamp. The P55 amplifier (Philbrick/Nexus Research Model P55

Solid-State Operational Amplifier), associated passive components, and dc balance is not part of the control loop. It is simply an amplifier for the meter (1 mA) which is used to monitor the error signal at the output of the P2A amplifier. The controlled variable (light intensity) level is primarily set by the 28-V supply which provides a dc bias at an appropriate level that is not obtainable from the P2A amplifier. Slight adjustment of the setpoint can be effected through the P2A amplifier dc balance.

An Automatic Balance

Automatic balances that produce recordable, weight-proportional outputs have recently become fashionable. They are particularly essential in thermo-gravimetric work. One approach involves controlling (holding fixed) the position of the "balance pans" with a feedback controller that delivers a weight-proportional output voltage suitable for recording. Such a system was designed [65] for a Wordon Quartz Products Inc. Model 4301 Fused Quartz Microbalance. The latter is designed for high-temperature thermo-gravimetric work in an evacuated chamber. The balance operates on a pivotal beam principle and is characterized by a 0.1 μg resolution. It is provided with electromagnets for restoring (position control) and damping. A concave mirror is coupled to a balance arm. A collimated light beam (slit image) impinging on this mirror is reflected in a direction that depends on the balance position, that is, on sample weight. Details of the controller are given in Fig. 8.28. The physical layout of the balance may be obtained from the manufacturers literature [66]. The principle of operation involves coupling the reflected light beam (feedback signal) to a pair of matched silicon solar cells (Centralab Type 52C) at the controller input (summing junction). Unless an equal amount of light impinges on each cell, a net difference is sensed and amplified by the first stage of the controller. Subsequent controller stages condition this signal so that a signal of first-order response (proportional at long times) is delivered to the restoring electromagnet coil and the damping coil is provided with a derivative response. In conventional terms the controller, which includes the coils, is a two-mode proportional-derivative controller. This controller action exerts a torque on the balance beam (controlled system) so that it maintains a fixed position corresponding to a negligible difference in light intensities seen by the solar cells. It is interesting to note that the automatic balance control network involves electronic, mechanical, electromagnetic, and photoelectric coupling.

The first stage of the controller (see Fig. 8.28) involves an operational amplifier (Burr-Brown Model 3065) and passive components configured as a precision difference amplifier to amplify the difference between the solar cell outputs. This first stage output is conditioned by two parallel stages. One consists of an Analog Devices Type 141A Operational Amplifier with

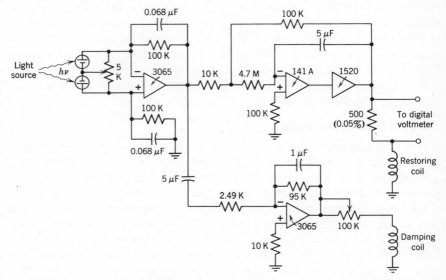

Fig. 8.28 Worden microbalance controller. amplifier 3065—Burr-Brown Model 3065 Operational Amplifier. amplifier 141A—Analog Devices Model 141A Operational Amplifier. amplifier 1520—Burr-Brown Model 1520 Current Booster Amplifier.

a Burr-Brown Type 1520 Current Booster which drives the restoring coil. The associated passive components are arranged to give a first-order response with a large time constant ($\simeq 250$ sec) and a dc gain of 10. The steady-state current applied to the restoring coil by this unit is proportional to sample weight. The voltage drop induced across a 500-Ω resistor by this current is the readout signal. The second signal conditioning path (Burr-Brown Model 3065 Operational Amplifier) gives a derivative response with a bandpass (upper frequency limit for true derivative response) of approximately 1 Hz. This signal is applied to the damping coil. For the application in question in which the weight variations of interest occur slowly, the response of this controller is adequate. Significantly faster controller response leads to instability, presumably because it allows the roll-off associated with the balance transfer function to contribute significantly before the $G_{OL} = 1$ point is reached. The attendant enhancement in the roll-off slope at unity open-loop gain is sufficient to cause instability.

Current-Controllers (Galvanostats)

A current controller (galvanostat) is readily constructed from a single operational amplifier, as shown in Fig. 8.29 [53]. Because the operational amplifier inputs draw negligible current, all the current through the input element R is "forced" through the system Z_f (characterized by an impedance

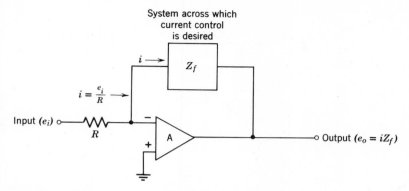

Fig. 8.29 Operational amplifier current control network.

Z_f). The latter may be any device across which we wish to effect current control. The resulting potential developed across the system ($= i \times Z_f$), which is frequently the readout of interest, is seen as the operational amplifier output e_o. In the context of the generalized control system of Fig. 8.1, the controller is the operational amplifier, the controlled system is the element Z_f, and the feedback network is the wire connecting Z_f to the input of the operational amplifier, the latter being the summing junction. The input signal r is the current across the input element ($r = i = e_i/R$). The feedback signal b and the controlled variable c are both identifiable as the current through the element Z_f ($b = c = i$).

Among the most prolific and demanding users of current controllers are electrochemists [54, 58, 62]. Electrochemical techniques with titles such as chronopotentiometry [67], galvanostatic transient measurements [62, 68], Heyrovsky's oscillographic polarography [69], controlled current faradaic rectification measurements [55, 68], and others involve controlled current. The circuit in Fig. 8.29 adequately controls the total current across a two-electrode cell. The amplifier output gives the total potential developed across the cell, including the ohmic potential drop (iR drop) associated with the current flow. For reasons discussed in Section 4 manifestations of cell iR drop on the readout signal are usually undesirable so that most modern electrochemical galvanostats employ the three-electrode cell principle (see Section 4). A typical circuit is shown in Fig. 8.30 [47, 54]. In this unit a controlled current is passed between the electrodes in the feedback loop of an operational amplifier (working and auxiliary electrodes), as in the simpler device in Fig. 8.29. The working electrode potential versus a reference electrode is sensed with a high-input impedance operational amplifier in the voltage-follower configuration (amplifier 2). Although residual iR drop sources still remain (see Section 4), this circuit is often satisfactory. It should

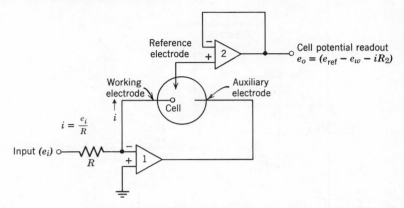

Fig. 8.30 Three-electrode galvanostat (electrochemical current controller): amplifier 1—operational amplifier controller; amplifier 2—operational amplifier voltage follower (for reference-working electrode cell potential readout); e_{ref} = potential of reference electrode versus electronic ground; e_w = potential of working electrode versus electronic ground; R_2 = cell ohmic resistance between working electrode and reference electrode probe.

be noted that the feedback control loop in Fig. 8.30 is the same as that in Fig. 8.29. The third electrode and voltage follower amplifier do not constitute part of the current control network but should be looked on as external readout signal-conditioning devices.

If we wished to eliminate iR drop effects completely from the cell potential readout, an additional amplifier would suffice, as shown in Fig. 8.31. Amplifier

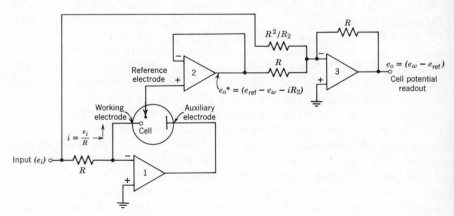

Fig. 8.31 Three-electrode galvanostat with compensation for cell ohmic potential drop: amplifier 1—operational amplifier controller; amplifier 2—operational amplifier voltage follower; amplifier 3—Operational amplifier adder (with inversion). Notation, the same as Figure 30.

3 of Fig. 8.31 adds iR_2 (R_2 = residual cell ohmic resistance) to the output of the voltage follower amplifier ($e_{ref} - e_{working} - iR_2$) and inverts the signal polarity to give the desired output ($e_{working} - e_{ref}$).

Being eminently difficult to satisfy, electrochemists actually find all of the foregoing galvanostat circuits inadequate in one important respect. The devices control the *total* cell current, part of which is applied to charging the electrical double layer as the potential varies (double-layer charging current) and part is utilized by the faradaic process (electrolysis process). The electrochemist, however, usually wishes to control the faradaic current and, in this framework, we must view the double-layer charging process as contributing an error to current control. Rigorous corrections for this error can be accomplished but with notable difficulty. Although the double-layer charging current is often negligible, it represents a substantial error in high-speed (short transient times or high frequencies) galvanostatic experiments. It is a tribute to the modern art of automatic control that a frequently viable solution to this problem can be found. The circuit of Fig. 8.32 represents a device which, under appropriate circumstances, will control the *faradaic* current across cell No. 1 ("sample" cell) while providing a potential readout (output of amplifier 3) free from iR drop contributions [70]. This is a modified version of a circuit proposed by DeFord [47] and later by Shults and co-workers [71] which did not provide for complete iR compensation. The control network has a galvanostat (Fig. 8.31 style—amplifiers 1, 2, and 3 with associated components) with a "sample" cell containing the solution under investigation, and a potentiostat (Fig. 8.22 Style—Amplifiers 4–6, etc.) whose "reference" cell contains only supporting electrolyte and solvent. The cell potential-output signal of the galvanostat (amplifier 3 output) is applied to the potentiostat input so that the potential changes induced in the sample cell are applied also to the reference cell. Because electroactive material of interest is absent, the resulting current flow in the reference cell is only double-layer charging current. The charging current signal obtained at the output of amplifier 6 is applied to the input of the galvanostat control amplifier. Assuming that proper adjustments are made, this operation adds a current equal to that required for charging the electrical double layer to the normal galvanostat input current (e_{in}/R) so that the latter is devoted solely to the faradaic process. This operation is valid, provided the electrical double layers at the two working electrode-solution interfaces are identical. If the electrode surfaces differ in their chemical characteristics (e.g., differing amounts of oxide film formation) or the electroactive species, which is present only in the sample cell, significantly influences the double-layer properties, this charging-current compensation scheme (and most others) is invalid. Fortunately, many situations exist in which such problems do not arise and more mundane sources of error (e.g., mismatch of reference electrodes) are readily handled.

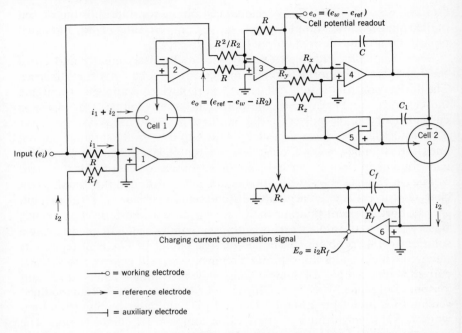

$e_o = (e_w - e_{ref})$
Cell potential readout

$e_o = (e_{ref} - e_w - iR_2)$

Input (e_i)

Charging current compensation signal
$E_o = i_2 R_f$

—o = working electrode

→ = reference electrode

—| = auxiliary electrode

Fig. 8.32 Three-electrode galvanostat with compensation for double-layer charging current and cell ohmic potential drop: amplifier 1—Operational amplifier current controller; amplifier 2—Operational amplifier voltage follower; amplifier 3—Operational amplifier adder; amplifier 4—Operational amplifier controller for reference cell potentiostat; amplifier 5—Operational amplifier voltage follower for reference cell potentiostat; amplifier 6—Operational amplifier current measuring amplifier for reference cell potentiostat; cell 1—Sample cell (cell under investigation—contains supporting electrolyte and electroactive material); cell 2—Reference cell (charging current generator—contains only supporting electrolyte); $i_1 = e_i/R =$ controlled faradaic current; $i_2 =$ electrical double-layer charging current; e_{ref}, e_w, R_2, R—same as Figures 30 and 31; $R_f, C_f, C_1, C, R_x, R_y, R_z, R_c$—same as Figure 22 (system operated with $R_x = R_y = R_z$); —o = working electrode; → = reference electrode; —| = auxiliary electrode.

From a control network viewpoint the circuit in Fig. 8.32 is quite interesting. Two feedback loops activate the controller (amplifier 1). One involves the working and auxiliary electrodes of the sample cell, as in the conventional galvanostats. The other involves the sample-cell potential readout system (amplifiers 2 and 3 and components), and the potentiostat-reference cell system. In other words, the feedback network of the current controller contains, within itself, another automatic control network! Although electrochemical units of this type have been operated successfully [70–71], the detailed stability characteristics have never been analyzed to our knowledge. Such a study would be challenging, interesting, and very helpful in assessing the bandpass limitations of circuits whose applications to date have involved only long-time experiments.

A Dual Potential Controller

At the cost of possibly overemphasizing the subject of potential control, particularly with regard to electrochemical measurements, we submit the circuit in Fig. 8.33 [72] as a somewhat unique example of the profound capabilities of modern automatic control systems. This circuit, which contains three operational amplifiers and four electrodes, enables simultaneous, independent control of the potentials of two working electrodes (W_1, W_2) versus a reference electrode. Amplifier 1 and its feedback loop act to hold the reference electrode at the potential $-E_1$ versus the electronic system ground. Amplifier 2 holds one working electrode (W_1) at ground potential so that its potential *versus the reference electrode* is E_1. Amplifier 3 holds the second working electrode (W_2) at the potential $E_2 - E_1$ versus ground or E_2 V versus the reference electrode. The control inputs are supplied at the $+$inputs of amplifier 1 ($-E_1$) and amplifier 3 ($E_2 - E_1$). The current flow associated with the potential control operation is between the auxiliary and working electrodes. Negligible current is passed through the reference electrode. Signals proportional to the currents through electrodes W_1 and W_2 are obtained at the outputs of amplifiers 2 and 3, respectively. This circuit has all the properties of the three-electrode cell configuration (above) with regard to eliminating many, but not all, sources of iR drop. This circuit

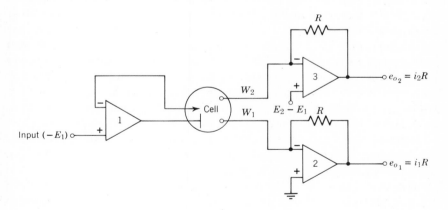

Fig. 8.33   Dual potential controller: $\rightarrow$ = reference electrode; $-|$ = auxiliary electrode; $\underline{W_1}$o = working electrode 1; $\underline{W_2}$o = working electrode 2; i_1 = current through working electrode 1; i_2 = current through working electrode 2; E_1 = potential of working electrode 1 versus reference electrode; E_2 = potential of working electrode 2 versus reference electrode; amplifiers 1, 2, 3 = Operational Amplifiers.

was designed for applications involving thin-layer cells [72] in which the residual iR drop contributions can have significant effects.

Reagent Concentration Controllers

Chemists frequently wish to control the concentration of a reagent involved in a chemical reaction. The numerous and varied underlying reasons include the desire to optimize conditions for a synthesis or to simplify conditions for a reaction rate measurement (i.e., maintain pseudo first-order conditions). Over most of the history of modern chemistry the chemist has resorted to naturally occurring control systems such as acid-base buffers to control pH or redox buffers to control the redox potential of a solution (i.e., to obtain a "poised" system). Although such techniques are often adequate, numerous situations still arise in which they do not represent a viable approach to concentration control. The necessary large excess of buffering agent may be undesirable, for example, when it influences a chemical reaction's pathway and/or rate. When precise concentration control is desired, chemical buffers may be inadequate; that is, the buffer solubility limits may preclude dissolving sufficient amounts to obtain the desired control. These and other problems arise with sufficient frequency that man-made automatic concentration controllers have been playing an increasingly important role in modern chemical research.

The convenience of controlling the concentration (or activity) of a number of solution components has been enormously enhanced by recent advances in the field of specific ion electrodes. The use of an electrode to sense an activity or concentration has obvious advantages in simplicity over other common instrumentation techniques such as spectrophotometry, gas chromatography, and mass spectroscopy. Until recently only the hydrogen ion concentration could be followed in this manner with high selectivity over a wide concentration range, thanks to the early development of the glass electrode. Accordingly, the commonest form of automatic concentration controller has been the pH controller (pH-stat). The complexity and expense attending other available instrumental measurement techniques suppressed wide utilization of automatic controllers for other components. Fortunately this situation has changed drastically. At the present time at least 14 ions, in addition to hydrogen, can be monitored with good selectivity over wide concentration ranges with the newly developed specific ion electrodes [73]. Further advances are anticipated [74]. Thus activity or concentration control systems based on a specific ion electrode measuring element can now be considered of fairly wide applicability.

A schematic of an activity-concentration control system of this type is shown in Fig. 8.34. It illustrates a system in which the controlled reagent is *added* by an automatic buret system or its equivalent. This implies unidirectional control. The control network design assumes that the processes occurring in the reactor lead to the removal, never the addition, of the controlled reagent. Of course, this is the usual situation encountered, although exceptions are not uncommon. Operational amplifier 1 and the liquid delivery system constitute the controller. The diode across amplifier 1 ensures that it delivers only negative outputs which we assume is consistent with the buret motor demands. The reactor and its contents (solution, stirring apparatus, etc.) represent the controlled system. The feedback network contains the specific ion electrode-reference electrode cell and operational amplifier 2. The amplifier-cell configuration shown provides an output equal to the cell potential without drawing current from the cell [53]. The summing junction involves resistive coupling (above). This control network delivers reagent at a rate sufficient to maintain the specific ion electrode potential (versus reference) equal to minus the input potential, thus controlling the activity of the reagent sensed by the specific ion electrode. If desired, we could insert a flow meter in the liquid delivery line whose readout would yield information on the rate of the reaction involving the controlled reagent. Alternatively, we could achieve the same end by monitoring the output of amplifier 1. In applying the circuit in Fig. 8.34 we should ensure that the polarity associated with the measuring cell potential is consistent with the requirement of negative feedback. The specific hookup shown in Fig. 8.34 is correct only if e_{in} is positive, the cell potential $E_s - E_r$ is negative, and the cell potential becomes increasingly negative with increasing reagent concentration. Although these requirements may seem

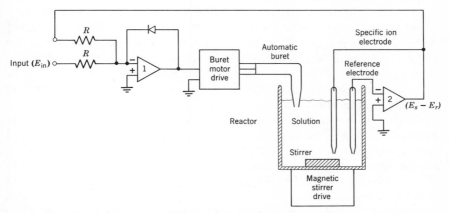

Fig. 8.34 Concentration controller based on liquid flow reagent delivery system: amplifier 1—controller amplifier (e.g., operational amplifier plus current booster to drive buret motor system); amplifier 2—operational amplifier; E_s = specific ion electrode potential versus electronic system ground; E_r = reference electrode potential versus electronic system ground.

rather specific, modification to other situations is usually trivial, amounting to little more than switching leads or signal polarities at appropriate points.

It should be recognized that the control network of Fig. 8.34 is non-linear by virtue of the logarithmic relationship between activity and cell potential. This also applies to Figs. 8.35 and 8.36 which are discussed below. Although the system is workable if amplifier 1 provides sufficient gain, quantitative application of principles described previously are applicable only for small deviations from the set point. This problem can be alleviated readily by inserting an antilogarithmic converter (available from operational amplifier manufacturers) at the output of amplifier 2. The system resulting from this modification can be viewed as a simple proportional controller.

The similarities between the concentration controller of Fig. 8.34 and a conventional potentiostat without positive feedback iR compensation (Fig. 8.22 without positive feedback loop) should be noted. The end result of both circuits is control of a cell potential. The potentiostat achieves this end by passage of current through the cell to *polarize* the working electrode to the appropriate potential versus a reference electrode. The concentration controller of Fig. 8.34 achieves the desired cell potential by the addition of the reagent to which the specific ion electrode responds. In the latter case the nature of the process is such that maintenance of a fixed cell potential necessarily implies maintenance of a fixed concentration of the relevant reagent throughout the solution (assuming adequate stirring). The similarities between the potentiostat and concentration controller become even more profound when we look more deeply into the events induced by the potentiostat and the definition of polarization. Polarization of the working electrode implies no more than the alteration by electrolysis or double-layer charging of surface *concentrations* of the solution species that influence the electrode potential. Thus in a real sense both devices in question effect concentration control. The main difference is that in most electrochemical techniques (e.g., polarography) the potentiostat-induced concentration variations occur only in the proximity of the electrode and are not manifested in the solution bulk during the observation period, whereas action of the concentration controller is manifested throughout the solution. Even this distinction, however, does not exist in all cases. In controlled potential coulometry [75] our objective is to alter the concentration of an electroactive species concentration throughout the solution (e.g., reduce the concentration to zero). With a cell characterized by a high electrode area to solution volume ratio and efficient stirring, the time required for even complete destructive electrolysis can be made very short—for example, about one minute [76]. Such rates of removal (or formation) of solution components are compatible with the needs of most concentration controllers.

Pursuing this line of discussion to its ultimate conclusion, we realize that in appropriate circumstances the potentiostat and concentration controller become identical; for example, the potentiostat of Fig. 8.22 without modification can serve as a concentration controller. A potentiostat is the most rational concentration controller in situations in which we wish to control the solution redox potential, that is, when the concentration ratio of oxidized and reduced forms of a redox couple must be controlled. If the cell design requirements stated above for rapid electrolysis are met, the potential setting of the potentiostat will determine the relevant concentration ratio *throughout the solution* (Nernst equation) unless the electrode reaction is irreversible or response requirements become too drastic. Such a concentration control application involving electrolytic generation or removal of reagents is unique on two counts: (a) it involves *in situ* generation or removal of reagent; (b) control is bidirectional, assuming the electrode reaction is reversible. *In situ* electrolytic reagent generation from a source contained within the reactor eliminates the complex valves, pumps, storage vessels, and flow-rate measuring equipment associated with systems of the type shown in Fig. 8.34. Rate of reagent addition is determined conveniently from the cell current. Bidirectional control is achieved because the potentiostat will carry out oxidation or reduction at the working electrode, depending on the requirements imposed by the events in the reactor. This feature obviously makes the controller more versatile and occasionally may prove essential with complex processes. Although, strictly speaking, a potentiostat can control only concentration ratios of redox couples, it can double as an absolute concentration controller whenever (a) electrolytic generation of the controlled reagent from an *in situ* reagent source is possible and (b) a large excess of reagent source can be tolerated or a reagent source of constant unit activity is available. For example, if bromine is the controlled reagent, condition (a) is fulfilled because bromide ion is an appropriate reagent source. In order for the potentiostat setting to control the bromine activity (not just the Br_2/Br^- ratio) we must have a sufficient excess of bromide ion so that its concentration will not change appreciably throughout the period of control. Condition (b) essentially states that this excess of bromide ion may be viewed as inert as far as the chemical process of interest is concerned. Condition (b) also acknowledges another common situation in which the potentiostat setting determines the absolute concentration of the controlled reagent. This occurs whenever the controlled reagent can be electrolytically derived from a pure solid or liquid; for example, when cupric ion is generated from a copper electrode or mercuric ion, from a mercury electrode.

If the special requirements that validate the use of a potentiostat as a concentration controller are not fulfilled, we can still realize the advantages attending *in situ* electrolytic generation of the controlled reagent with a network of the type shown in Fig. 8.35. This device is a simple modification of the control network of Fig. 8.34 in which an *in situ* electrolytic cell for reagent generation or removal replaces the liquid-flow system for reagent addition. The concentration of the controlled reagent is monitored by a separate specific ion electrode-reference electrode cell (see Fig. 8.34).

Details of cell design for electrolytic reagent generation are not given here. Requirements are essentially the same as for coulometric titrations. The reader is referred to the literature on the latter subject [75] for cell-design considerations. In the same literature he will find cells for *external electrolytic generation* of a reagent and should recognize them as still another possibility for concentration control network design.

In the foregoing discussion the capability for bidirectional control is mentioned as one of the advantages attending electrolytic reagent generation-removal. We might ask whether bidirectional control is feasible in the many cases in which the electrolytic scheme is inappropriate, that is, when a flow system must be used as in Fig. 8.34. By now the reader should have sensed that an optimistic outlook is warranted and that the answer to such

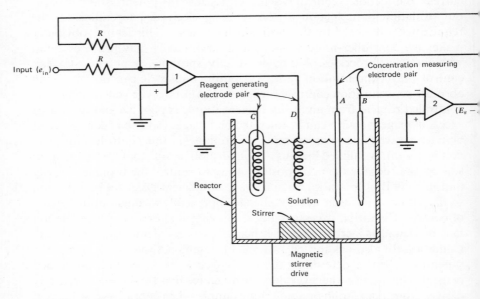

Fig. 8.35 Concentration controller based on *in situ* electrolytic generation and removal of reagent: amplifier 1—controller amplifier (e.g., operational amplifier plus current booster, if necessary); amplifier 2—Operational amplifier; A = specific ion electrode; B = reference electrode; C = counter electrode of reagent generating pair in separate compartment; D = reagent generating electrode.

inquiries will usually be affirmative. Figure 8.36 outlines a modification of the network in Fig. 8.34, which yields bidirectional control of pH. Two automatic buret delivery systems are employed, one containing acid, the other base. The control amplifier output (amplifier 1) is applied through a relay to the automatic buret motors, the relay position determining which motor is activated. The controller output is also applied to a two-state trigger circuit (amplifier 3 and components) whose response characteristics are defined by (8.30) and (8.31). The trigger output is applied to the relay coil to control the relay position. The sign of the controller output determines the trigger output state and thus the relay position. With proper adjustment of the e_{in} value (see Fig. 8.36), the controller output is applied to the acid-containing buret motor when the pH exceeds the desired level and to the base-containing buret motor when the pH is too low.

Examples considered here have emphasized feedback networks that utilize specific ion electrodes for measurement of activities or concentrations. It should, however, be recognized that feedback networks based on other concentration-activity measurement schemes (spectrophotometric, conducti-metric, etc.) can be substituted in place of electrode detection without grossly altering other aspects of the control networks in Figs. 8.34 to 8.36.

Automatic Gain Control

Automatic gain control (AGC) is widely applied in electronic circuitry. Most family TV sets contain this device. In the chemical laboratory a useful application is stabilization and control of an oscillator amplitude. A rather crude oscillator (with respect to amplitude stability) can be converted to an ultrastable source with the aid of a circuit of the type whose block diagram is shown in Fig. 8.37 [77]. An interesting aspect of this circuit is its use of an electronic multiplier, a *nonlinear* device now available in small, low-cost, reasonably high performance modules (see also Fig. 8.18). The multiplier output is the product of the oscillator output times the integrator output. The multiplier output is rectified and filtered. The resulting dc signal, e_{dc}, is applied to the input of a high-gain (small RC) integrator. A reference voltage, E_{ref}, is applied to another input. When $e_{dc} = -E_{ref}$ (i.e., when the multiplier output amplitude ΔE is $\pi/2 \times E_{ref}$), the net integrator input current is zero and the output of the integrator is steady, as is the multiplier output. If the oscillator amplitude drops, the integrator inputs become unbalanced and the integrator output increases until balance is again achieved, that is, when $\Delta E = (\pi/2)E_{ref}$. Similarly, an increase in oscillator amplitude will stimulate a drop in the integrator output until $\Delta E = (\pi/2)E_{ref}$. Figure 8.38 shows a specific circuit diagram [77] of an AGC circuit based on the principle of Fig. 8.37. Amplifiers 1 and 2 and their associated circuitry constitute a precision rectifier-filter. Amplifier 3 and its passive components

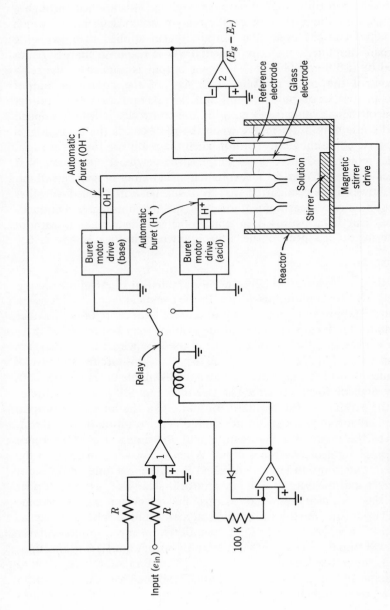

Fig. 8.36 Bi-directional pH controller: amplifiers 1 and 2—same as Figure 34; amplifier 3—operational amplifier; E_g = glass electrode potential versus electronic system ground; E_r = reference electrode potential versus electronic system ground. NOTE: Although not shown in this schematic, a unity-gain inverting amplifier may be required at the input to *one* of the buret motor drives. This need will arise if the buret motor drives operate only on one polarity.

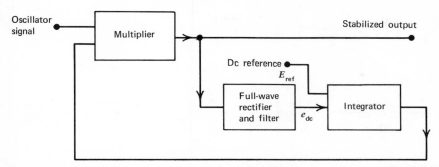

Fig. 8.37 Block diagram of oscillator amplitude control network. Permission to reprint was granted by the Burr-Brown Research Corp.

make up a high-gain integrator whose output e_I is limited to $0 \leq e_I \leq 10$ V. This AGC loop maintains a constant multiplier output for oscillator amplitudes ranging from 2 to 10 V [77].

Power-Line Conditioners

Power-line regulation is a familiar operation to chemists. Sola transformers and similar devices have been employed for many years to stabilize the 60-Hz line source for equipment sensitive to line fluctuations. Unfortunately most "classical" line regulators achieve long-term stabilization but do not protect against short transient interferences (as generated by desk calculators, IBM card punches, and other digital readout equipment) and various *RF* interferences. As every chemist knows, sources of these troublesome interferences

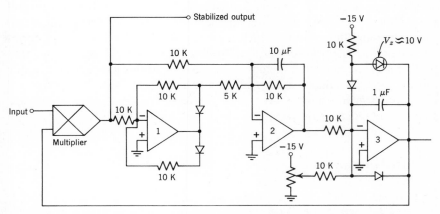

Fig. 8.38 Automatic gain control network: amplifiers 1, 2, 3—operational amplifiers (Burr-Brown Model 3064); multiplier = Burr-Brown Model 4029. Permission to reprint was granted by the Burr-Brown Research Corp.

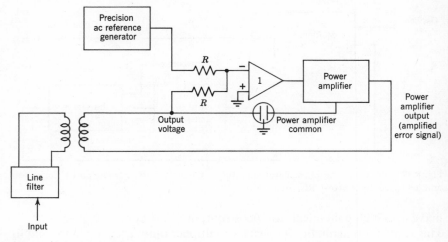

Fig. 8.39   Power line conditioner.

are becoming increasingly common in the chemical laboratory. Thanks to implementation of modern feedback control ideas, a new generation of power-line conditioners that are extremely effective in removing line transients, etc., have become available. They possess characteristics such as 50-μsec recovery times, load and line regulation better than 0.1%, output harmonic distortion less than 0.2%, and output power of 1 to 2 kVA. The schematic in Fig. 8.39 [78] illustrates the basic principle underlying one common approach to such devices. The power-line output is compared to an ac reference generator via a resistive summing junction. The error signal is amplified by a high-gain preamplifier, followed by a power amplifier. The power-amplifier output, which is proportional to the error signal, drives one side of the line transformer, thus forcing the output voltage to equal that of the reference generator. Actual circuits based on this idea appear notably more complicated than is shown in Fig. 8.39 because of a variety of peripheral devices designed to protect against current and/or voltage overloads. Figure 8.39 indicates only the basic feedback control network.

References

1. J. M. Sturtevant in *Technique of Organic Chemistry*, A. Weissberger, Ed., Vol. 1, Part I, Interscience, New York, 1947.
2. H. W. Bode, *Network Analysis and Feedback Amplifier Design*, Van Nostrand, Princeton, New Jersey, 1945.

3. H. Chestnut and R. W. Mayer, *Servomechanisms and Regulating System Design*, Vol. 1, 2nd. ed., Wiley, New York, 1959.

4. F. E. Nixon, *Principles of Automatic Controls*, Prentice-Hall, Englewood Cliffs, N.J., 1953.

5. E. M. Grabbe, S. Ramo, and D. E. Woolridge, Eds., *Handbook of Automation, Computation and Control; Vol. 1, Control Fundamentals*, Wiley, New York, 1958.

6. D. M. Considine, Ed., *Process Instruments and Controls Handbook*, McGraw-Hill, New York, 1957.

7. I. M. Horowitz, *Synthesis of Feedback Systems*, Academic, New York, 1963.

8. P. S. Buckley, *Techniques of Process Control*, Wiley, New York, 1964.

9. L. A. Zadeh and C. A. Desoer, *Linear System Theory*, McGraw-Hill, New York, 1963.

10 H. E. Koenig, Y. Tokad, and H. K. Kesavan, *Analysis of Discrete Physical Systems*, McGraw-Hill, New York, 1967.

11. C. J. Savant, Jr., *Control System Design*, McGraw-Hill, New York, 1964.

12. E. B. Canfield, *Electromechanical Control Systems and Devices*, Wiley, New York, 1965.

13. W. I. Caldwell, G. A. Coon, and L. M. Zoos, *Frequency Response for Process Control*, McGraw-Hill, New York, 1959.

14. C. R. Kelley, *Control Eng.*, **15**, 75 (May 1968).

15. W. C. Carter, *Instr. Control Systems*, **40**, 107 (January 1967).

16. R. V. Churchill, *Operational Mathematics*, McGraw-Hill, New York, 1958.

17. A. Erdelyi, ed., *Tables of Integral Transforms*, Vol. 1, McGraw-Hill, New York, 1954, p. 230.

18. J. T. Tou, *Digital and Sampled Data Control Systems*, McGraw-Hill, New York, 1959.

19. E. I. Jury, *Sampled Data Control Systems*, Wiley, New York, 1958.

20. H. E. Merritt and R. E. Hohn, *Control Eng.*, **14**, 61 (December 1967).

21. Burr-Brown Research Corp., "Handbook of Operational Amplifier Applications," Burr-Brown Research Corporation, Tucson, Arizona, 1963, p. 46.

22. T. S. Gray, *Applied Electronics*, Wiley, New York, 1957.

23. H. Nyquist, Regeneration Theory, *Bell System Tech. J.*, **11**, 127 (1932).

24. Instrument Society of America, "Dynamic Response Testing of Process Control Instrumentation," *ISA Standard S26*, Instrument Society of America, Pittsburgh, Pa., 1968.

25. Analog Devices, "A Comprehensive Catalog and Guide to Operational Amplifiers," Analog Devices, Cambridge, Mass., January 1968, p. 29.

26. Burr-Brown Research Corp., *Fall 1968 Catalog*, Burr-Brown Research Corp., Tucson, Ariz., 1968, p. 16.

27. J. M. Reiner, *The Organism as an Adaptive Control System*, Prentice-Hall, Englewood Cliffs, N.J., 1968.

28. W. H. McAdams, *Heat Transmission* 3rd ed., McGraw-Hill, New York, 1954.

29. H. J. Stoever, *Applied Heat Transmission*, McGraw-Hill, New York, 1941.

30. J. O. Hougen, O. R. Martin, and R. A. Walsh, *Control Eng.*, **10**, 114 (September 1963).

31. R. P. Sandell and N. H. Cealgske, *ISA J.*, **3**, 482 (1956).
32. A. Krigman, *Instr. Control Systems*, **42**, 67 (January 1969).
33. A. Krigman, *Instr. Control Systems*, **41**, 65 (January 1968).
34. E. D. West, in *Treatise on Analytical Chemistry*, I. M. Kolthoff and P. J. Elving, eds., Part I, Volume 8, Chapter 93, Interscience, New York, 1968.
35. Kepco, "Kepco Power Supplies," Kepco, Flushing, N.Y., 1967, p. 16.
36. Philbrick Researches, *Applications Manual for Computing Amplifiers*, Philbrick Researches, Dedham, Mass., 1966, pp. 32–33.
37. Burr-Brown Research Corp., *Handbook of Operational Amplifier Applications*, Burr-Brown Research Corp., Tucson, Ariz., 1963, pp. 43–44.
38. Analog Devices, Inc., *Applications Manual for Models 201, 202, 203 and 210 Chopper Stabilized Operational Amplifiers*, Analog Devices, Cambridge, Mass., 1967, p. 4.
39. P. Harriott, "Process Control," McGraw-Hill, New York, 1964.
40. P. W. Murrill, *Automatic Control of Processes*, International Textbook, Scranton, Pa., 1967.
41. M. H. Aronson, Ed., *Instruments and Automation*, **31**, 1518 (September 1958).
42. Conoflow, *Bulletin T-100*, Conoflow, Blackwood, New Jersey, 1969.
43. E. B. Canfield, *Electromechanical Control Systems and Devices*, Wiley, New York, 1965, pp. 188–192.
44. C. J. Savant, Jr., *Control System Design*, McGraw-Hill, New York, 1964, pp. 263–279.
45. L. O. Brown, Jr., *AIEE Trans.*, **70**, 1890 (1951).
46. G. L. Booman, *Anal. Chem.* **29**, 213 (1957).
47. D. D. DeFord, Division of Analytical Chemistry, 133rd Meeting, ACS, San Francisco, April 1958.
48. H. Gerischer and K. E. Staubach, *Z. Elektrochem.* **61**, 789 (1957).
49. M. T. Kelley, D. J. Fisher, and H. C. Jones, *Anal. Chem.*, **31**, 1475 (1959).
50. *Ibid.*, **32**, 1262 (1960).
51. G. L. Booman and W. B. Holbrook, *Anal. Chem.*, **35**, 1793 (1963).
52. *Ibid.*, **37**, 795 (1965).
53. C. N. Reilley, *J. Chem. Ed.*, **39**, A853, A933 (1962).
54. W. M. Schwarz and I. Shain, *Anal. Chem.*, **35**, 1770 (1963).
55. D. E. Smith, in *Electroanalytical Chemistry*, A. J. Bard, Ed., Vol. 1, Chapter 1, Dekker, New York, 1966.
56. J. W. Hayes and C. N. Reilley, *Anal. Chem.*, **37**, 1322 (1965).
57. P. Valenta and J. Vogel, *Chem. Listy.*, **54**, 1279 (1960).
58. R. W. Murray, *Anal. Chem.*, **35**, 1784 (1963).
59. E. R. Brown, T. G. McCord, D. E. Smith and D. D. DeFord, *Anal. Chem.*, **38**, 1119 (1966).
60. E. R. Brown, D. E. Smith, and G. L. Booman, *Anal. Chem.*, **40**, 1411 (1968).
61. G. Lauer, *Anal. Chem.*, **38**, 1277 (1966).
62. K. J. Vetter, *Electrochemical Kinetics*, Academic, New York, 1967.
63. G. C. Barker, in *Transactions of the Symposium on Electrode Processes*, E. Yeager, Ed., Wiley, New York, 1961.
64. P. A. Loach and R. J. Loyd, *Anal. Chem.*, **38**, 1709 (1966).
65. J. E. Lester and R. J. Loyd, unpublished work, Department of Chemistry, Northwestern University, Evanston, Ill., 1968.

66. Wordon Quartz Products, "Data Sheet 252-3,4 Fused Quartz Micro-Balance," Wordon Quartz Products, Houston, Texas, 1968.
67. D. G. Davis, in *Electroanalytical Chemistry*, A. J. Bard, Ed., Vol. 1, Chapter 2, Dekker, New York, 1966.
68. P. Delahay, in *Advances in Electrochemistry and Electrochemical Engineering*, P. Delahay, Ed., Vol. 1, Chapter 5, Interscience, New York, 1961.
69. R. Kalvoda, *Techniques of Oscillographic Polarography*, Elsevier, New York, 1965.
70. D. E. Smith, unpublished work, Department of Chemistry, Northwestern University, Evanston, Ill., 1968.
71. W. D. Shults, F. E. Haga, T. R. Mueller, and H. C. Jones, *Anal. Chem.*, **37**, 1416 (1965).
72. L. B. Anderson and C. N. Reilley, *J. Electroanal. Chem.*, **10**, 295 (1965).
73. Orion Research Inc., *Comprehensive Listing of Specific Ion Electrodes*, Orion Research, Cambridge, Mass., April 1, 1968.
74. C. J. Coetzee and H. Freiser, *Anal. Chem.*, **40**, 2071 (1968).
75. D. D. DeFord and J. W. Miller, in *Treatise on Analytical Chemistry*, I. M. Kolfhoff and P. J. Elving, Eds., Part I, Volume 4, Chapter 49, Interscience, New York, 1963.
76. A. J. Bard, *Anal. Chem.*, **36**, 1125 (1964).
77. Burr-Brown Research Corp., "Multipliers/Dividers"; *Bulletin PDS-201B*, Burr-Brown Research Corp., Tucson, Ariz., July 1968.
78. International Electronic Research Corp., "Dynamic Line Corrector": *Bulletin 509-3/15/63*, International Electronic Research Corp., Burbank, Calif. 1963.

Chapter **IX**

COMPUTERS IN CHEMICAL RESEARCH

Murray C. Goddard and John Figueras

---

1   INTRODUCTION

Man has distinguished himself as a tool-using animal. Computers are tools; they differ from most other tools in that they provide an intellectual means of interacting with models of the external world; they lead the way to a new approach to problems. Computers obviously can accomplish humdrum, clerical work as well as sophisticated, rapid calculations that would otherwise be intolerably long. Less obvious but more important is the fact that they give man a new, penetrating insight into his problems. The point of view that the intelligent user can gain through the interactive discipline of working with a computer is one of the greatest boons of computer use.

The field of computer applications has had its rapid growth since World War II. The volume of literature available in this young field is overwhelming and often redundant. In this chapter we have brought together the elements needed by chemists who may wish to do scientific computing or apply the computer as a tool for laboratory process control. Our aim is to build up sufficient background for understanding the vocabulary and concepts, the operations that are performed, and the necessary combinations of equipment and programs. Programming techniques are illustrated with examples that should suggest to chemists the potential uses of computers. No reader should expect to learn to program a computer solely from studying this chapter; reference to complete programming texts and suppliers manuals would be required to supplement our illustrations.

Practical applications require the study of manufacturers' literature and other texts [1]. Computer manufacturers furnish extensive educational material because they recognize that the education of new users of computers is essential. Our intent is to supply a framework that will suggest uses a chemist might wish to explore and to provide a basis for further study. Both analog- and digital-computing components and techniques are described.

The chapter is divided into three relatively self-contained sections. In the first we include a short general history of computers and their applications. The second contains a discussion of the fundamental principles of computing and brief descriptions of typical electronic and electromechanical means of implementing them. The third gives some details of programming both analog and digital computers; typical problems are discussed to help build a bridge from the theory of programming to its practice.

Types of Computer

Computers fall into two categories: analog and digital. *Analog computers* simulate one continuous variable by means of another; for example, distance may be represented in an analog computer by a voltage or speed by the pointer and dial of a speedometer. *Digital computers* operate with discrete variables, much as a child counts on his fingers. The differences between analog and digital computers are one of degree; in theory each can do the tasks of the other, since a multiplicity of discrete levels approach a continuum, whereas coarse differences in continuous variables can be made to simulate digital operations. Hardware differences, however, do affect the different ways of using the two methods of computing, which may lead to different insights.

The analog computer is primarily associated with the continuous solution of differential equations, particularly nonlinear differential equations, whereas the digital computer is most often associated with solutions to algebraic problems. In control use the analog computer copes most naturally with proportional problems and problems in which the memory of previous individual measurements is less important than averages or integrals. It normally uses only one independent variable, simulated by *time*. The digital computer provides large memories of individual measurements and easy access for the true-false type of logic; it can also be programmed to simulate continuous variables. Analog and digital techniques may be used together, as exemplified by a beam balance that employs both fixed weights and a slide-bar.

Applications

Computers also differ according to their intended applications such as calculating, control, data collection, graphics, and information storage and retrieval. These calculations may include any that could be done with a desk calculator (a digital machine) or a slide rule (an analog computer). Because electronic devices are used, calculating can be done in less than one millionth of the time required by a human being. This speed differential opens up solutions to a vast range of calculations formerly inaccessible with manual techniques. Further, such high-speed calculations can provide almost instantaneous control of laboratory experiments; new experiments can now be imagined and tried. In addition to speed, computer control of experiments can provide reliability, precision, and safety beyond the capability of human beings. When collecting data, a computer-based system can screen them, control the amount permanently retained, and find statistical parameters, such as averages.

Computer-generated graphic displays are becoming increasingly common. A graph is the most ordinary means of output from an analog computer. The experimenter can interact with the analog model while viewing the effects on a graphical output. Electronically generated displays of mathematical models provide an excellent way to gain insight into a problem. The use of interactive, graphic terminals to access remote, time-sharing digital computers promises to grow rapidly in the near future.

Storing and retrieving information is our most common problem. Computers can be programmed to be particularly helpful in its solution. One of the reasons for the usefulness of computers in this function is that they can search their index files in many ways; for example, letters may be filed sequentially as they are received. A computer-readable index of the file which included the filing date, the writer, and one or more subjects would permit retrieval of all the letters from one person or all the letters on some particular subject that arrived after a particular date.

History

Modern digital computers are based on the design principles derived by Charles Babbage in his plans for an "analytical engine" [2]. This early nineteenth century effort was not completed, basically because at that time machines could not be built to the required tolerances. Babbage planned to use cards to feed both data and computing instructions to his machine, much as we do today.

George Boole developed the logical algebra that is the basis for arithmetic and mathematical logic about the middle of the nineteenth century. He showed that arithmetic and other algebras could be derived from his logical algebra. The application of Boolean algebra provides a powerful tool for simplifying logical problems, including those encountered in designing digital equipment.

James Clerk Maxwell provided the next necessary ingredient of our modern computers when he laid the theoretical basis for electrical engineering in the latter part of the nineteenth century. His field equations are a complete mathematical basis for analyzing electrical circuits; they are the basis of electrical engineering.

Subsequent electrical engineering developments, for example, DeForest's grid-controlled amplifying vacuum tube, patented before World War I, were followed by others, such as the Eccles-Jordan flip-flop circuit, patented shortly after World War I. The demand for large volumes of computation in World War II was met by the first automatic digital computers. IBM and the Bell Labs built computers based on telephone relays; the first publicly announced electronic digital computers were the Mark I at Harvard (1944) and the ENIAC (Electronic Numerical Integrator and Calculator) at the University of Pennsylvania. The ENIAC, first publicly demonstrated in 1946, contained 18,000 vacuum tubes. ENIAC also marked the first step in the use of acronyms in the computer field; acronyms now supply a major part of the jargon, possibly lending an air of expertise to its practitioners that obscures the primitiveness of this largely undeveloped field. A group at Harvard even named a programming language for use in computer-aided instruction MYNORCA (acronym spelled backward).

2 BASIC PRINCIPLES

The basic principles of computers are simple enough to be taught to elementary school children as part of "modern math." The theory is based on numbers, Boolean algebra, logic diagrams, and truth tables. Applications are based on algorithms, methods of modeling, simulation, feedback loops, sampling theorems, statistics, and other fields. Some understanding of these concepts will be of value in any use of computers [3]. In most applications these "bare bones" of the machine will protrude when the computing system fails or has "bugs."

Number Systems

All of us frequently use a variety of number systems. The simplest and oldest is the *tally* in which a mark is made for each of the objects to be counted. Perhaps the fifth item is tallied as a mark cutting across the first four (////) to create a distinctive graphic symbol for this group of tally marks.

This invention of symbols for numbers greater than one facilitates handling of moderately large numbers. The *Roman* system of numerals extends to higher grouping of V for 5, X for 10, L for 50, C for 100, and so on. With this system one can conveniently list how many items are in a given set. The sum of the symbols is the tally being represented. One disadvantage, however, is that as the set grows larger the corresponding set of symbols also grows larger. To count an infinite set of items would require an infinite set of symbols.

The Romans also developed the idea that the meaning of a symbol could change with its position; a lesser symbol placed in front of a greater symbol subtracts from it. This convention allows us to write IV instead of IIII.

Although the Roman system does well enough for counting, for example, how many fighting men there are in a legion, it makes addition and subtraction difficult, requires a multiplicity of rules for multiplication, and makes the representation of fractions almost impossible. A complex society requires a more efficient number system.

One technological solution was made to all of these problems; the Hindus invented and the Arabs developed a system of numbers that combined two attributes of the Roman system: symbols for each different number from 1 through 9 and a special symbol (0) just to hold position. In this notation meaning depends on the symbol and its position. The nine symbols replace the tallies from I to $IIIIIIIII$, and the position indicates a multiple of ten. The first position is multiplied by 10^0 ($= 1$), the second by 10^1 ($= 10$), the third by 10^2 ($= 100$), and so on, counting positions from a beginning point to the left. Thus

$$
\begin{aligned}
4231 &= 4 \times 10^3 = 4000 \\
&+ 2 \times 10^2 = 200 \\
&+ 3 \times 10^1 = 30 \\
&+ 1 \times 10^0 = 1 \\
\hline
&4231
\end{aligned}
$$

The *Arabic system* is closed; there are exactly 10 symbols and every combination of them has a single specific meaning in terms of a tally. Further, the rules for addition, subtraction, multiplication, and division are simple enough for elementary school children to master in a few years (800 years ago, using the Roman system, most mathematicians could not multiply with facility, to say nothing of dividing).

Vestiges of other numbering systems remain in daily use; for example, we use a system of 12 for the hours of a day, a system of 60 for minutes and seconds, and a system of 360 for degrees. The British use a system of 20 and

12 for money, and we use a binary fraction system for distance (e.g., $\frac{1}{2}$, $\frac{1}{4}$, $\frac{1}{8}$ inch). The numbers based on 12, 60, and 6×60 had the advantage of being divisible by many integers without dropping fractions, which would be almost intolerable in commerce.

Binary Numbers

A generalization of the above procedures allows us to construct number systems on any *base* or *radix*. The simplest system is the unary system, which is identical with the tally system. A binary system has a base or radix of 2 and two symbols. The symbols are usually represented by 0 and 1, but they can be just as well represented by "on" and "off," "+" and "−," or any other complementary pair of symbols. This on-off characteristic makes the binary system natural for electronic and magnetic circuits that exist in two (and only two) states.

Consider a binary number such as 11001:

$$11001 = 1 \times 2^4 = 16$$
$$+1 \times 2^3 = 8$$
$$+0 \times 2^2 = 0$$
$$+0 \times 2^1 = 0$$
$$+1 \times 2^0 = \underline{1}$$
$$25 \text{ (in base 10).}$$

The appendix includes tables and instructions for converting between binary, octal, hexadecimal, and decimal numbers.

When adding numbers in any number system, a "carry" must be made when the sum equals or exceeds the base of the number system. In the binary system, for example, $1 + 0 = 1$ and $1 + 1 = 0$, carry 1. Binary multiplication is much simpler than decimal multiplication because the table to be memorized is simpler. The rules for binary multiplication are

$$0 \times 0 = 0$$
$$0 \times 1 = 0$$
$$1 \times 0 = 0$$
$$1 \times 1 = 1$$

The multiplier and multiplicand in binary multiplication can be arranged just as they are in decimal multiplication; for example

$$
\begin{array}{lr}
10111 & (23_{10}) \\
\underline{101} & \underline{(5_{10})} \\
10111 & \\
00000 & \\
\underline{10111} & \\
1110011 & (115_{10})
\end{array}
$$

In binary multiplication the partial products are formed by copying the multiplicand if the particular multiplier was 1 and by copying 0 if the multiplier was zero. The binary addition of the third column from the left in the example requires that the 1 from the carry from the column to its right be added to the $1 + 1$ from the partial products. The $1 + 1 = 0$, carry 1, so that the triple sum is $1 + 1 + 1 = 1$, carry 1.

Just as decimal long division is based on the multiplication of trial quotients by the divisor, so is binary division; for example,

$$
\begin{array}{r}
10111 \\
101\overline{)1110011} \\
101 \\
\overline{100} \\
000 \\
\overline{1000} \\
101 \\
\overline{111} \\
101 \\
\overline{101} \\
101 \\
\overline{0}
\end{array}
$$

"Borrowing" in subtraction is analogous to carrying in addition. Just as the decimal 200 can be thought of as $199 + 1$, in binary notation 1000 can be thought of as $111 + 1$. The third subtraction in the division example is $1000 - 101$. This may be thought of as

$$
\begin{array}{r}
111 + 1 \\
-101 \\
\overline{10 + 1} = 11
\end{array}
$$

that is, $1000 - 101$ is 11 in binary numbers. Note that the quotient (10111) times the divisor (101) is equal to the dividend (1110011), as shown in the previous multiplication example.

The binary system is important to digital computers because the condition of SIGNAL and NO SIGNAL is easy to achieve with various electrical, mechanical, and pneumatic devices. The binary system minimizes the problem of measuring how much signal is present, thus minimizing a source of uncertainty. The rules for addition and subtraction in a binary system are simpler than for most other systems of numbers and therefore much easier to memorize or derive than the rules in other number systems, for example the decimal system. A similar simplicity exists for multiplying. Examination of Table A.2a in the appendix shows the price paid for the simplicity of the binary number system: many more positions are required to represent a given number; therefore many more additions and carries must be performed to add two binary numbers than to add the equivalent decimal numbers.

BCD Codes

Sometimes a four-bit binary code is used to represent the decimal digits 0–9. Table 9.1 gives an example. Sets of these *Binary Coded Decimal* (BCD) codes are used to represent decimal numbers. The position of each digit is represented by parallel sets of counters or by the sequence of signals on

Table 9.1   A BCD Code

Decimal Digit	Binary Equivalent
0	0000
1	0001
2	0010
3	0011
4	0100
5	0101
6	0110
7	0111
8	1000
9	1001

one counter. At the next count after 9 the counter is reset and a carry is made to the next counter. By using schemes like this decimal machines are made from essentially on-off binary devices such as flip-flop and switches. Four binary devices are made to count decimally.

Octal, Hexadecimal Codes

The long string of ones and zeros that forms a binary number is difficult to read and write. A person can easily learn to translate short groups of binary digits to and from other number systems; with a little practice this can be done as a mental exercise without recourse to pencil and paper. The radix or base of these other number systems is two raised to the third or fourth power.

Computers often display the settings of registers with strings of lights: a light is lit for each 1 and unlit for each 0 in the binary number. Sometimes these lights are grouped by three's to facilitate reading the contents of the register as octal (base eight) numbers or by fours, leading to hexadecimal (base 16) numbers. The appendix contains tables for translating between these number systems.

Table 9.2

(a) Octal Digits		
Octal	*Binary*	*Decimal*
0	000	0
1	001	1
2	010	2
3	011	3
4	100	4
5	101	5
6	110	6
7	111	7

(b) Position Multipliers

$\downarrow$ Position Point

Position 4 3 2 1 0 -1 -2

x x x x x . x   x

(c) Position	Multiplier
0	$8^0 = 1$
1	$8^1 = 8$
2	$8^2 = 64$
3	$8^3 = 512$
4	$8^4 = 4{,}096$
5	$8^5 = 32{,}768$
	etc.
-1	$8^{-1} = \frac{1}{8}$
-2	$8^{-2} = \frac{1}{64}$
	etc.

Octal numbers are usually represented by the first eight decimal digits (0–7). Part (a) of Table 9.2 lists the binary and decimal equivalents of the octal numbers; parts (b) and (c) list the position multiplier for the first few positions of an octal number. Positions are counted from the position point; positive positions starting with zero are counted to the left, negative positions, to the right. In a decimal system the position point is the decimal point.

Hexadecimal numbers require 16 symbols; the 10 decimal digits (0–9) and first six letters of the alphabet (A–F) are commonly used. Table 9.3 lists the binary and decimal equivalents of these hexadecimal numbers.

Boolean Algebra

Boolean algebra is concerned with the logical rules governing connectives that connect variables such as classes or names. George Boole, an English mathematician, invented this algebra more than a hundred years ago to facilitate logical discussions [4]. This section reviews briefly some aspects of Boolean algebra that have proved to be useful when applied to digital problems.

As in any algebra, Boolean algebra contains symbols, operators, and propositions. In ordinary algebra the symbols x, y, z stand for numbers. The operators such as $+$, $-$, $\times$, $\div$ indicate what is to be done with the symbols: $x + y$ means that x and y are to be added together.

The propositions are logically acceptable ways in which the symbols and operators can be combined; for example, in ordinary algebra $x \cdot y = y \cdot x$; that is, it does not matter which symbol is written first when multiplying two numbers together. The rules we follow for ordinary algebra apply only to handling numbers; not all are appropriate to an algebra designed to handle logical connections between classes.

In Boolean algebra the symbols stand for classes of things. A letter of the alphabet signifies the members of a class. The class may consist, for example, of all the paper clips in a box or all the apples in a basket.

Specifying some common characteristic of a class also automatically specifies the complementary members of that class; that is, when we speak of all the good apples in a basket, the complementary class is the rest of the apples in the basket, the bad apples. If B represents all the good apples, then

Table 9.3

Hexadecimal Digits			Position Multipliers	
Hex	*Binary*	*Decimal*	*Position*	*Multiplier*
0	0000	0	0	$16^0 = 1$
1	0001	1	1	$16^1 = 16$
2	0010	2	2	$16^2 = 256$
3	0011	3	3	$16^3 = 4{,}096$
4	0100	4		etc.
5	0101	5	-1	$16^{-1} = \frac{1}{16}$
6	0110	6	-2	$16^{-2} = \frac{1}{256}$
7	0111	7		etc.
8	1000	8		
9	1001	9		
A	1010	10		
B	1011	11		
C	1100	12		
D	1101	13		
E	1110	14		
F	1111	15		

Table 9.4   Rules of Boolean Algebra

(1a) $A + A = A$	(1b) $A \cdot A = A$	
(2a) $A + \overline{A} = 1$	(2b) $A \cdot \overline{A} = 0$	Special distributive law
(3a) $A + 1 = 1$	(3b) $A \cdot 1 = A$	
(4a) $A + 0 = A$	(4b) $A \cdot 0 = 0$	
(5a) $A + B = B + A$	(5b) $A \cdot B = B \cdot A$	
(6a) $\overline{(A + B)} = \overline{A} \cdot \overline{B}$	(6b) $\overline{(A \cdot B)} = \overline{A} + \overline{B}$	DeMorgan's theorem
(7a) $A + (B + C)$	(7b) $A \cdot (B \cdot C)$	
$\quad = (A + B) + C$	$\quad = (A \cdot B) \cdot C$	Commutative laws
(8a) $A + (B \cdot C)$	(8b) $A \cdot (B + C)$	
$\quad = (A + B) \cdot (A + C)$	$\quad = A \cdot B + A \cdot C$	Associative laws
(9) $\overline{(\overline{A})} = A$		
(10) $\overline{1} = 0$		
(11) $\overline{0} = 1$		
(12) If $A + B = 0$, then $A = 0$ and $B = 0$		
(13) $A + \overline{A} \cdot B = A + B$		

its complement $\overline{B}$ stands for the bad apples in the basket. $\overline{B}$ stands for "not-B." The symbol " $'$ " sometimes replaces " $^{-}$ ", that is, B' is equivalent to $\overline{B}$.

Taken together the elements of the class form all the elements in that universe: the good and bad apples together form the class of all the apples in that basket. The universe class is given the symbol 1. Its complementary class is the class with no elements, 0.

The symbols used for operators in Boolean algebra differ from those used in ordinary algebra. The line over the top of a symbol or a prime, as previously defined, is the NOT operator. The symbol " $+$ " is often used for OR. Thus $A + B$ stands for the set of objects in either set A or set B or both. The operator AND is represented by a dot like that used to indicate multiplication in ordinary algebra. Thus $A \cdot B$ stands for the class common to both classes A and B. Occasionally the dot is omitted: AB stands for $A \cdot B$.

The sign " $=$ " can be translated into English as "if and only if." Writing $A = B + C$ means, for example, that A is true if and only if B or C are true or both B and C are true.

The most useful relationships of Boolean algebra may be deduced from the definitions given; they can be proved by examining all possible cases. Proofs are not presented here in most cases. Table 9.4 is a table of rules of Boolean algebra. These rules are sufficient to derive many useful results with Boolean algebra.

Venn Diagrams

The Boolean relations can be represented by geometric diagrams called Venn diagrams after the English logician, John Venn. A rectangle represents all the elements in the "universe" being discussed; a circle in the rectangle encloses the elements of a set. The rectangle in Fig. 9.1 represents "1," and so rule 2a ($A + \bar{A} = 1$) becomes the obvious statement that everything is either inside the circle or outside it. Likewise rule 2b ($A \cdot \bar{A} = 0$) says that no elements are common to both the inside and the outside of the circle.

In the Venn diagram in Fig. 9.2 the universe is divided into regions A and $\bar{A}$ and into regions B and $\bar{B}$. The sum of all the subareas can be written

$$A \cdot B + A \cdot \bar{B} + \bar{A} \cdot B + \bar{A} \cdot \bar{B} = A \cdot (B + \bar{B}) + \bar{A}(B + \bar{B}) \quad \text{(rule 8b)}$$
$$= A + \bar{A} \quad \text{(rules 2a, 3b)}$$
$$= 1 \quad \text{(rule 2a)}$$

The application of the rules of Boolean algebra correctly showed that the sum of the four subareas equals the whole area; the Venn diagrams and the Boolean algebra provide two ways of looking at the same ideas.

By referring again to Fig. 9.2 consider all the area outside of the region $A \cdot B$, that is, $\overline{A \cdot B}$.

$$(\overline{A \cdot B}) = \bar{A} \cdot B + \bar{A} \cdot \bar{B} + A \cdot \bar{B} \quad \text{(by inspection of Fig. 9.2)}$$
$$= \bar{A} \cdot (B + \bar{B}) + A \cdot \bar{B} \quad \text{(by rule 8b)}$$
$$= \bar{A} + A \cdot \bar{B} \quad \text{(by rules 2a and 3b)}$$
$$= \bar{A} + \bar{B} \quad \text{(by rule 13)}$$

This illustrates DeMorgan's theorem (rule 6). By inspection of the figure we see that all the region outside $A \cdot B$ is included in either $\bar{A}$ or $\bar{B}$ and thus find rule 6 by direct inspection.

DeMorgan's theorem can be used to relate the AND and OR operators to NAND and NOR (which stand for NOT AND and NOT OR). These operators are important since simple electrical circuits, such as a transistor switch, implement the operators NAND and NOR directly because such circuits switch "off" when an input signal is turned "on" and vice versa. When we apply DeMorgan's theorem, expressions implemented by AND, OR circuits can be translated into circuits equivalent to NAND and NOR; for example, a NAND gate with two inputs, A and B, will be "on" signal if

Fig. 9.1 Venn diagram.

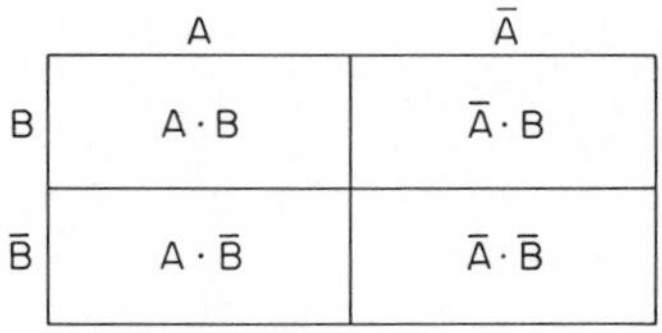

	A	$\bar{A}$
B	$A \cdot B$	$\bar{A} \cdot B$
$\bar{B}$	$A \cdot \bar{B}$	$\bar{A} \cdot \bar{B}$

Fig. 9.2 Venn diagram.

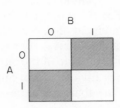

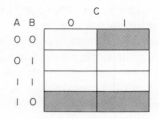

Fig. 9.3 Truth table, two-element.   **Fig. 9.4** Truth table, three-element.

$\overline{(A \cdot B)}$. By DeMorgan's theorem this is equivalent to $\overline{A} + \overline{B}$, and the gate will be "on" if either A is not "on" or B is not "on."

Truth Table

A "truth table" is a form of Venn diagram. Figure 9.3 shows a two-element truth table. The rectangle encloses a universe that includes areas of A and B and areas that are not A ($\overline{A}$) and not B ($\overline{B}$). The 1 and 0 on the left stand for A and $\overline{A}$, for example. The shaded areas in the truth table in Fig. 9.3 represent the expression $\overline{A} \cdot B + A \cdot \overline{B}$. This is obviously equivalent to $\overline{A \cdot B + \overline{A} \cdot B}$ which also comes from DeMorgan's theorem.

Figure 9.4 illustrates a three-element truth table for the function $\overline{A} \cdot \overline{B} \cdot C + A \cdot \overline{B} \cdot \overline{C} + A \cdot \overline{B} \cdot C$. Inspection of the diagram shows that the expression can be simplified to $\overline{A} \cdot \overline{B} \cdot C + A \cdot \overline{B}$. The same result could have been found by manipulating the Boolean expression, but such simplifications can often be found more easily from a truth table. Another expression can be found by considering the unshaded areas: $\overline{(B + \overline{A} \cdot \overline{B} \cdot \overline{C})}$. One expression may be easier to implement than another in a particular case.

As one further illustration, consider the problem of designing an adder for binary arithmetic. Addition is done by combining two numbers to form a sum. The first number is called the augend, the second, the addend. First

Table 9.5 Binary Addition

Carry-In $C1$	Augend A	Addend B	Sum S	Carry-Out $C2$
0	0	0	0	0
0	0	1	1	0
0	1	0	1	0
0	1	1	0	1
1	0	0	1	0
1	0	1	0	1
1	1	0	0	1
1	1	1	1	1

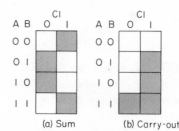

Fig. 9.5 Truth table, binary addition.   (a) Sum   (b) Carry-out

a sum is formed by using the low-order (right-hand) digits. A sum greater than the base (or radix) less one (1 for the binary system or 9 for the decimal system) generates a 1 carry-out to the next higher position; this carry-out becomes a carry-in that is added to the digits in the next higher position (to the left); the sum then becomes a combination of a 1, which is carried-in, a digit from the augend, and a digit from the addend. Represent the augend by A, the addend by B, and the carry-in by $C1$. The two outputs of the adder are the sum S and the carry-out $C2$. Table 9.5 and Fig. 9.5 show all eight possible cases of binary addition with carry-in. The shaded areas of Fig. 9.5a show when $S = 1$ and the shaded areas of Fig. 9.5b show when $C2 = 1$; that is,

$$S = \bar{A} \cdot \bar{B} \cdot C1 + \bar{A} \cdot B \cdot \bar{C1} + A \cdot \bar{B} \cdot \bar{C1} + A \cdot B \cdot C1$$

and

$$C2 = \bar{A} \cdot B \cdot C1 + A \cdot \bar{B} \cdot C1 + A \cdot B \cdot \bar{C1} + A \cdot B \cdot C1.$$

Simplifications for these expressions can be found by inspection of the truth tables in Fig. 9.5.

$$S = (A \cdot B + \bar{A} \cdot \bar{B}) \cdot C1 + (A \cdot \bar{B} + \bar{A} \cdot B) \cdot \bar{C1}$$
$$C2 = A \cdot B + (A \cdot \bar{B} + \bar{A} \cdot B) \cdot C1$$

The term $(A \cdot \bar{B} + \bar{A} \cdot B)$ is "exclusive or"; that is, it is true if either A or B is true but excludes both being true.

Modeling and Simulation

One of the most powerful ways of using a computer, either analog or digital, is simulation. Indeed, as implied by their name, analog computers simulate physical systems with analogous physical systems that follow similar differential equations.

The performance of many physical systems can be analyzed with similar differential equations. Consider, for example, a mechanical system in which acceleration is opposed by a counterforce. Newton's second law can be expressed as

$$F = ma, \tag{9.1}$$

where F = force,
   m = mass, and
   a = acceleration.

If the system is to be stable, another force must tend to bring the object back as it is displaced. If this force is proportional to the displacement, as with a linear spring,

$$F = -kx,$$ (9.2)

where k = constant, and
   x = displacement.

Since these forces are equal and opposite, by using d^2x/dt^2 for acceleration we have

$$\frac{d^2x}{dt^2} + \frac{kx}{m} = 0,$$ (9.3)

which has a sinusoidal solution:

$$x = \cos(\omega t + \theta).$$ (9.4)

Here ω is an angular frequency and θ is the angle of the starting position, at which we declared t to be 0.

In an electric circuit that consists of a capacitor and an inductor in parallel a back emf is generated in the inductor as a function of the rate of change of current:

$$L\frac{di}{dt} = -e,$$ (9.5)

where L = inductance,
   i = current
      = dq/dt, the rate of change of charge q (so $di/dt = d^2q/dt^2$), and
   e = emf or voltage.

The voltage across the capacitor is proportional to the charge

$$\frac{q}{C} = e,$$ (9.6)

where C = capacitance.

From the definition of current the rate of change of current equals the second derivative of charge, and

$$\frac{d^2q}{dt^2} + \frac{q}{LC} = 0.$$ (9.7)

The solution to this equation is

$$q = \cos(\omega t + \theta).$$ (9.8)

The electric circuit simulates the mechanical problem because the structure of the differential equations is the same. Building a circuit with chosen values of L and C can simulate a mechanical system with given values of m and k. More complex mechanical systems can be simulated by more complex electric circuits; indeed, nonlinear differential equations can be simulated, in which the restoring force is proportional to a nonlinear function of the displacement, as with many ordinary springs. Analog computers, which easily integrate by accumulating charge on a capacitor, simulate physical systems or sets of equations in this way. Digital computers can function similarly by using special subroutines to perform the integrations. In these operations the computer simulates the functioning of a real system by operating with the same differential equations.

In modeling the computer is forced to reach the same results as the system being studied, without regard to how it reaches those results; for instance, suppose you wish to solve a transcendental equation such as $\tan X = X$. In your first algebra course you probably learned to plot both terms, $\tan X$ and X, and found the solution(s) where the graphs intersect. In an analog computer one function generator can be made to generate a voltage proportional to a tangent, $\tan V$; connecting the output of this tangent function generator to its input satisfies the equation, and the voltage (after some very short transient) will be proportional to one of the answers. In a digital computer one simple approach is given by these directions: guess a value of X, find the value of $\tan X$, and find the difference; increasing the value of X by some small increment ΔX and repeating the operation will provide another difference. If the second difference is greater than the first, change the sign of ΔX and repeat the second operation. If the sign of the differences reverses, divide ΔX by two and repeat the operation. If the difference is smaller than some chosen minimum value, X is a solution to the problem. Repeating these steps a finite number of times will give a solution.

Feedback Loops

The process described above for solving the transcendental equation $\tan X = X$ used a form of feedback, both in the analog and the digital methods described. The concept of feedback is fundamental to self-regulating systems.

The governor for a steam engine was an early feedback system. Two rotating weights tend to fly out farther as they rotate faster. They exert more force on the arms that retain them, and that force operates a brake or valve that retards the rotary motion. Similar feedback mechanisms can be made to operate on all sorts of systems. In every case the output of the system is compared with some standard and the difference is fed back to modify the behavior of the system. Obviously the modification must be in a direction to reduce the difference if the system is to be stable. Furthermore, the change of output cannot lag the correction too much or the system will oscillate.

3   ANALOG COMPUTER COMPONENTS

Operational Amplifiers

Operational amplifiers are the heart of an analog computer; the size or "power" of an analog computer is often stated in terms of the number of amplifiers it contains. These amplifiers are often combined with other elements to perform particular special-purpose computing jobs [5].

An operational amplifier is a high-gain, direct-coupled, negative-feedback amplifier that can multiply a variable voltage by a constant greater than one. The operational amplifier can also provide an algebraic sum of a number of voltages, produce a voltage proportional to the time integral of one or more variable voltages, and provide many other mathematical operations.

Figure 9.6 is a block diagram that illustrates the general use of an operational amplifier. The specifications for the amplifier will become apparent with its application. The amplifier, represented in Fig. 9.6 by the large box with the $-A$, is a dc amplifier with a very high gain (A) that produces an output voltage (V_0) opposite in sign to the input. The inversion of sign is necessary because a feedback impedance Z_f connects the output back to the input. If the amplifier did not invert, the positive feedback would increase the input so that the output would try to become infinitely large, a useless situation generally.

The input voltages (V_1, V_2, V_3, etc.) connect to the input through impedances Z_1, Z_2, Z_3, etc., so that each contributes an input current i_1, i_2, i_3, etc. The voltage at the input to the amplifier is V_g. The input current i_g of the amplifier is the sum of the currents at that point:

$$\frac{V_0 - V_g}{Z_f} + \sum_j \frac{V_j - V_g}{Z_j} = i_g. \tag{9.9}$$

The current through an impedance equals the voltage across the impedance

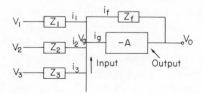

Fig. 9.6 Block diagram of an operational amplifier.

divided by the impedance; for a resistor this becomes Ohm's law ($i = E/R$), but the output voltage of the amplifier is related to the input voltage.

$$V_0 = -AV_g. \tag{9.10}$$

In an operational amplifier the input current i_g is very small (usually $< 10^{-10}$ A). The other currents are typically many orders of magnitude greater than i_g, so i_g can be ignored. In practical operational amplifiers the gain A is at least 10^4, with many amplifiers having gains of 10^6 or more. The voltage V_g remains fixed (usually at "ground") and may also be neglected. In this case (9.9) becomes

$$V_0 = -\sum V_j \frac{Z_f}{Z_j}. \tag{9.11}$$

This approximation is satisfactory for most high-gain operational amplifiers. The error of the approximation can seldom be detected separately from small random electrical variations or "noise." If the gain decreases, as at high frequencies, or if the input current i_g is within several orders of magnitude of the branch currents, the approximation becomes less satisfactory, and simulation of mathematical operations with the operational amplifier may be in error.

Note that if the input impedance of the amplifier is high (making the input current low) and the gain of the amplifier is high, the output voltage depends only on the input voltages and the input and feedback impedances; the output is *independent* of the characteristics of the amplifier. This means that the output can be made to simulate different functions of the input by changing the input and feedback impedances, using the same operational amplifier. Achieving a stable, accurate output becomes relatively easy. When high precision and long-term stability are required, the input and feedback impedances may be mounted in an oven, with controlled temperature and humidity.

The stability of an operational amplifier is measured by its freedom from drift and high-frequency noise. Higher stability costs more and usually reduces some other quality of the amplifier, such as its ability to recover after being driven to its limit. High slewing rates (the rate of change of output voltage with time) also indicate an ability to amplify high-frequency noise.

The gain of most operational amplifiers drops with increasing frequency, which means increasing errors for higher frequency signals. The interpretation of the words "high" and "higher" depends on the particular requirements and on the specifications given by the manufacturer for a particular amplifier. Phase shifts (the lag in time between applying a sinusoidal voltage and outputting that sinusoid) are not constant in operational amplifiers, which may distort complex waveforms. Integration virtually eliminates any concern with phase shift, and so phase shift may not be important in the selection of operational amplifiers.

Linear Network Components

Multiplication by a Constant

In one common use an operational amplifier multiplies a voltage by a constant by using resistors in both the input and feedback circuits. In this case (9.11) becomes

$$V_0 = -V_1 \frac{R_f}{R_1}. \tag{9.12}$$

If the feedback resistor is 1 M and the input resistor is 100,000 Ω,

$$V_0 = -10V_1. \tag{9.13}$$

Changing the feedback resistor to 100,000 Ω also makes

$$V_0 = -V_1. \tag{9.14}$$

The resistor network allows one to multiply the input voltage by any of a wide range of negative constants. Multiplication by a positive constant requires that two amplifiers be used in series; the first may provide the desired constant, whereas the second merely inverts the output of the first and changes the sign from negative to positive.

Using the example with the resistive elements to illustrate the approximations involved with an operational amplifier, assume that the gain of the amplifier is 10^5 and that the input current is -10^{-10} A; assuming a value of 1 M for the feedback resistor and of 100,000 Ω for the input resistor, (9.9) becomes

$$\frac{V_0 - 10^{-5}V_0}{10^6} + \frac{V_1 - 10^{-5}V_0}{10^5} = -10^{-10}, \tag{9.15}$$

using the relation

$$V_g = 10^{-5}V_0. \tag{9.16}$$

Equation 9.15 reduces to

$$(1 - 11 \times 10^{-5})V_0 = -10V_1 - 10^{-4}. \tag{9.17}$$

The expansion of the inverse of a binomial such as $(1 - \Delta)$ is

$$(1 - \Delta)^{-1} \simeq 1 + \Delta, \tag{9.18}$$

with an approximate error of Δ^2. Equation 9.17 becomes

$$V_0 = -10.0011V_1 - 0.000100011. \tag{9.19}$$

If V_1 is 1 V, V_0 is -10.0012 V, an error of 1.2 mV in 10 V, or approximately 0.01 %. This illustrates the magnitude of error to which these approximations lead.

Fig. 9.7 Linear attenuator.   **Fig. 9.8** Attenuator and operational amplifier.

An attenuator divides a voltage by a value less than one. Figure 9.7 is a typical circuit that divides by using an attenuator. It consists of a potentiometer ("pot") with a resistance R. The arm of the pot divides the resistance R by some fraction k. The output of the arm, loaded by the resistance R_L, is the output voltage V_0, which results from the input V_1. The load R_L introduces a loading error, which can be calculated:

$$\frac{V_0}{V_1} = k - \frac{k}{1 + R_L/(1 - k)kR}. \tag{9.20}$$

The loading error becomes zero and $V_0/V_1 = k$ if the load R_L becomes infinite; in other words, the loading error is zero if the load is disconnected.

The loading problem is circumvented on analog computers by using an operational amplifier. Connect the input voltage to the potentiometer, as in Fig. 9.7, and make the input resistor in Fig. 9.6 (Z_1) the load resistor R_L. To set the potentiometer to some desired value the input to the amplifier R_L is grounded. A high-impedance voltmeter, such as a vacuum-tube voltmeter (VTVM), measures the voltage at the arm of the potentiometer when a standard voltage, such as 10.000 V, is applied to the input of the potentiometer. If the potentiometer is to provide an input of 0.434, for example, the arm is adjusted until the voltmeter reads 4.34 V; this fraction is the input to the operational amplifier net that follows. The method takes advantage of the fact that the input voltage of the operational amplifier is a "pseudo-ground."

The common computer diagram symbol of a circle is used for the attenuator, a triangle, for the amplifier; the circuit with the attenuator is illustrated in Fig. 9.8. The number of the potentiometer (Np) is usually written in the circle and the number of the amplifier (Na), in the triangle. The dividing ratio or potentiometer setting (S) is written next to the circle, and the ratio of the feedback to the input resistor (G) is written over the input line to the operational amplifier.

Integration

Use of a capacitive feedback impedance and a resistive input impedance in an operational amplifier gives a circuit that can perform integration.

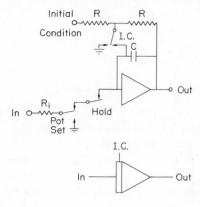

Fig. 9.9 Integrator.

Here (9.9) becomes

$$C\frac{dV_0}{dt} = -\frac{V_1}{R}.$$

(9.21)

because the displacement current through a capacitor is the product of the capacitance and time rate of change of the voltage across it. Solving for V_0 gives

$$V_0 = -\frac{1}{RC}\int_{t_0}^{t} V_1 \, dt.$$

(9.22)

The pictorial symbol for an integrator is a small rectangle on the input side of the triangle symbol for the operational amplifier, as in Fig. 9.9. A 1-μF feedback capacitor and a 1-M input resistor give an amplifier gain of unity. Other values give other gains.

The output voltage at the instant at which integration starts (t_0) is the constant of integration. Relay circuits switch the amplifier from an initial setting to integration at the time t_0. Another relay, the Hold relay, stops the integration at time t. Still another relay circuit discharges the capacitor after the end of the integration and resets the integrator.

Figure 9.9 shows the general arrangement of relays and impedances for a typical operational amplifier. In a general-purpose analog computer these connections are brought to a patch-panel so that connections can be easily made. Plugs and wires needed to connect up the desired circuits for the particular problem are assembled on a patch-board that is then plugged into the patch-panel.

Differentiation

Operational amplifiers are connected as differentiators by making the input impedance a capacitor and the feedback a resistor; the output voltage depends directly on the time rate of change of the input:

$$V_0 = -RC\frac{dV_1}{dt}.$$

(9.23)

A pulse of noise, that is, a fast change in the input voltage, may then produce a larger output than the more slowly varying input signal. Differentiation tends to amplify high-frequency noise, whereas integration "smooths" noise by averaging it over the period of integration. Integration tends to be an accurate operation, whereas differentiation tends to be an inaccurate operation.

Nonlinear Components

Multiplication by a Variable

Analog multipliers are either electromechanical or electronic devices. The electromechanical multipliers use a servomotor to move the arms of a "gang" or set of potentiometers. One of these potentiometers is connected from the plus reference voltage to the minus reference voltage. Any difference between one of the variable input voltages, x, and the voltage at the arm of this potentiometer is amplified and applied to the servomotor so that it moves to reduce the difference to zero. When the difference is zero, the input impedance of the difference amplifier is infinite, and the shaft position is at (x/ref) of full travel. If a second potentiometer in the set has voltages plus and minus y applied to its ends, the voltage at its arm becomes (xy/ref) (see Fig. 9.10).

Any load on this arm will produce an error in the product, which can be corrected automatically by connecting the arm of each potentiometer being

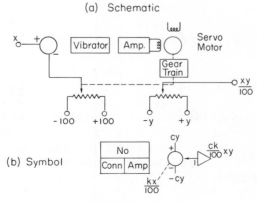

(a) Schematic

(b) Symbol

Fig. 9.10 Servo multiplier.

used to matched input resistors leading to operational amplifiers. Since the servomotor drives the arms to the point at which the output from the reference potentiometer equals the input x, the loading error of all the potentiometers is automatically corrected.

A number of electronic methods of multiplying exist. They respond to changes in the x-variable more rapidly than the servo multiplier, which must overcome the mechanical inertia of the servomotor, shaft, and potentiometer arms. Electronic multipliers may be less accurate than servo multipliers and may be more expensive.

Function Generators

Other devices generate other mathematical functions. One kind of function generator depends on a set of straight-line approximations. Diodes that switch at chosen voltages bring in various resistor loads to generate the functions. The function generators are set up by sequentially setting a series of potentiometers to produce desired outputs at chosen input voltages.

The function generator can be set as a squaring circuit; two squares can be connected to form a quarter-square multiplier. One squaring circuit produces an output proportional to $(x + y)^2$ and the other, an output proportional to $(x - y)^2$. These outputs are summed to provide the product

$$xy = \tfrac{1}{4}[(x + y)^2 - (x - y)^2], \tag{9.24}$$

which is the basis for some electronic multipliers.

Another kind of device depends on some physical characteristic of an electronic device: for example, the current through a transistor with a grounded base is proportional to $\exp(-E/kT)$, where E is the voltage, k is Boltzmann's constant, and T is the absolute temperature of the junction. When such a device is connected as the feedback impedance of an operational amplifier, the output of the amplifier will be proportional to the log of the input voltage. To minimize the temperature dependence of such an element, a second transistor is packaged in thermal contact with the first. Connected as the feedback element of a second operational amplifier and fed with a fixed voltage, this second output is subtracted from the first in a third operational amplifier, as in Fig. 9.11. If the gains of the two operational amplifier units (A and B) are equal, any variation of output of one because of a temperature change is canceled by the change in output of the other.

Logging devices can be used to multiply by adding logarithms; the antilog function is formed by connecting the transistors in the input legs of the amplifiers. Multiplying by logarithms implements

$$xy = \text{antilog}(\log x + \log y). \tag{9.25}$$

Logging

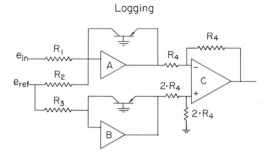

Fig. 9.11 Logging (from G. A. Philbrick Researchers, Inc. data sheet).

Division is performed by placing a multiplier in a feedback loop around an operational amplifier. The output of the amplifier is used as the y-input of the multiplier, the divisor is the x-input of the amplifier, and the output of the multiplier becomes a unity-gain input to the amplifier.

Conversion to and from polar coordinates can be made by using a resolver. A resolver resembles a servo multiplier, and the potentiometers are constructed so that the output is proportional to the sine or cosine of the angle through which the arm is turned. The variable corresponding to the angle replaces the x-input of the servo, and the input to the other potentiometers corresponds to the radius vector R. The output is proportional to $R \sin \theta$ or $R \cos \theta$.

Similarly, a general-purpose function generator can be made with a potentiometer that is tapped at a number of points so that the voltage at those points can be set externally. The desired function is then approximated by a series of straight lines.

Input/Output Devices

Buffer Amplifiers

Some operational amplifiers have differential inputs, one that provides an output opposite in sign to the input and one that provides an output having the same sign as the input. Another use of such a differential amplifier is to provide an output proportional to the difference in two inputs, as in Fig. 9.12. If a signal source creates a voltage difference between two lines, any noise common to the two lines can be rejected by the differential amplifier.

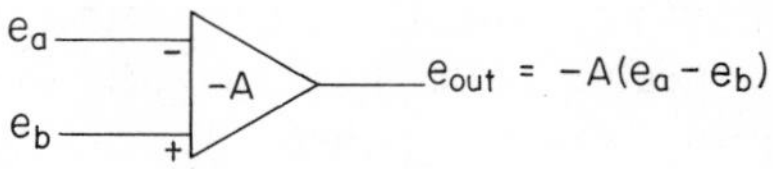

Fig. 9.12 Difference amplifier.

e_a

e_b

$-A$

$e_{out} = -A(e_a - e_b)$

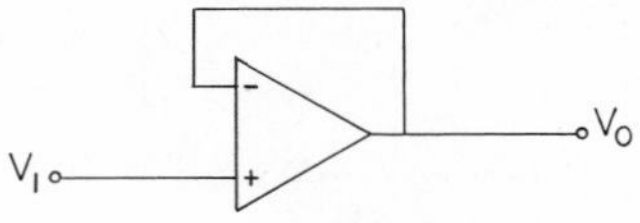

Follower Circuit

Fig. 9.13 Follower circuit.

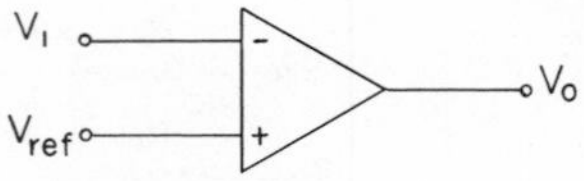

Fig. 9.14 Trigger.

In still another connection the differential amplifier can be used as shown in Fig. 9.13. The input is connected directly to the noninverting or positive input and the output is fed back to the inverting input with no feedback impedance. Ignoring any offset voltage, the output will equal the input

$$V_0 = V_1. \tag{9.26}$$

However, the input source will "see" only the input impedance of the differential amplifier, whereas the output impedance will be a fraction of an ohm. Connected this way, the differential amplifier acts as an impedance transformer—that is, a buffer.

Many signal sources produce a voltage that is limited by the current drawn; their calibration depends on the load presented to them. The buffer amplifier prevents the load on the output from affecting the calibration of the input source. This is an important consideration when externally generated signals are processed by an analog computer. Other buffering arrangements than the differential amplifier can be arranged.

Trigger and Sample-and-Hold Circuits

A differential amplifier can also supply a trigger voltage (see Fig. 9.14). When V_1 is greater than V_{ref}, the output voltage is at the negative limit of the amplifier. When V_1 drops to a lower value than the reference voltage, the output of the amplifier switches to the positive limit. With some amplifiers care must be taken to prevent output limiting from slowing down the switching time. Such a circuit is used typically to switch an integrator relay from "hold" to "sample."

Electronic switches can be made to operate in extremely short times; for example, much less than a microsecond. They are, indeed, digital circuits. One use for these switches is to make "sample and hold" circuits. In many arrangements of processing external signals with an analog computer a desired source may be present only for a short time. If this variable is to be a constant in following operations, it must be "memorized." One way to do this is to trigger an integrator from "reset" to "sample" for a short fixed length of time. During that time the voltage to be memorized is integrated; returning to a "hold" condition provides an output proportional to the average input voltage.

If we assume that the voltage to be sampled remains constant during the sampling process, the output according to (9.22) is

$$V_0 = - \frac{V_1 t}{RC}, \tag{9.27}$$

with an initial voltage across the capacitor of zero. The values of t, R, and C determine a gain constant; for example, the gain is unity if the integration time is 1 sec, the resistance 1 MΩ, and the capacitance 1 μF.

Displays

Common output devices for analog computers are digital voltmeters, X-Y recorders, and multichannel strip-chart recorders (see Chapter VI). When problems can be reset and rerun rapidly, the output can be displayed on a cathode-ray-tube (CRT) oscilloscope. A permanent record of output can be made by photographing the face of the CRT. Most oscilloscopes provide a constant time sweep across the tube face; special oscilloscopes have identical X-axis and Y-axis amplifiers that allow two variables to be plotted against each other.

4 DIGITAL COMPUTING COMPONENTS

Logic and Computing Circuits [6]

Basic Logic Circuits: AND, OR, NOT

Many physical systems can be arranged to implement the logical AND, OR, and NOT (see p. 210); for example, the mixing faucets at a washbasin may form an OR implementation. Water flows from the tap if either the hot *or* the cold faucet is on. The switches in housewiring form other simple logic circuits. In Fig. 9.15 an output current can flow if either switch A or switch B is operated; this is an OR circuit. The AND circuit is illustrated in Fig. 9.16; and output current can flow only if both switch A and switch B are closed. Figure 9.17 illustrates the NOT circuit, which lets current flow when A is closed and not flow when A is open ($\overline{A}$). The Venn diagrams in Fig. 9.18 illustrate these three basic logic circuits. The rest of the box, not

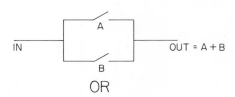

Fig. 9.15 OR circuit.

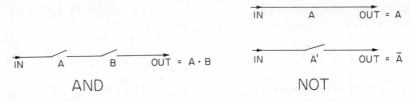

Fig. 9.16   AND circuit.   Fig. 9.17   NOT circuit.

enclosed by the region $A + B$, $A \cdot B$, or A, illustrates the inverted gates NOR, NAND, and NOT.

Inverted gates are simpler to build with electronic circuits than direct gates; for example, if switching is done by diodes and summing by a circuit junction, both must be followed by a stage of amplification. The amplification prevents the load connected to the output from directly affecting the input sources (within the limits of the amplifier). Single-stage amplifiers invert so that the operation implemented is OR followed by NOT or AND followed by NOT. DeMorgan's theorem allows easy transformations between the direct and inverted gates.

The Boolean expressions for the inverted gates may appear to be more complicated than the expressions for direct gates. This illustrates one unfortunate aspect of Boolean algebra: the simplest appearing expression may not be implemented with the simplest circuit; simplicity relates both to the expression and to the particular circuitry.

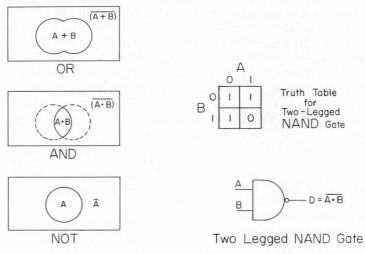

Fig. 9.18   Venn diagrams.   Fig. 9.19   NAND gate.

DeMorgan's theorem applied to a NAND gate provides an OR function with inverted components:

$$\overline{A \cdot B} = \overline{A} + \overline{B}. \tag{9.28}$$

Applying a single input to a NAND gate merely inverts that input. The usual symbol for these NAND gates is shown in Fig. 9.19 along with a truth table for a two-legged NAND gate.

Higher Level Circuits

The Flip-Flop

The most widely used storage element is a flip-flop. The bistable multi-vibrator, or flip-flop, was patented by Eccles and Jordan shortly after World War I; just as the basic design for digital computers has existed since the time of Charles Babbage, more than a hundred years ago, the electronic circuits needed for a fast electronic computer have existed since 1920. The pressures of World War II brought these possibilities to a realization.

A flip-flop acts like a pan of water pivoted at the center (see Fig. 9.20). Whichever way the pan is left it remains: it is bistable. A flip-flop can be made of two NAND gates connected as shown in Fig. 9.21. The output of NAND gate NG1 is connected to one input of NAND gate NG2 and the output of NG2 is connected to one input of NG1. Assume that the input S to NG1 and the input R to NG2 are set to 1 or ON. If NG1 is ON or 1, both inputs to NG2 are 1, and, by the NAND operation, NG2 has a "0" output; since one input (S) to NG1 is 1 and the other (NG2) is 0, by the NAND function NG1 must be ON. Conversely, if NG1 is 0, NG2 must be 1 and therefore NG1 remains 0.

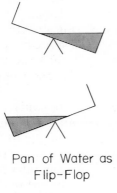

Pan of Water as
Flip-Flop

Fig. 9.20 Flip-flop water analog.

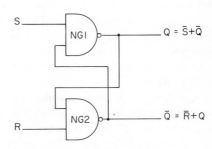

Fig. 9.21 Flip-flop NAND gates.

Assume that NG1 is 1 and NG2 is 0. If the input R to NG2 is changed to 0, NG2 will flip to 1 and NG1 will flop to 0. Restoring R to 1 will not affect the output. Thus changing the state of the appropriate input to the flip-flop will cause the outputs to change their states. A flip-flop "remembers" a transition from 1 to 0 on an appropriate line. Flip-flops form memories, shift registers, and counters.

The Multivibrator

By appropriate changes in the circuits that form a bistable multivibrator a monostable multivibrator can be formed; for instance, a circuit could be arranged to allow only a transient voltage to pass from NG2 to NG1 by inserting a blocking capacitor in the lead from NG2 to NG1 in Fig. 9.21. Now when R is changed 1 to 0 to cause the output of NG2 to switch from 0 to 1 and thereby force NG1 from 1 to 0, the transient from NG2 to NG1 "leaks off" after a time. NG1 no longer sees the input from NG2 as 1, and so it switches back to 1, returning NG2 to 0; that is, this monostable multivibrator will change its output for a while after receiving an input pulse, but it will then return to its only stable state. Multivibrators of this type are used to provide fixed delays and to provide timing pulses. A "clock" can be made by connecting an output of a multivibrator to its own input.

Triggers

A monostable multivibrator can be designed to produce an output pulse when the input reaches some particular voltage. At that point the multivibrator "triggers." The "squaring circuit" or "Schmitt trigger" is used to transform slowly changing waveforms to fast-rising pulses that are more suitable for operating digital logic circuits.

Gates

The word "gate" has been used before to describe certain logic circuits. If the gate is "open," a current or pulse can pass through, but if the gate is "closed" the current or pulse cannot pass through. Figure 9.19 shows a NAND gate. As shown in its truth table, the state of leg A can be used to "gate" leg B: if leg A is 1, the output of the gate is $\bar{B}$, the opposite of the B-input: if leg A is 0, the output of the gate is 1 and does not respond to changes in the B-input.

Gates and flip-flops require some finite length of time to switch from one state to another. At some point in the switching operation the output may be ambiguous. A common method of avoiding uncertainty is to "strobe" or "clock" the final gates of any logic device by using a pulse with fast rise and fall times. These pulses are generated repetitively by an internal clock, and all gates are considered to be in their final state at the end of the clock pulse.

Conglomerate Circuits

Memories, Counters, and Registers

Flip-flops like the one illustrated in Fig. 9.21 "remember" pulses that have been fed to them; for example, four such flip-flops could be arranged as a register and four bits that represent a binary number could be put on the R inputs momentarily; that is, the R inputs would remain 1 for every 1-bit and would momentarily go to 0 for every 0-bit, whereas the S inputs would remain 1 for every 0-bit and would change to 0 momentarily for every 1-bit. The outputs $\bar{Q}$ of the NAND gates (NG2) would remain 1 for each of the 1-bits in the number and 0 for each of the 0-bits in the number. The outputs from the NG1 gates would represent the inverse (one's complement) of the number; that is, the register "remembers" the input bits.

Flip-flops can be arranged to change state for each input pulse that arrives; that is, for the first pulse the output might change from 0 to 1, for the next pulse it would change from 1 to 0, and so on. A series of flip-flops can be connected as shown in Fig. 9.22 to count the incoming pulses. Each flip-flop changes the state of its outputs when the input T goes from 1 to 0. A series of flip-flops converts a serial input into a parallel output.

Assume that the A outputs of all the flip-flops are initially set to 0 by making all the R inputs 0 for a short time. All the B outputs are at the 1 level. Now let the train of pulses shown be an input to FF1. The table at the right of Fig. 9.22 shows the levels of the A-outputs of the four flip-flops. Obviously this chain forms a binary count of the first 15 input pulses.

A shift register is similar to a counter; it consists of a series of flip-flop gates connected so that the binary number memorized by the flip-flops

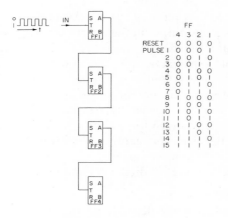

Fig. 9.22 Binary counter.

Table 9.6 Action of Shifting

Shift Pulse	FF4	FF3	FF2	FF1
0	0	1	0	1
1	1	0	1	0
2	0	1	0	0
3	1	0	0	0
4	0	0	0	0

shifts each time a shift pulse is introduced. Suppose we had a register with four bits that contains the number 0101. Table 9.6 indicates the settings of the flip-flops after each shift-left pulse. A shift register converts parallel outputs coming simultaneously from each register to serial outputs from the last register.

Magnetic Core Memories [3]

A magnetic core is a small annulus (ring) of soft magnetic material. Three wires are looped around or through this annulus: an input winding, a sensing winding, and an output winding. A given amount of current, i, through the input winding will cause the magnetic field in the annulus to saturate in one direction. A current $\frac{1}{2}i$ through the sensing winding will cause no increase in the magnetic field if the current is in a direction to add to the field, for the magnetic field is already saturated. If, however, the current in the sensing winding creates a field opposing the residual field, the field is decreased by one-half, thus inducing a current in the output winding. An input current of one polarity makes the magnetic field a 1, whereas the input current of the opposite polarity sets the magnetic field to the opposite direction, defined as 0. A pulse of current through the sensing winding will produce a simultaneous output in the output winding if the magnet was set to 1 and no output if the magnet was set to 0. The sensing current does not change the state of the magnetic core; therefore the "reading" is nondestructive. The numbers can be sensed by gating currents through sensing windings and gating the outputs of the output windings into flip-flops.

Magnetic-core memories generally respond more slowly than flip-flop memories, but they cost much less per bit and require no power until they are sensed. Since the electronic gates that control the sensing currents can be addressed in any sequence, magnetic-core memories are used for the large random-access storage in digital computers.

Acoustic Memories

Another form of memory depends on the transmission of mechanical stresses through a wire, a surface, a liquid such as mercury, or a solid such as glass. Since such waves can be heard when transmitted through air, if they are at the proper frequencies, these memories are called "acoustic delay lines" or "acoustic memories." At one end of the line a piezoelectric crystal is stressed by an electric field; it transmits its movement to the transmitting materials. The wave is detected at some later time by another piezoelectric crystal, which produces a voltage as it is strained by the wave. After amplification this output voltage is fed back to the input of the delay line. The relative times of the pulses can be treated as creating binary 0 or 1 states. Such acoustic memories are serial, and the information they contain can be detected only at some fixed time after it has been put into the memory.

Other Memory Mechanisms

Any other physical phenomenon that takes two unambiguous states can be used as a digital memory. Many means have been investigated, including photographic stores (as discrete dots or as gratings of various frequencies) and superconductivity. None of these is in common use, but any future methods will depend on the detectability of two states of some physical property.

Magnetic Film Memories: Disk, Drum, and Tape

Magnetic memories can be ranked by their cost per bit of storage capacity and by the degree of randomness with which the stored information can be made on flexible tape, on drums with multiple read and write heads, or on disks with both fixed and movable read and write heads. All of these means detect the magnetic field as it cuts the windings of a read head, and all of these memories are sequential, not random. Multiple heads provide simultaneous reading of tracks recorded on the magnetic material, but within a track the binary data are retrieved sequentially.

Magnetic memories can be ranked by their cost per bit of storage capacity and by the degree of randomness with which the stored information can be retrieved. Magnetic-core memories are the most expensive and can be accessed randomly; that is (within the electronic capability of the computer), any information stored anywhere in a core memory can be read within a few microseconds at most. Magnetic-drum memories cost less per bit than core memories and can store only a fixed amount of information, depending on the area of the drum surface and layout of heads; the information is accessible when the position at which it is stored rotates under the read-heads. The average access time for a magnetic drum is one-half the period of rotation of the drum.

Magnetic disks have either fixed or movable read-heads. A disk with fixed multiple read-heads requires an average of a half-period of rotation of the disk to access any point on the disk. Many disks have movable read-heads which must be indexed along a radius to the track that contains the

Table 9.7 Standard Code

b7		0	0	0	0	1	1	1	1
	b6	0	0	1	1	0	0	1	1
	b5	0	1	0	1	0	1	0	1
b4 b3 b2 b1									
0 0 0 0		NULL	DC$_0$	ƀ	0	@	P		
0 0 0 1		SOM	DC$_1$	!	1	A	Q		
0 0 1 0		EOA	DC$_2$	"	2	B	R		UNASSIGNED
0 0 1 1		EOM	DC$_3$	*	3	C	S		
0 1 0 0		EOT	DC$_4$ (STOP)	$	4	D	T		
0 1 0 1		WRU	ERR	%	5	E	U	UNASSIGNED	
0 1 1 0		RU	SYNC	&	6	F	V		
0 1 1 1		BELL	LEM	' (APOS)	7	G	W		
1 0 0 0		FE$_0$	S$_0$	(	8	H	X		
1 0 0 1		HT / SK	S$_1$	)	9	I	Y		
1 0 1 0		LF	S$_2$	*	:	J	Z		
1 0 1 1		V$_{TAB}$	S$_3$	+	;	K	[		
1 1 0 0		FF	S$_4$	, (comma)	<	L	\		ACK
1 1 0 1		CR	S$_5$	−	=	M	]		①
1 1 1 0		SO	S$_6$	.	>	N	↑		ESC
1 1 1 1		SI	S$_7$	/	?	O	←		DEL

NULL	Null/tab	DC$_1$–DC$_3$	Device control
SOM	Start of message	DC$_4$ (stop)	Device control (stop)
EOA	End or address	ERR	Error
EOM	End of message	SYNC	Synchronous idle
EOT	End of transmission	LEM	Logical end of media
WRU	"Who are you?"	S$_0$–S$_7$	Separator (information)
RU	"Are you . . .?"	ƀ	Word separator (space, normally nonprinting)
BELL	Audible signal		
FE$_0$	Format effector	<	Less than
HT	Horizontal tabulation	>	Greater than
SK	Skip (punched card)	↑	Up arrow (exponentiation)
LF	Line feed	←	Left arrow (implies/ replaced by)
V$_{TAB}$	Vertical tabulation		
FF	Form feed	\	Reverse slant
CR	Carriage return	ACK	Acknowledge
SO	Shift out	①	Unassigned control
SI	Shift in	ESC	Escape
DC$_0$	Device control reserved for data link escape	DEL	Delete/idle

data to be read. Such disks cost less per bit of information stored, but the access time to random positions may range as high as a hundred milliseconds.

Magnetic tapes provide the cheapest magnetic form of mass storage of data. The tape drives are generally complex and expensive because the physical positioning specifications must be precise to minimize reading errors and to start the tape and accelerate it to its designed reading speed in a few milliseconds. Such tapes may require minutes to provide access to information placed at random points on the tape. Other, less expensive digital magnetic tape recorders use smaller reels, which have less mechanical inertia, and other schemes that pack less data into each unit area of tape, but require less elaborate drives and electronics.

Paper Memories: Cards and Tape

Punch cards and punched paper tape are other common methods of storing machine-readable data and words. Both media normally use codes to represent alphabetic characters, decimal digits, and special characters such as punctuation. The cards are most often punched with a Hollerith code. Hollerith codes are punched into 12 rows along 80 columns of the card, with one character punched in each column. Since the 12 bits in one column could be used to represent 2^{12} or 4096 different characters, their restriction to the alphabet, decimal digits, and a few special characters is highly inefficient. Tradition, bolstered by large investments in equipment for punching, verifying, reading, and interpreting (printing the characters punched on the same card), has generally inhibited efforts to adopt more efficient schemes. Rejection of all unused codes does provide a form of error checking.

Punched paper tape has provided the cheapest method of storing machine-readable data. These tapes were developed primarily for automatic information transmission and recording systems, such as teletypewriters. A common punched paper tape uses seven of a possible eight rows punched across a paper tape 1 in. wide. These punched columns are spaced at intervals of $\frac{1}{10}$ in. The information is stored as one alphabetic character, decimal digit, or special character per column. The code that is becoming most common for this representation is the USASCII (United States of America Standard Code for Information Interchange) (see Table 9.7).

Error Checking and Correction

Since many external devices—peripherals—use special codes to represent symbols that can be understood by people, a major problem in data communication is the translation of these codes. One of the problems in any translation or transmission is the detection of errors. In punched paper tape the eighth hole is often used to provide a "parity" check bit. This bit is punched (if needed) to provide an even number of bits in the character (or an odd number). Parity-check circuits on punches and readers detect whether an odd or an even number of holes has been punched and signal if "bad" data occur. The parity bit is sometimes called a vertical redundancy check (VRC).

A number of characters may be recorded as a block. If an odd-even redundancy check is made along each *row* or bit as the characters are recorded, a final character can be inserted at the end of the block to give every row an odd (or an even) parity. This is called a lateral redundancy check (LRC). When reading back the data, a lateral redundancy check will indicate any single reading error in a row. Usually the sender is requested to retransmit the block of data when an error has been detected.

More elaborate error checks can be performed, always at the cost of recording more information than the minimum required to designate the characters. Abramson [7], for example, discusses error-checking codes in "Information Theory and Coding." Error-checking codes increase the reliability of message transmission at the cost of sending more information. Information theory provides quantitative methods for evaluating the trade-offs between reliability and redundancy.

5   THE STRUCTURE OF A DIGITAL COMPUTER

Basically a digital computer consists of input/output (I/O) devices, a central processing unit, and a memory (see Fig. 9.23). The central processing unit (CPU) usually controls both the I/O units and the memory. The CPU contains registers and means of gating signals to various devices over cables or "busses."

Internal Communications

As an example, let us assume that we are dealing with a computer that works with a 16-bit word, which means that 16 bits are transmitted simultaneously

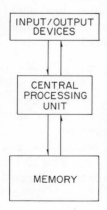

Fig. 9.23 Block diagram of a digital computer.

throughout the machine and that the memory is designed to hold 16-bit words. If the machine is designed to have up to eight input devices and eight output devices, each device can be provided with a "name" or "address" of four bits; for example, placing signals corresponding to 0001 on the first four bits of a word might turn on the gates to a paper-tape reader, whereas 0010 might turn on the gates to a paper-tape punch, and so on.

Each word of memory and each device or register that can be operated on directly by the central processing unit can be considered as having an "address." Thus, if a "word" of 16 bits in memory can be read into the arithmetic register by a single command of the CPU, that word has an "address." Access to a particular bit in that word generally requires some logical manipulation of that word; the particular bits are *not* considered addressable. The word "address" and similar terms, such as "word," "location," and "position," have not yet been given commonly agreed on precise meanings, though the word "address" is most often used as described above.

Each input/output device has a unique logic circuit connected to the first four lines of a 16-line cable or bus. This unique circuit will produce a pulse only if the four bits for its particular address are present. The output of the address-gate is connected to one leg of an AND gate for the rest of the lines of the bus; for example, the last eight lines of the 16-line bus might be connected to the eight bits generated by the hole-sensors in the paper-tape reader so that when the device 0001 is addressed the word present in the paper-tape reader is connected to a register in the central processing unit. Other lines can be used to determine whether the paper-tape reader was in a position to provide a character and to instruct it to advance to the next character after the first one is read.

Although this transfer takes place between the paper-tape reader and the register in the CPU, none of the other I/O devices can be connected because 0001 is the unique address of the paper-tape reader. Each device can be addressed similarly in a unique manner. The clock pulses ensure that each set of gates has time to react properly before the information transfer takes place.

More transfers take place between the register(s) of the CPU and the memory than with the I/O devices. Correspondingly, more elaborate schemes are usually resorted to for addressing the memory. Special registers help generate a memory address; for example, assume that our machine has $8192 (= 2^{13})$ different addressable positions of memory, each with 16 bits of storage. The unique address for putting data into the memory (or retrieving it from the memory) is generated as for an I/O device but by using 13 lines of a memory bus. The logic associated with the memory prepares the gates so that in the next clock cycle the data may be sent between the memory and the register.

The addresses for the memory may be generated in a number of ways. A direct 13-bit address may be transmitted from the address register in the CPU; but this address may come from a word already put into the address register, by adding one to the preceding address in the address register (thus addressing the next position in memory), or by adding another number to the contents of the address register. The second number can be a smaller number of bits—say, eight—that provide a relative address. At the time the program for a particular calculation was generated, these relative addresses would have to be calculated. Relative addressing provides a trade-off between truly random access to the memory and the number of bits that have to be used to address the memory from sequence to sequence of calculations.

Registers

Some central processing units have index registers that provide high-speed counts of internal events. Each index register has its own address; each time the register is addressed its contents are transferred to an arithmetic register or another register and the index register is incremented by one. Such index registers can provide for simpler programming and faster computing.

Arithmetic Unit

The central processing unit will have one or more arithmetic registers. These registers also have their own addresses. Generally they will add the number sent them to their contents, and as a rule shift operations can also be performed: a number in the register is shifted one position to the right or left and an index register is decremented simultaneously; shifting is completed when the index register reaches zero.

Binary multiplication consists of shifting and adding. The series of instructions that causes such multiplication can be stored in memory and called forth in sequence each time a multiplication takes place or direct hardware multipliers can be constructed. A hardware multiplier generally operates faster that the "software" multiplier.

Complementary Arithmetic [8]

Subtraction is usually performed by finding the complement and adding the result; that is, all negative numbers are stored as their two's complement. The procedure is similar to casting out nines.

Suppose you wish to subtract 7 from 16. Since we are dealing with two-digit numbers, we can consider seven as $(100 - 7 = 93)$, and add 16 to 93, discarding all numbers after the first two digits:

$$\begin{array}{r} 16 \\ +93 \\ \hline 109 \end{array}$$

the desired answer. The 93 may be found by adding whatever is necessary to each column of the (negative) number to get 9 and adding 1 to the result. Consider that the number 7 has a 0 in the ten's column and a 7 in the one's column (07). To get to 9 in each column add 9 to the ten's column and add 2 to the one's column to arrive at 92; now add 1 to the 92 to get 93.

Binary arithmetic is similar. Find the two's complement of a number by changing every 1 to a 0 and every 0 to a 1 (to get the one's complement) and then adding 1 to the result.

$$7_{10} = 00111_2$$
$$11000_2 \text{ (one's complement)}$$
$$+1_2$$
$$-7_{10} = 11001_2 \text{ (two's complement)}$$

(Here the subscript 10 refers to the number as a decimal, whereas 2 means the number is binary.) Now perform the subtraction by adding the two's complement.

$$
\begin{array}{rcr}
16_{10} = & & 10000_2 \\
-7_{10} = & + & 11001_2 \\
\hline
9_{10} = & & 01001_2
\end{array}
$$

Since nine equals $2^3 + 2^0$, the answer is correct.

Intuitively, adding one to the nine's complement (in the decimal example) makes the sum of the complement and the negative number "overflow" the number of digits being used; in the two-digit case the added one makes the 99 become 100, but the 1 in 100 is dropped when we are limited to two digits. Therefore adding a complement and ignoring the "overflow" digit (if any) is equivalent to subtracting. Overflow is the generation of a quantity beyond the capacity of the storage facility [9].

The advantage of using two's-complement arithmetic in a binary digital calculator is that by performing this operation both positive and negative numbers can be treated similarly; the operation of subtraction is eliminated. The one's-complement is available at the other output of flip-flop registers and is converted to two's complement by adding one.

Input/Output Units

Switches and Lights

Among the many input/output devices used with digital computers switches and lights are almost universal. Almost all digital computers have at least one bank of switches containing one switch for each bit of a word. These switches can be set manually and addressed from the central processing unit. Similarly, almost all digital computers have at least one bank of lights as an output device. The bank will have one light for each bit of a machine word. A bank of these lights is often connected to each register in the CPU, so that when the machine is halted the operator can read the contents of each register. Obviously these forms of input and output are binary, although the computer operators usually learn to read them in octal or hexadecimal notation. These I/O devices are normally used only for trouble shooting; the conversion tables (see the appendix) for binary, octal, hexadecimal, and decimal are helpful in learning to use and interpret these switches and lights.

Keyboard and Typewriter

A keyboard and character printer, like a typewriter, form the next most common input/output devices. Frequently the two units will be combined, as in a teletype (TM) unit or an IBM Selectric (TM) typewriter. The keyboard operates a set of switches which generates character codes—usually USASCII or, with IBM, EBCDIC, a code described in their manuals. These codes are generally eight-bit codes. The USASCII code, for example, is arranged so that characters that appear on one key (on a normal typewriter keyboard) differ by only one bit, and the generation of these codes is simplified. The character printer depends on a series of gates to select the solenoids that will operate the printing mechanism.

The typewriter and keyboard are each addressed by the central processing unit, and each provides a "ready" signal when it has a character to transmit or receive. Note that a translation from the man-readable character to or from a binary code is performed by the keyboard and associated printer device. If the internal machine codes are USASCII, as they are for many machines, no further translation is required. In other machines the codes are translated in the CPU. Obviously a translation process must take place if a string of decimal characters is to be translated into a single number stored in one word (or word-set) in the machine. Keyboards and associated printers usually have a capacity of 10 to 15 characters a second.

Card Readers and Punches

Card readers and card punches were adapted from business machines. Cards have the advantage of easy editing just by replacing one card with a corrected one, but they have the disadvantage of requiring bulky special storage; further, dropping a large deck can be near-disaster unless the cards are numbered sequentially.

Card readers and punches are addressed by the central processing unit and provide a "ready" bit similar to that from the keyboard/printer. The codes generated are normally read as bits by the CPU and must be translated there into machine codes. Card readers operate at speeds of one to about 20 cards per second, whereas the top speed of punches is around 12 cards per second. Each card can normally contain 80 characters. These readers and punches are complex electromechanical devices and require expert maintenance. Further, cards punched in computer-operated punches are not "interpreted"; that is, the characters punched in the card are not also printed along the top of the card. Without interpretation cards are difficult for people to read, particularly when the card contains anything other than decimal digits.

Paper Tape Reader and Punch

Punched paper tape is commonly used as a source of machine-readable input and output. Paper-tape punches and readers are less expensive and less complicated than card punches and readers. Tape punches normally operate at rates of 10 to more than 100 characters per second and tape readers operate at rates varying from 10 to several hundred characters per second. A reader that accepts 10 or 15 characters a second provides a tedious means of putting a program into a computer. Paper tape is difficult to edit, compared with punch cards, but the data cannot get out of sequence. The speed and invariable sequence, along with the relatively low cost of readers and punches, make paper tape an attractive medium for recording digital data. Most measuring apparatus originally intended for either graphical recording of output or human reading produces data at a rate slower than many tape punches can punch the data.

Tape punches and readers should normally use the USASCII code; other codes have been used in the past, but there appears to be no good reason not to standardize on the American Standard code. Tape punches and readers are addressed by the central processing unit in much the same way as the other peripheral equipment. Paper tapes are oily and will pick up dirt. Tapes are not easy for humans to read and require special storage. Special boxes are available, as are motor-driven tape winders and special unwinders. Some digitally controlled machine tools read from paper tape.

Line Printer

A common form of output from large, general-purpose digital computers is printed by a line printer. Line printers print an entire line at one time rather than character-by-character, as typewriters do. Line printers are complex electromechanical machines that can write approximately one to 20 lines a second. Each line contains about 100 to 150 characters; 120 characters per line are common. Some small printers provide 10 to 20 characters (usually digital) like a printing desk calculator. Line printers are addressed by the central processing unit in the same way as other peripherals, but more data must be transmitted to specify all the characters in each line. Even 1200 lines per minute and 150 characters per line call for only 3000 characters per second, a slow rate for a CPU that is clocked every microsecond or so.

Graphic Displays

X-Y PLOTTERS

Digital plotters provide another output for digital computers. Most digital plotters use one stepping motor to move the paper in small increments along one axis and a second stepping motor to move a pen in equal increments at right angles to the paper motion. These motors move in small enough increments (0.01 in. or less) so that the short straight lines appear to form continuous curves when viewed from a reasonable distance. The steppers can move 200 or 300 steps a second; hence such plotters can form one of the fastest man-readable outputs available. Since each stepping motor can do only one of three things (move forward, move backward, or remain still) on each command, the plotter is usually addressed with a single word that is interpreted in the computer as any combination of the possible movements. Another bit is used to command the pen to be up or down in the writing position. The plotter is addressed as are the other I/O devices, but it often does not furnish a signal to indicate either that the last instruction has been completed or that the pen and paper are in any particular position. This lack of feedback to the computer means that special care must be taken to position the pen properly and to wait long enough for each step to be completed before taking the next. Most plotting programs provide counts of the number of steps moved from the initial position of the pen.

CATHODE-RAY TUBES

The cathode-ray tube (CRT) provide another input/output device. Two different kinds of CRT are used as output devices. In one form the tube operates an electrostatic memory, which can continue to present (for as long as several minutes) anything written on the tube face with the cathode ray. These storage tubes can be "erased" in about half a second. They provide an image of less than optimum brightness and contrast and commonly hold up to 4000 characters at a time.

The second kind of CRT display operates much like an ordinary television receiver. The electron beam is caused to scan a series of closely spaced lines that fill the face of the tube and repeat 30 or more times a second so as not to appear to flicker when viewed normally. The characters are formed by turning the beam on and off at the right times, just as the TV image is formed by modulating the beam in synchronism with the horizontal raster. Whereas the raster is generated by TV sweep circuits, the brightness control is supplied either directly by a computer or from an auxiliary memory in the CRT display. Since such displays require instruction at each of about 400 points along each of about 500 lines, they require 200,000 data points every thirtieth of a second, or 6,000,000 pieces of data per second. This is a high enough rate to utilize the capability of many computers; for this reason such displays are usually provided with high-speed character generators and a local buffer memory. Acoustic delay lines often provide such buffer memories, though a randomly addressable core memory can also provide the buffer storage.

Cathode-ray-tube displays are often intended for use by one or two individuals at a time and do not normally provide a permanent copy of the display. Such permanent copies can be provided either by the other computer output devices or by some form of photographic copy of the display on the tube face. A major attraction of a visual display is that the observer can interact with what he sees. Most displays are provided with a keyboard for the user to write with. The keyboard output is displayed on the tube and can be "read" by the CPU. Usually a small bright mark called a "cursor" is displayed at the point on the tube at which the next symbol from the keyboard will be displayed.

LIGHT PENS

One novel method of interacting with a refreshed display uses a "light pen." A light pen consists of a photosensitive receptor which detects the light generated at the CRT when the pen is pressed against the face of the tube. The coincidence of the raster position of the CRT beam and the momentary detection of light by the light pen are correlated to provide the computer with the location of the light pen. Programs stored in the computer can then use the data generated with the light pen; for example, the light pen, with proper programs, can be used to sketch line drawings on the face of the CRT.

SCRATCH PADS

Another form of interactive input is often used in conjunction with a CRT. One form of tablet is made of many horizontal lines that are insulated from a set of vertical lines. The change in capacitance between a horizontal and vertical line, caused by bringing a stylus close to the tablet, provides the computer with the X-Y coordinates of the stylus. With suitable programming of the computer, the stylus can be used to "draw" on the CRT. Various other electronic schemes can also let the computer "sense" the instantaneous coordinates of the stylus.

Other I/O Units

OPTICAL AND MAGNETIC PRINT READERS

Optical and magnetic print readers form still another input device to digital computers. These devices read special printing, check identification, pencil-marked ("mark sensed") examination forms, and so on. More adaptable optical character readers will soon be forthcoming, but for the near future their complexity will make them too expensive for any but a highly specialized use.

MICROFILM OUTPUT

Computer output to microfilm (COM) provides a cheap method of preparing large volumes of output that can be read by humans. The characters for these microfilm systems are formed on special cathode-ray tubes. The characters are formed either by shadow masks in the electron beam or by electronic character generators that cause the beam to "draw" each character. Writing speeds of 90,000 characters a second are available. Graphical output to microfilm is also available. These microfilm output devices often operate separately from a general-purpose digital computer; the computer output is first recorded on magnetic tape in the desired format for rerecording by the microfilming unit.

AUDIO OUTPUT

Some output by audio devices has been tried, but the present applications have been limited mainly to commercial applications such as banking. Switching a magnetic tape recorder on and off with a computer is relatively simple, but practical devices that provide more than a few audible words in random sequence are not yet commonly available. Storage of audio messages in digital form requires too much core memory to be practical at present.

A–D AND D–A CONVERTERS [10]

To connect laboratory apparatus to a digital computer the signals have to be "interfaced" to the computer. Electrical analog signals are converted to digital form with a digital voltmeter or an analog-to-digital (A–D) converter. These devices depend on sampling. If the samples are taken before any significant change can take place in the analog voltage, all is well, but if the voltage changes rapidly various problems develop.

Analog-to-digital converters require some finite length of time to make a conversion; high-speed devices may operate at one bit per microsecond, though lower speeds often cost less and provide other advantages. During the time the conversion takes place the converter is usually disconnected from the signal source and the voltage is "held" (see page 224). The most common high-quality sample-and-hold device uses an operational amplifier in an integrating circuit. The integrator is switched on for a short time and then switched to a "hold" mode. The on or "aperture time" usually ranges from a few nanoseconds up to seconds and must be considered when selecting the A–D converter. The signal is "averaged" over the aperture time. Other converters, and many digital voltmeters, use passive circuits to smooth the input voltage so that it cannot change by as much as half the value represented by the least significant bit in the time it takes to make one conversion. Such low-pass filters usually consist of resistor-capacitor circuits and act like integrators combined with an exponential decay.

Analog-to-digital converters can be interfaced with logic circuits so that they can be addressed by the central processing unit like other devices. They usually provide one bit to indicate a "ready" status and accept one bit to initiate the conversion of one sample.

Digital-to-analog (D–A) converters provide an analog voltage output from digital computers. These devices are relatively simple compared with A–D converters. Since they provide analog voltages in discrete steps, which normally are not present in analog signals, some care must be taken to filter or "smooth" the output voltage. Digital-to-analog converters are addressed in the same way as other peripherals.

SWITCHES, RELAYS, AND POWER TRANSISTORS

The contact closures provided by switches and relays can be fed to a computer as inputs. These signal sources must be buffered from the central processing unit to generate the voltages correctly for the computer and also to prevent spurious voltages from being picked up by the computer. This "noise," which can be extremely bothersome, causes the computer to operate in a random, nonrepeatable fashion difficult to identify and correct. Relay and solenoid coils generate such noise when the current through them is suddenly interrupted.

The computer output signals can also be used to operate power transistors that, in turn, can operate relays and solenoids or other devices. The connection of the digital computer to an outside world of apparatus depends on the functions being translated into voltages, switch closings, solenoid operations, etc.

Nonelectric Computing Components

Pneumatic and Fluid Devices

Many nonelectric computing components are possible. Pneumatic controllers find wide use in industry. Fluid amplifiers and switches have been developed to provide all the analog and digital operations required for general purpose computers. The working fluid can be a gas or a liquid. Cost of components and lack of a cheap, large memory analogous to magnetic cores have thus far restricted the use of fluidic computers.

Mechanical Devices

The earliest computers were mechanical. The digital computer designed by Babbage in the first half of the nineteenth century depended on gears and levers. Physically large analog computers were designed and built before World War II with "ball and disk" integrators. Similar devices were built into special-purpose analog computers for aerial bomb sights and course plotters for ships during that war.

Mechanical computing elements have many obvious applications today. They tend, however, to be used more often in special purpose computing applications for they are not so easy to switch from application to application as electronic components.

6   ANALOG COMPUTING TECHNIQUES

General Considerations

Analog computing is done by using the elements described in Section 3, which include passive elements such as resistors, capacitors, and wire "patch cord" connections and active elements such as operational amplifiers, switches, and relays. More complex hardware performs such operations as multiplication, division, and function generation.

The accuracy of an analog computer depends on the application as well as on the individual components used. Since drift is a problem, computations that run over very long times, such as hours, may become inaccurate unless particular precautions are taken. Comparison to carefully established references can help control drift.

Closed-loop operation of systems of operational amplifiers can improve the over-all accuracy of the system. Integration, which always takes place with time as a variable, "averages" changes that occur during the time of integration.

Problems for Analog Computers

Analog computers can solve both static and dynamic problems, though their use with dynamic problems is more common. Analog computers are usually applied by simulating a system, which must first be analyzed. The input-output characteristics of each element must be established, usually in terms of differential or integral equations. The output of each element becomes the input of the succeeding element. Corresponding computing blocks are constructed; the computing blocks will simulate the real system to the extent that input-output specifications are strictly analogous to actual relationships between system variables. The accuracy of the result deteriorates with inaccuracies of the components of the analog computer (usually a fraction of one percent).

Once the system has been specified in terms of differential equations (either a single equation or simultaneous equations) the solution can be found on an analog computer by following a fairly straightforward procedure. This procedure may be illustrated in the solution of an ordinary linear differential equation with *one* independent variable, which will be related to time on the computer.

Assume that we have a third-order equation:

$$\frac{d^3x}{dt^3} + A\frac{d^2x}{dt^2} + B\frac{dx}{dt} + Cx = F(t), \tag{9.29}$$

where x = a dependent variable, to be represented by a voltage,
          t = an independent variable, to be represented by time,
A, B, and C = constants,
          $F(t)$ = driving force that varies with the independent variable, to be represented by a function generator.

The steps are the following:

1. Assume the highest derivative exists as a voltage.
2. Integrate successively on the highest derivative to produce the dependent variable.
3. Generate the highest derivative.

Following the example above, we find

$$\frac{d^3x}{dt^3} = -A\frac{d^2x}{dt^2} - B\frac{dx}{dt} - Cx + F(t). \tag{9.30}$$

In Fig. 9.24a the third derivative d^3x/dt^3 is assumed to be the input to an integrator, shown as a rectangle on the input of a triangle (which represents the operational amplifier with standard input and feedback networks). Since the operational amplifier always inverts, the output $(-d^2x/dt^2)$ is the negative integral of the input.

As shown in Fig. 9.24b, a chain of three integrators produces the variable x from the third derivative as an input. Note that each stage provides an integral of its input and a sign reversal.

The third derivative is just the sum of four terms, as shown in (9.30). The first three terms are multiplied by constants and are negative. The output dx/dt must be inverted by an operational amplifier to provide the desired negative factor. Each of the three terms is multiplied by a constant, shown in Fig. 9.24c as a circle. If any constant A, B, or C is larger than one, the attenuator is set to the constant divided by 10, and the result is multiplied by 10 at the input to the next operational amplifier summing network.

In Fig. 9.24c the inputs to the integrator of the highest derivative are summed to form that derivative. An integrator forms a sum by connecting several input resistors to the same input point to which the feedback capacitor is attached. The driving force $F(t)$ is assumed to have been formed by some other function-generating circuit.

This approach is generally satisfactory for solving both linear and non-linear differential equations. Note that the over-all circuit forms multiple

(a)

(b)

(c)

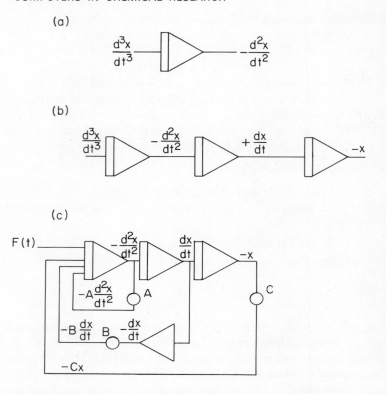

Fig. 9.24   Block diagram of analog computing problem (*a*), (*b*), (*c*).

feedback loops. Also note that each loop contains an *odd* number of amplifiers; an even number would provide a positive feedback and the circuit
would be unstable. Also, initial conditions must be set on each integrator.
The initial condition is represented by the voltage on the output of the
integrator at the instant at which integration begins.

Scaling

Operational amplifiers are limited to output over a fixed voltage range.
Since the variables are represented by voltages, any scale may be chosen
to relate the variable and the voltage. The best scale will provide the highest
possible output from all operational amplifiers involved but will not allow
any amplifier to exceed its design limit at any time during the calculation.
High output is required to minimize the proportional effects of drift and noise,
which are usually small voltages. The scale factor must usually be changed
if the dynamic range exceeds 100:1.

To choose the scaling first list the variables in the problem and all their derivatives that are the output of operational amplifiers. Then estimate maximum values of the variables and their derivatives. Calculate the scale factors as the ratio of the maximum computer voltage (often 10 or 100 V) to the maximum value of the variable or derivative. This ratio is usually rounded down to simplify these preliminary calculations; rough calculations with a slide rule suffice to find the ratios. Finally, list the computer variables (the problem variables times the scale factors).

The independent variable, which is represented by time in the analog computer, must also be scaled. If τ is the independent variable in the problem, we may write

$$\frac{dx}{d\tau} = \beta \frac{dx}{dt},$$ (9.31)

or

$$t = \beta\tau.$$

Time scaling is normally done after voltage scaling; the time scaling is introduced as an attenuator β on the input of an operational amplifier. The time scale on all the integrators in a given problem must be the same, but, if the independent variable in the problem is time, the problem can be arranged to run in real time, faster than real time or slower than real time. Obviously, if an experimental piece of apparatus is supplying some variable, such as $F(t)$, the time scale must be unity and the problem must be run in real time. In other cases time scales may be chosen to provide the user with better insight into the problem; for example, a reaction that requires days may be scaled to approach completion in minutes in its analog representation. In no case may time scales be chosen that require the analog computer components to operate faster than allowed by their design specifications; for example, servo multipliers must operate slowly enough so that the output will not lag the input significantly; usually a servo requires several seconds to slew over its entire output range.

Example

The problems of analog computing, including the choice of scale factors and time scales, can be illustrated with an example. Assume that the data, concentration C at various times, were found in a bench-scale study of a chemical reaction; Table 9.8 gives these data. Assuming that the reaction followed the equation

$$\frac{dC}{dt} = -kC^n,$$ (9.32)

the problem is to find the rate constant k and the order n that best fit the experimental data.

Table 9.8

Time (min)	Concentration (moles/ft³)
0	1.250
1	1.110
2	1.010
3	0.910
4	0.825
5	0.770
6	0.715
7	0.670
8	0.625
9	0.590
10	0.555
15	0.435
20	0.375
25	0.303
30	0.264
40	0.208
50	0.172

Equation 9.32 can be programmed directly on an analog computer by using log circuits to implement the following:

$$C^n = 10^{n \log C}. \qquad (9.33)$$

Such a circuit is shown in Fig. 9.25. Figure 9.11 shows one means of simulating logarithmic functions by using a transistor with a grounded base. This use of a transistor depends on the relation that the impedance of the transistor is a function of the current flowing through it (see Section 3).

Another approach, however, can be used to avoid having n appear as an exponent. Differentiating (9.32) with respect to t gives

$$\frac{d^2 C}{dt^2} = -knC^{n-1}\frac{dC}{dt}. \qquad (9.34)$$

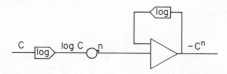

Fig. 9.25   Block diagram of implementation of rate constant.

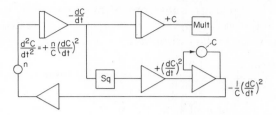

Fig. 9.26   Initial block diagram of analog of chemical rate equation.

Substituting (9.32) into this result for $-kC^n$ gives

$$\frac{d^2C}{dt^2} = \frac{n}{C}\left(\frac{dC}{dt}\right)^2. \tag{9.35}$$

The analog of this equation can be programmed as in Fig. 9.26. A squaring circuit in this diagram is shown as a square with "Sq" written in it. The multiplier is shown as a square with "Mult" written in it; the servo multiplier drives the potentiometer with C written beside it.

Now consider the values of the variables of the analog computer circuit shown in Fig. 9.26. The maximum values for each amplifier are listed in Table 9.9, which also gives the scale factors, chosen to convert each maximum to 100 V or less, and the computer variables actually implemented by this analog circuit.

The maximum value of C given was 1.25 moles/ft^3. A scale factor of 80 converts this to a maximum of 100 V. Thus the analog circuit will produce

Table 9.9   Estimating Scale Factors

Variable	Maximum Probable Value	Scale Factors	Computer Variables
C	1.25 moles-ft^{-3}	80	$80C$
$\dfrac{dC}{dt}$	2.33×10^{-3} moles-ft^{-3}-sec^{-1}	40×10^3	$40 \times 10^3 \dfrac{dC}{dt}$
$\left(\dfrac{dC}{dt}\right)^2$	5.44×10^{-6} moles^2-ft^{-6}-sec^{-2}	16×10^6	$16 \times 10^6 \left(\dfrac{dC}{dt}\right)^2$
$\dfrac{1}{C}\left(\dfrac{dC}{dt}\right)^2$	4.36×10^{-6} moles-ft^{-3}-sec^{-2}	20×10^6	$20 \times 10^6 \dfrac{1}{C}\left(\dfrac{dC}{dt}\right)^2$
$\dfrac{d^2C}{dt^2}$	17.42×10^{-6} moles-ft^{-3}-sec^{-2}	5×10^6	$5 \times 10^6 \dfrac{d^2C}{dt^2}$

a variable $80C$. The maximum slope of an exponential curve occurs at the beginning, so the maximum value of dC/dt can be estimated from the change in C that occurred in the first minute.

$$\left(\frac{dC}{dt}\right)_{max} \cong \frac{1.25 - 1.11}{60} = 0.00233 \text{ mole-ft}^{-3}\text{-sec}^{-1}. \qquad (9.36)$$

Choosing a scale factor of 40×10^3 for this means the maximum output of that circuit need be only 93.3 V; the scale factor was rounded down for convenient figuring and to provide the possibility of a small upward adjustment, should the estimate of a maximum have been too low. The computer variable then becomes $40 \times 10^3(dC/dt)$.

Assume that the maximum value of the squared slope is the square of the maximum value of the slope, or 5.44×10^{-6} mole^2-ft^{-6}-sec^{-2}. An appropriate scale factor for this variable is one hundredth of the square of the scale factor for the slope, or 16×10^6. Squaring circuits normally provide an output that is scaled just this way.

The greatest output of the dividing circuit will occur when both inputs are at their maxima, or 4.36×10^{-6}. Scaled to provide a maximum of 100 V out, this gives a scale factor of 20×10^6 and a computer variable of $20 \times 10^6(1/C)(dC/dt)^2$. The dividing circuit normally provides the $\times 100$ additional scale factor. Because we cannot be sure (without further testing) that the maximum output of this dividing circuit will occur at the maxima of both inputs, we insert an attenuator into one input. This potentiometer will be set initially at one, but it can easily be used to decrease the scale factor of this variable, should the amplifier become overloaded while the problem is being run.

The order constant n will probably be less than four, and the maximum value is found from (9.35) by using four times maximum of $(1/C)(dC/dt)^2$. This maximum is 17.42×10^{-6} mole-ft^{-3}-sec^{-2}. A scale factor of 5×10^6 will restrict this maximum voltage to less than 100 V and makes the analog computer variable $5 \times 10^6(d^2C/dt^2)$.

As implemented in the analog computing circuit, (9.35) becomes

$$5 \times 10^6 \frac{d^2C}{dt^2} = \left(\frac{n}{4}\right)\left\{\frac{[40 \times 10^3(dC/dt)][40 \times 10^3(dC/dt)]}{100}\right\}\left(\frac{100}{80C}\right) \qquad (9.37)$$

The terms in this equation are written to show the division by 100 automatically provided by the squarer and the multiplication by 100 provided by the dividing circuit.

The circuit contains two integrators; these are shown in Fig. 9.27, together with the input and output computer variables for each. Each integrating amplifier is usually arranged to supply a gain of 0.1, 1, or 10. Preceding each

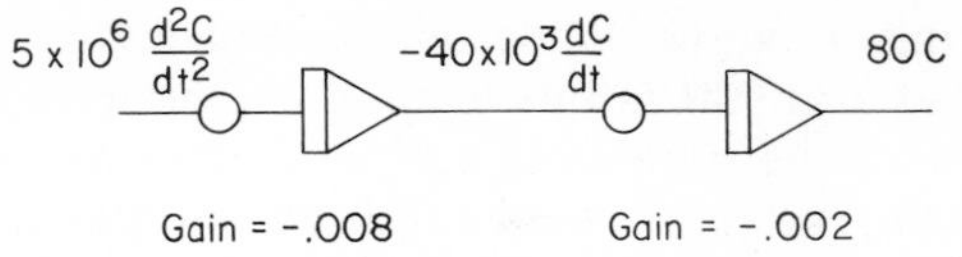

$$5 \times 10^6 \frac{d^2C}{dt^2}$$

$$-40 \times 10^3 \frac{dC}{dt}$$

$$80\,C$$

Gain = −.008   Gain = −.002

Fig. 9.27 Block diagram of integrators and potentiometers.

input by a potentiometer provides a further gain control between zero and one. Small setting errors, however, become high percentage errors when the attenuation is great; therefore small gain settings of the potentiometers should be avoided.

Dividing the output by the input of the first integrator shows that the gain required by this stage is -0.008. Similarly, we find that the gain required for the second stage is -0.002. The gains can be changed to -0.8 and -0.2, respectively, by speeding up the integrators a hundred times, that is, by changing the time scale of the problem by a factor of 100. Since time is the same variable for both integrators, only a single time-scale factor can be used in one analog computing circuit.

The original problem ran for 50 min, or 3000 sec. Our change of time scale, using $\beta = 0.01$, means that the problem will run on the computer in 30 sec. This is a good choice, for the squaring and dividing servo motors will not have to run too fast, yet we shall not have to wait too long for a result. These times are also compatible with plotting the results on an ordinary X-Y plotter. (The characteristics of these plotters are discussed in Chapter VII.)

Figure 9.28 shows the analog computer circuit used for this problem. The circuit requires five operational amplifiers (A_1–A_5), six potentiometers

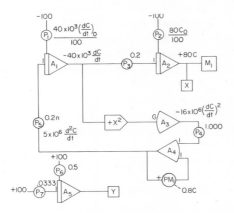

Fig. 9.28 Final block diagram of analog of chemical rate equation.

(P_1-P_6), one squaring circuit (X^2), and one multiplier (M_1 and PM_1). The blocks marked X and Y are the inputs to an X-Y plotter.

The gain of each of the potentiometers is written beside the symbol. Thus, including the time scaling, P_3 is set to 0.200 and the input to the integrator A_2 is set to 1; P_4 is set to 1.000 and will be left there unless amplifier A_4 becomes overloaded while the problem is being executed. If P_4 were reset, P_5 would have to be readjusted also. As indicated in Fig. 9.28, the gain (including time scaling) of 0.8 is combined with the order scaling $(n/4)$ and P_5 is set to $0.2n$.

Assume that the plotter works over an area of 10×15 in.; make the 10-in. axis the Y-axis and the 15-in. axis the X-axis. If the gain along the Y-axis is 10 V/in., a voltage change of 100 V will be sufficient to cover the range available on the plotter. The Y-axis can be used to represent time by driving it with a voltage that changes linearly with time. An integrator with a constant input provides such a linear voltage ramp. Since the problem is to take place in 30 sec, P_7 should be set to provide the unity input to integrator amplifier A_5 with 3.33 V, and the output will swing 100 V in 30 sec. This setting of P_7 is related to the time-scaling factor β.

The connections shown at the top of the integrators provide the initial condition for the integrators. To provide for swinging the Y-axis (time axis) from plus to minus the potentiometer P_6 can be fed with $+100$ V and set to 0.500, providing an initial voltage of $+50$ V on the output of A_5. This voltage will change -3.33 V/sec while the problem runs, reaching -50 V after 30 sec, or 50 scale-minutes. Thus each inch along the Y-axis will correspond to 5 min.

Before running the problem the outputs of all the amplifiers should be checked at some intermediate value. Adjusting the initial condition potentiometers to chosen values will set such voltages throughout the circuit, once an arbitrary value of n is chosen; for example, assume that the initial condition of $+80$ V is impressed on amplifiers A_1 and A_2 and that n is set to 2. Since the computer variable generated by A_2 is $80C$ and the output is $+80$ V, C must be 1 mole/ft^3. Similarly, the value of dC/dt from A_1 is $(+80 \text{ V})/(-40 \times 10^3)$, or -2×10^{-3} mole-ft^{-3}-sec^{-1}.

The value of d^2C/dt^2 is found from (9.35). At this static test condition $d^2C/dt^2 = (2/1)(-2 \times 10^{-3})^2 = +8 \times 10^{-6}$ mole-ft^{-3}-sec^{-2}. Since the scale factor for A_1 is $-40 \times 10^3/\beta$, the input to A_1 must be

$$\frac{-40 \times 10^3}{0.01} \frac{d^2C}{dt^2} = -40 \times 10^3 \times 10^2 \times 8 \times 10^{-6} = -32 \text{ V}.$$

For a static check set the initial condition potentiometers P_1 and P_2 to -80 V to provide $+80$ V from A_1 and A_2 and check to find -32 V at the unity input to A_1. Any other value at the input to A_1 indicates an error in scale factors or in setup.

Over the length of the run the value of C will change from 1.25 moles-ft^{-3} to nearly zero. A useful scale factor for plotting along the 15-in.-long X-axis would be 0.1 mole-ft^{-3} = 1 in. The output of A_1 is scaled to $80C$ and 0.1 mole-ft^{-3} will be represented by 8 V; therefore the X-axis amplifier of the X-Y plotter should be adjusted to 8 V/in.

Before starting any solutions the original data are plotted by using the symbol " $+$ " on the graph positioned in the X-Y plotter and using the scales chosen. The initial value of C in the data is 1.250 moles/ft^3. Since the output of amplifier-integrator A_2 is $80C$, its initial value must then be 80×1.250, or $+100$ V; P_2 must be set to provide -100 V into the integrator because the amplifier inverts the input voltage; P_6 has already been set to provide $+50$ V to the Y-axis of the plotter, the pen is adjusted to 0 sec and 1.25 mole-ft^{-3} on the graph with these voltages present.

The potentiometers P_1 and P_5 will be adjusted between runs until the plot falls on all the given data points. For initial values we expect dC/dt to be -2.33×10^{-3} mole-ft^{-3}-sec^{-1}. Since the gain of this stage is -40×10^3, the output is $+93.333$ V. For the first trial P_1 should be set to provide -93.333 V to A_1. Selecting n as 1 initially, the potentiometer P_5 should be set to provide a gain of 0.2000.

In the first trial, plotted with other trials in Fig. 9.29, the analog curve undershot the plotted points. Subsequent runs could not reach the plotted points, even though P_1 was set to its maximum value. The range of P_1 was changed by changing the scale factor for dC/dt to 32×10^3. To maintain the scale factor of 80 for C, P_3 had to be changed to 0.25. If one leaves P_4 at 1.000, the output of the squaring circuit and amplifier A_3 is $10.24 \times 10^6(dC/dt)^2$ and the output of the dividing circuit and amplifier A_4 has a scale factor of 12.8×10^6. Again assuming n might range as high as 4, we find a scale factor of 3.2×10^6. Using β still as 0·01, the setting of P_5 becomes 0·25n.

The best match of the analog curve and the plotted points occurred when P_1 was 0.8284 and P_5 was 0.4940. Since the setting of P_5 was 0.25n, we find $n = 1.976$. Now we can find k from the initial setting of the integrator. From (9.32)

$$k = -C_0^{-n}\left(\frac{dC}{dt}\right)_{t=0}. \tag{9.38}$$

Use of the scale factor -32×10^3 gives

$$\left(\frac{dC}{dt}\right)_{t=0} = -\frac{100 \times 0.8284}{32 \times 10^3}. \tag{9.39}$$

Using $C_0 = 1.25$ moles/ft^3, we employ logarithms to find $k = 1.666$.

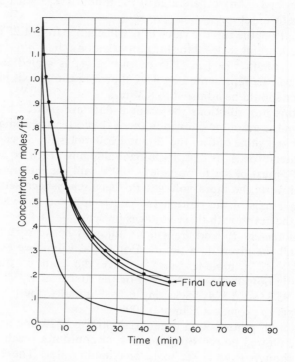

Fig. 9.29   Output plot for chemical rate equation example.

This example has illustrated one application of an analog computer in the analysis of laboratory data. A nonlinear differential equation was assumed and the experimental data were fitted by the analog simulation. From the fit the two constants were evaluated. The application illustrated the use of operational amplifiers, servo multipliers and dividers, potentiometers, variable scaling and time scaling, use of an X-Y plotter, and a necessary readjustment of scale factors in the face of computer results. Unless n is an integer no general solution for (9.32) exists; hence the solution without a computer would have been exceedingly tedious.

Most of the mathematical techniques that have been developed for analysis of differential equations can be applied with analog computing. As illustrated, analog computers can handle some nonlinear differential equations. The analog computer simulates the system symbolized by the differential equation(s).

Other Problem Types

If we use a time scale of unity, parts of the real system can be connected with the analog computer; of course, the real part must be interfaced with electronic signals so that the output of that part will control a voltage and the input to that part will be controlled by a voltage.

Some statistical problems can be solved easily with an analog computer; for example, rms error can be generated directly and continuously, and other error terms can often be generated with ease. The variables of the system can be adjusted manually to minimize the error signal on repeated runs.

Partial differential equations and boundary value problems must be approached in relatively roundabout ways with an analog computer because the only independent variable available is time. Techniques for dealing with them are described in the literature; hybrid computers (partly analog, partly digital, with information flowing between these sections) offer an attractive means of attacking partial differential equations and boundary value problems.

The greatest value of an analog computer is the insight the user gains in solving his problem. The sequence of formulating the problem in the form of differential equations, designing computer elements to simulate the parts of the equations, scaling, and examining the problem in such detail invariably leads the user to further insights. Because situations, once set up, can be tried again and again, "feel" can be developed for the problem and for the effects of various changes in inputs. Changes made between runs, however, should not be just "dial twiddling" but should reflect careful thought and trial calculations of the slide-rule variety.

7   DIGITAL COMPUTER TECHNIQUES

Machine Language Programming

A program for a digital computer consists of a sequence of instructions that enables the computer to manipulate symbols. The symbols actually manipulated by an electronic digital computer are voltages, currents, and magnetic fields in the various elements of the computer, whose on-off characteristics permit coding of binary digits 0 and 1.

The binary numbers are, in turn, symbols. The same symbols can also represent numbers, alphabetic symbols, or any symbols designated by the programmer. "As (the programmer) Humpty Dumpty said to Alice in scornful tone: 'When *I* use a word, it means just what I choose it to mean—neither more nor less.' " (*Through the Looking Glass* by Lewis Carrol.)

The computer program causes sequences of the following operations to occur:

1. Combining two symbols to generate a third.
2. Altering the order of making combinations by "executing a conditional jump."
3. Changing the content of memory.
4. Reading data into memory from an input device or reporting data out of memory on an output device.

These operations can be illustrated on a simple computer. The program will go through a selected number of cycles, then change the contents of a memory location. This little machine needs three registers in its CPU (central processing unit). The first, called ACC, is a five-bit accumulator; it adds any five-bit word brought to it to those already in the register. The second register, called CR, is a five-bit control register. The third is a three-bit address register called ADR. Three bits can address eight positions (000 to 111 in Table 9.2) so that the computer will need a memory of eight words containing five bits each.

Each five-bit word can, in some circumstances, be considered in two parts: a two-bit command and a three-bit address. Let the two bits at the left-hand end of the word represent the four basic commands, as shown in Table 9.10. The remaining three bits address a word of memory.

Let the input to this simple computer be a set of five toggle switches in a row; each switch corresponds to one bit of a five-bit word. A toggle switch with the toggle down will represent 0; with the toggle up, 1. The output is shown by a set of five lights.

Table 9.10   Symbolic Representation of Computer Commands

---

00   add the word stored at the address (given by the last three bits) to the contents of ACC, and move to the next sequential address.

01   take the address of the next instruction from the last three bits of this command word if the left-hand bit in ACC is 1; otherwise execute the instruction at the next sequential address. This is called a "jump."

10   store the contents of ACC at the address given with this command, clear ACC, and go to the instruction at the next address.

11   read an input word if the last bit at the right of the address given with this command is 1 and go to the instruction at the next address; write an output if the bit is 0.

Pick a number such as 3 and enter it into the toggle switches as a negative number (see Section 5);

$$3_{10} = 0 \quad 0 \quad 0 \quad 1 \quad 1$$
$$\quad\quad 1 \quad 1 \quad 1 \quad 0 \quad 0 \quad \text{(the one's complement)}$$
$$\quad\quad\quad\quad\quad +1$$
$$-3_{10} = 1 \quad 1 \quad 1 \quad 0 \quad 1 \quad \text{(the two's complement)}$$

To represent this number all the toggle switches are up except for the next to last on the right-hand end.

Table 9.11 A Machine Language Program

Memory Address	Memory Contents
0 0 0	1 1 0 0 1
0 0 1	0 0 1 1 1
0 1 0	0 1 0 0 1
0 1 1	1 0 1 1 0
1 0 0	1 1 0 0 1
1 0 1	0 1 1 0 1
1 1 0	1 1 1 1 1
1 1 1	0 0 0 0 1

The positions of the words in the memory must have addresses. The eight words can be numbered or addressed from 0 to 7 decimal or 000 to 111 in binary (see Table 9.2). Assume that the eight words of memory are filled by some operation that preceded this description. Each word of memory consists of five bits, as shown in Table 9.11. Note that the memory addresses are not the same as the memory contents. The addresses are the sequence of binary numbers (see also the appendix), whereas the contents of the memory are five-bit binary numbers stored at those addressable locations.

In this computer the first step clears ACC and loads the contents of address 000 into CR. According to the program, this is

Before Step 1: ADR = 000   CR = 00000   ACC = 00000
After   Step 1: ADR = 000   CR = 11001   ACC = 00000

The first two bits of the word now in CR (11) tell the computer, according to Table 9.10, to place the contents of the switch register in ACC and increment the address pointer ADR by 1.

Step 2:   ADR = 001   CR = 00111   ACC = 11101

The first two bits of the word now in CR (00) tell the computer to add the word stored at address 111 to the word in ACC and proceed to the next address.

Step 3:   ADR = 010   CR = 01001   ACC = 11110

The value in ACC occurred because the content of address 111 is 00001; 11101 + 1 = 11110.

The first two bits of the word in CR (01) tell the computer to go to the address given by the last three bits in CR, since the first bit in ACC is 1.

Step 4:   ADR = 001   CR = 00111   ACC = 11110

The command in CR (00) is like Step 2. Adding 1 to ACC gives

Step 5:   ADR = 010   CR = 01001   ACC = 11111

The command in CR (01) again jumps to address 001 because the first bit in ACC is 1; this is like Step 4.

Step 6:   ADR = 001   CR = 00111   ACC = 11111

As in Steps 3 and 5, 1 (the word stored at address 111) is added to ACC (11111 + 1 = 00000).

Step 7:   ADR = 010   CR = 01001   ACC = 00000

This time, since the first bit in ACC is 0, the command 00 in CR tells the computer to go to the next sequential address.

Step 8:   ADR = 011   CR = 10110   ACC = 00000

The first two bits in CR (10) now tell the computer to store the contents of ACC at the address 110, clear ACC, and go to the next sequential address. Address 110 changes from 11111 to 00000.

Step 9:   ADR = 100   CR = 11001   ACC = 00000

This instruction (11) tells the computer to read the contents of the switch register once again and to proceed to the next address.

Step 10:   ADR = 101   CR = 01101   ACC = 11101

The first two bits (01) of this instruction tell the computer to jump to address 101, since the first bit in ACC is 1. Because this is the address at which the machine has already arrived, the computer will cycle with these values until some other stop is provided: for example, pull the plug because we did not give this computer any means of recognizing a STOP command.

This program illustrates the fundamental operations of the computer: combining symbols, making conditional jumps, changing the content of

Table 9.12 Assembler Mnemonic List

English Word		Binary Word	
ADD		00000	
JUMP		01000	
STORE	XXXXX	10000	
READ		11000	
LABEL	XXX	00XXX	(where each name is replaced by an address)
SWITCH		00001	

memory, and reading an input. At the end the contents of memory address 110 were changed from 11111 to 00000. The program cycles the number of times indicated by the two's complement originally set in the switch register; the number of cycles could have been set from 0 to 16 and other operations could have been performed that number of times, had the memory been larger.

Assembler Programming

A program can be written to translate words that represent operators into binary numbers that become a program; for example, an assembler program for our hypothetical computer would generate or "assemble" binary words on finding the series of binary numbers equivalent to the English words in Table 9.12.

Further, the assembler program combines (logical OR) all the words written on one line. The preceding program could then be written in assembler language and translated to the program given by the assembler (Table 9.13).

To generate the binary numbers for the machine-language program the assembler must often have access to the source statements twice. On the first pass the assembler must generate the addresses for labels C, D, and E. Only then can the machine codes that refer to these addresses be generated.

Table 9.13 Assembler Program

Source Statement		Generates
LABEL A:	READ, SWITCH	11001
LABEL B:	ADD LABEL E	00111
	JUMP, LABEL B	01001
	STORE, LABEL D	10110
	READ, SWITCH	11001
LABEL C:	JUMP, LABEL C	01101
LABEL D:	STORE 11111	11111
LABEL E:	STORE 00001	00001

Assemblers use a computer to change one set of symbols, which are mnemonic, short English words, into another set of symbols, binary numbers that constitute a program. This translation of symbols is the essence of programming.

Subprograms

Many operations must be done over and over—such as input and output operations—and subprograms provide one means of avoiding rewriting these routines every time one is needed. The subroutine usually occupies some sequential set of addresses in memory.

When the subprogram is needed, the address of the *second* word of the subroutine is written as the address of a jump; this jump-to-subroutine instruction also causes the address of the next step in the main-line program to be stored as the first word of the subprogram. The last word of the subprogram is then a jump to take the address of the next step as stored in the first word of the subprogram. This sequence of program steps permits the subprogram to be entered as many times as desired from the calling program, always storing the desired return address.

Higher Level Languages

Subprograms can be written to perform any function that is within the capabilities of a computer. In particular, subprograms called by a single symbol or mnemonic word or particular order of symbols (syntax) can cause one to a larger number of program steps to be performed. The subprogram can, indeed, call other subprograms as part of its own sequence of instructions.

Systems of subprograms are designed to interpret more complex statements than those that generate a single instruction, as the assembler does. Such languages are given mnemonic names, such as FORTRAN (FORmula TRANslation), ALGOL (ALGOrythmic Language), COBOL (Common Business Oriented Language), and PL/I (Programming Language I). By handling more of the generation of the machine-language codes these languages allow programs to be written by people with no understanding of the internal operation of the computer.

Two separate phases of computer operation occur for each program. In the first phase, called *compilation*, the program is read from some suitable medium (such as punched cards) into the computer memory and undergoes suitable translation as discussed later; in the second phase, called *execution*, numerical data are read as needed (input) and the logical-mathematical operations required by the program are carried out to yield results (output). The whole program is stored in computer memory, and each program step is called out of memory and carried out during execution.

The two phases of programs written in higher level languages, compilation and execution, do not always have to be deferred until an entire program is entered into the computer. Each line can be compiled and executed as it is entered. This kind of operation assumes that the programmer is entering his program into the computer himself—at a keyboard, for example. The computer program that "monitors" this kind of input can also immediately indicate to the programmer any programming errors that it detects. Such dynamic interaction can occur with time-sharing computers that serve many "terminals" almost simultaneously. Because this interactive use of computers makes efficient use of people, time-sharing will grow rapidly and probably will soon become the most common method of using computers. Commonly used interactive languages include BASIC, APL (A Programming Language) [14], MULTICS, and others.

By the steps outlined symbol translation techniques have been developed so that sophisticated mathematics—the manipulation of other symbols—can be programmed without any detailed worry by the user about where the program and data are stored in memory. These higher level languages, particularly FORTRAN and ALGOL, are extremely useful for scientific programming. Every competent working scientist needs to be familiar with a higher level language such as FORTRAN.

Only with a working knowledge of programming scientific problems on a digital computer can a scientist develop a "feel" for the ease or difficulty with which any particular operation can be programmed. Further, as in analog-computer programming, the scientist who programs some of his own problems gains deeper insight into those problems.

Programming requires close attention to detail and to logical procedures. Most of the insight into a problem comes in finding a logical way to write the program and then discovering by executing the program whether there were holes in the logic. Because electronic digital computers operate around a million times faster than a man on a desk calculator, programs that contain errors—"bugs"—will usually run across the error and reach some ridiculous result in a few seconds.

Higher level languages, however, require large programs to compile them (to translate them into machine language) and so do not fit as well on small computers as on larger ones. The sort of computer needed for the control of processes in a laboratory usually need not be large; the control of a process often requires special subprograms, written for that particular system.

The phase of computer operation in which the program in high level language (called the *source* program) is translated into machine language is called *compilation*. During compilation several other operations are carried out besides translation: storage positions are allocated in memory for the

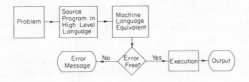

Fig. 9.30   Flow chart showing problem solving on a digital computer.

variables and arrays, any special routines or special functions previously stored in computer memory are called into the program if needed, and the program is screened for certain kinds of error. If errors are found, the program will not compile, and a message to this effect is issued by the computer. If no errors occur, compilation is successful, and the computer moves into *execution*, the next phase of operation. During execution the computer actually carries out the commands contained in the program, using numerical data that may have been read into the computer during the execution step. The whole process is outlined in Figure 9.30.

8   FORTRAN

There are many higher level languages, some developed for special purposes. The most popular languages in current scientific use are FORTRAN and ALGOL, the latter having widespread application in Europe. PL/I is a recent (1965) language of great flexibility developed for scientific and business computing. We propose to exemplify the characteristics and uses of a typical higher level language by means of an abbreviated presentation of the FORTRAN IV language. Enough detail is given to permit the reader to write programs for a small computer having a FORTRAN compiler, but other sources should be consulted for a complete description (see Bibliography).

The vocabulary and grammar of FORTRAN are closely related to ordinary mathematical language to facilitate use by nonprofessional programmers. FORTRAN was adopted as a standard computer language by ASTM.

Elements

Statement Types

FORTRAN statements are instructions to the computer expressed in FORTRAN language. There are four types of statement:

SPECIFICATION STATEMENTS provide information to the computer describing the data; for example, it is necessary to distinguish between literal (alphabetic) data and numerical data or to inform the computer that a certain number is an integer and not a decimal number. Specification statements appear first before any other statements in the FORTRAN program.

ARITHMETIC STATEMENTS define the operations to be carried out on the data.

INPUT/OUTPUT STATEMENTS permit the transfer of information (data) between the computer and input or output units such as card readers, printers, tape and disk units, and curve plotters.

CONTROL STATEMENTS. The program is a list of instructions, which are normally executed in sequence, starting at the beginning of the list. Control statements are used to alter this normal sequence of processing. It may be necessary, for example, to execute a given instruction several times, and this can be accomplished by inserting a suitable control statement. Control statements also provide for branching to other parts of the program.

The Character Set

The character set used in FORTRAN contains 48 symbols that occur on keypunches and typewriters. Alphabetic characters are in upper case only:

A–Z (alphabetic)
0–9 (numeric)
blank = + − * / ( ) , . $ ' (apostrophe).

Variable Names and Constants

A FORTRAN statement is an instruction to a computer. It may be viewed as a sentence that contains nouns and verbs. The nouns are *variable names* and *constants* and the verbs are *operations* or *descriptions*. Variable names are certain allowed combinations of alphabetic and numeric symbols from the character set which play a role in FORTRAN analogous to the role of x or a in algebra. In FORTRAN a *variable name is a label assigned to an address in computer memory*. The *value* assigned to that variable at a given time during execution of the program is the number stored at the address having that variable name as its label; for example, the letter I is a valid name for a variable in FORTRAN. The FORTRAN expression I = 3 is a command to the computer to store the number (integer) 3 at an address in memory having the label I. In this expression I is a variable; the symbol 3 is a *constant*. A constant is a number used without change from one execution of the program to another.

Variable names may be of any length up to five symbols (on small computers) and may be composed of letters and numerals, subject to the restriction that the initial symbol must be alphabetic. The following are examples of valid FORTRAN variable names:

RATE   SEEK2   A34FB X X6   NONE   TIME

Blanks may not be included in FORTRAN names. It is good practice to assign variable names that have meaning in terms of the problem; thus a variable representing a height might be called HT or HITE in the program.

A peculiar feature of FORTRAN is that numbers with decimal points (called *real* numbers in the programming manuals) are treated quite differently from integers. This is a consequence of the fact that the two different kinds of number are stored differently in computer memory. In general, integers are written and punched without decimal points; real numbers, on the other hand, must always appear with decimal points. The following examples illustrate the two classes of number:

INTEGERS   3   5699   23

REAL NUMBERS   3.242692 3.0 3. 0.002 38895.77

Note that commas may *not* be used to mark off thousands in large numbers. We shall see that there are many practical programming advantages in distinguishing between the two kinds of number. One immediate example is *counting*, which requires integer arithmetic rather than decimal arithmetic. Variable *names* likewise fall into two categories, depending on whether the value of the variable represented by the name is a real or an integer quantity. According to convention, names that represent integer quantities start with any of the letters I through N inclusive, whereas names that represent real numbers must start with any of the letters A–H or O–Z. Variables whose allowed values are real numbers are called *real variables*, whereas those whose allowed values are integers are called *integer variables*. The following are examples of names of integer and real variables:

INTEGER VARIABLE NAMES: IRATE   N   KKK   LUNCH   J88

REAL VARIABLE NAMES: ALL   Z67   RATE   DIST   X   HAHA

As a memory-aid note that the first two letters (I, N) of the word INTEGER give the alphabetic range of the first letter of the normal name of integer variables; the other letters of the alphabet are used for real variables.

FORTRAN Statement Cards and Data Cards

FORTRAN statements are punched onto a standard statement card, shown in Figure 9.31. Any standard IBM card may be used as long as the following spacing requirements are satisfied. FORTRAN statements are punched in columns 7–72; at least the first six columns are left blank (statements may be indented as much as desired) and the statement must not go beyond column 72. If desired, statements may be numbered in the first

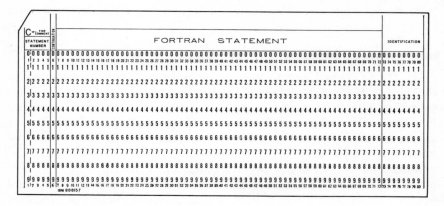

Fig. 9.31 A FORTRAN statement card.

five columns of the card. It is not necessary—in fact, it is undesirable—to number every statement in the program. On the other hand, it is often necessary to refer to a statement within an instruction and such reference is by means of a statement number. Statements do not need to be numbered sequentially, but each statement number must be unique within a given program. One use of statement numbers is described in the next section.

Column 6 on the FORTRAN statement card is reserved for continuation. Instructions that require more space than is provided by columns 7–72 can be carried over to a second card by punching any number from 1 through 9 into column 6 of the continuation card. The continued statement may commence in column 7 and must terminate by column 72. More than one continuation card may be used. The number of allowed continuation cards varies with the computer; for example, on the IBM 1130 computer five continuation cards are permitted, whereas 19 are allowed with the IBM 360 computer.

During execution of the program, and under control of the program, data may be required for computation. Such data are commonly entered from punched cards. One of the jobs facing the programmer is to specify the form and location of the input data. The data are read into computer memory by means of a READ statement; the form and location of the data on the input medium (usually a punched card) are specified by a FORMAT statement which is keyed to the READ by a statement number assigned to the FORMAT. Similarly, computer results may be written out of computer memory with a WRITE statement, but a FORMAT statement associated with the output determines the layout of the results on the printed page: titles, column headings, indentation and spacing, the number of lines to be printed on a page, and so on. Thus a FORMAT statement is required for each input/output operation.

Input/Output Statements: FORMAT

Data to be entered into a computer for subsequent computation may be recorded on a variety of input media. Punched paper tape is often used for collecting data from automatic devices such as spectrophotometers and may be used as an input medium to the computer. Magnetic tape serves a similar purpose. For most scientific computing, however, the usual input medium is the punched card and the input device is the card reader. The nature of the input device is specified by a number; for the IBM 1130 computer, for example, the number 2 is associated with the model 1442 card reader. This number will vary from one computer to another and must be obtained from the computer center.

The command to read data from the input medium is

$$READ(a,b) \ A,B,C \ldots$$

where a is the number associated with the input device, b is the statement number of a FORMAT statement which describes the input data, and A,B,C . . . are names of variables. On encountering this command the computer will transfer control to the input device and read from the input numerical values, which are then stored at memory locations labeled A,B,C . . . etc. Let us consider a more specific example:

$$READ(2,5) \ IRATE$$
$$5 \ FORMAT(I3)$$

On encountering the READ command the computer will go to the card reader (specified by the number 2) and read a punched card. The FORMAT statement, which describes the input data, is contained in statement number 5. According to this FORMAT, the input datum is contained in the first three columns of the punched card and is an integer (I3). The computer is to store the three-digit integer found there in an area of memory location labeled IRATE.

FORMAT Statements

FORMAT statements are *always* numbered and may appear any place in the program after the specification statements. Many programmers lump all FORMAT statements together so that they are readily accessible for alterations. The statement number for FORMAT statements must appear in columns 1–5; the word FORMAT may start in column 7 or later, and the statement cannot go beyond column 72. For long FORMAT statements, continuation cards may be used. The FORMAT statement always has the form FORMAT(. . . . . .), with formatting information contained within the parentheses.

In what follows we assume that data (including sign) are entered into the computer via punched cards, read in a card reader with logical unit number 2. Each kind of datum—real, integer, or alphabetic—requires its own FORMAT description, which not only specifies the type of datum but also tells how many positions on the punched card are devoted to it. The FORMAT descriptions follow.

I-FORMAT

The FORMAT description for integers is In, where I designates integer and n designates that n spaces on the punched card are used to contain the number; for example, I10 is a FORMAT specification for an integer stored in a 10-position field on a punched card. Successive FORMAT specifications indicate the use of successive fields on the punched card. Thus FORMAT-(I10,I5,I2) reserves the first 10 spaces on the punched card for the first integer, the second five spaces for a second integer, and finally two spaces for the third integer. An example of the use of this FORMAT is the following:

$$\text{READ}(2,10) \ \text{IX,IY,IZ}$$

$$10 \ \text{FORMAT}(I5,I9,I5)$$

The computer is instructed to read three values (integers) from a punched card at the card reader (logical unit 2) and store the values at storage positions labeled IX, IY, and IZ. The first value occurs in the first five positions of the punched card, the second value occurs in the next nine positions, and the third value occurs in the next five positions.

According to this READ command, three values are read simultaneously from one punched card. If one wished to read three separate cards, the commands would be

$$\text{READ}(2,11) \ \text{IX}$$

$$\text{READ}(2,11) \ \text{IY}$$

$$\text{READ}(2,11) \ \text{IZ}$$

$$11 \ \text{FORMAT}(I5)$$

These commands provide for entering the values of IX, IY, and IZ on separate cards. A common FORMAT is to be used for all three READs, and only one FORMAT statement is required; in each case the integer to be read appears in the first five positions of the punched cards. In punching integer data it is important that each datum be *right-justified* in its field. If this is not done, the computer will fill in the right-hand part of the field with zeros; for example, if the number 5 is punched into the third space on the card with a FORMAT I5, the number read into the computer will be 500, not 5.

F-FORMAT

REAL NUMBERS

A FORMAT description for real numbers is Fw.n, where F designates a real quantity, w designates the number of spaces on the punched card to be used, and n designates the number of digits following the decimal point; for example, F10.3 designates that 10 positions are reserved on the punched card for a real number with three digits after the decimal point; 3.456. Note that one of these spaces is occupied by the decimal point. As long as the decimal point appears in the number, the real quantity can be spaced anywhere within the field of 10 spaces. If the decimal point is not punched, the number must be right justified in the field. The following example shows the use of F-FORMAT for reading in the values of three real numbers to be stored at storage locations labeled A, DIST, and Y.

READ(2,6) A,DIST,Y

6 FORMAT(F10.3,F5.2,F6.0)

The first number is contained in the first 10 positions on the punched card and has three digits after the decimal point; the second number occurs in the next five positions and has two digits after the decimal point; the third number occurs in the next field of six positions and has no numbers after the decimal point. The last number, Y, in the list with FORMAT description F6.0 is still a real (decimal) number and *not* an integer, even though the FORMAT description specifies that there are no digits following the decimal point. This example underscores the fact that the FORMAT description is primarily a description of a piece of datum as it is represented on the input (or output) medium and has nothing to do with the internal representation of that datum in the computer. Thus FORMAT F6.0 specifies that on the input medium the real variable Y will occur in a field of six positions and the decimal point is to follow any numbers appearing in this field, no provision being made to enter digits that might occur after the decimal point.

If the decimal is punched on the data card, that positioning of the decimal over-rides the FORMAT specification for that datum; for example, the number 3.04 occurring any place in the first 10 positions of a punched card could be read as 3.04 on a FORMAT specification of F10.0, F10.4, or F10.6. If the decimal is not punched, careful attention must be paid to the FORMAT and positioning of the data on the card. The number 345 right-justified in a field of five and read in under FORMAT(F5.2) would appear in the computer as 3.45; that is, if the decimal point is not punched, it is "inserted" as indicated by the FORMAT specification.

E-FORMAT

A second FORMAT specification is used for real numbers written in exponential (scientific) notation; namely, Ew.n, where E designates an exponential quantity to the base 10, w designates the number of spaces on the punched card to be used, and n designates the number of digits following the decimal point.

The FORMAT E12.2 requires 12 positions to be reserved on the punched card for entering a number in E-FORMAT with two digits after the decimal point. As is the case for real numbers in F-FORMAT, the appearance of a decimal point overrides the FORMAT specification and therefore the number $5.67E+07$ (which represents 5.67×10^7) could appear anywhere inside the 12-digit field specified by the FORMAT E12.2.

Mixed Data Types

Data of mixed types, for example, integer and real, can be read from a card using proper variable names with corresponding suitable FORMAT descriptions. The following READ statement provides for the entering of two integer values and one real number into computer memory:

$$\text{READ}(2,3) \quad \text{NN,ITEM,BATR}$$

$$3 \ \text{FORMAT(I2,I2,F5.0)}$$

Note that the sequence of FORMAT descriptions parallels the sequence of variables in the READ statement; the FORMAT description must agree in type with the variable types implied by the variable names. In the above example the first two numbers are integers entered in successive pairs of spaces on the punched card, the next five spaces thereafter being reserved for the real value of BATR.

WRITE Commands

Data are retrieved from computer memory for output by means of a WRITE statement. The command

$$\text{WRITE(3,5)} \quad \text{A}$$

is an instruction to the computer to print out the current value stored in memory location labeled A on the output device (line printer) with logical unit designation 3. The printing is to be done under control of a FORMAT statement number 5, which describes the nature of the data to be printed and where it is to be located on the line.

Carriage Control

The output of data resembles data input in many respects; that is, the data to be printed must be described by format specifications and the specifications must agree in number and kind with the data items appearing in the output list. There is one respect in which the output FORMAT for a line printer differs significantly from input, and this is the requirement that each FORMAT description commence with a character for controlling the position of the printer carriage; this character is enclosed in apostrophes at the beginning of the FORMAT description; for example, FORMAT(' ',F5.1). The blank enclosed in apostrophes is the *carriage control*; it may be replaced with the following symbols, which control the position of the printer carriage as shown:

blank—single space before printing
0—double space before printing
1—skip to a new page before printing
+—no space before printing

The carriage control provides for spacing between lines or for transferring to a new page. An example of an output operation, including carriage control, follows.

WRITE(3,5)   A,I

WRITE(3,6)   BRY,Z

5 FORMAT(' ',F6.1,I8)

6 FORMAT('0',2F10.4)

The first WRITE keyed to FORMAT statement 5 provides for printing out A and I, using the first six spaces of the printed line for the value of A and the next eight for the value of I. The second FORMAT causes the printer to turn up two lines before it begins printing; the first 10 positions of the next printed line are used for the value of BRY and the second 10 for the value of Z. Thus there will be one line of space between these two sets of values.

FORMAT specifications for output must be chosen large enough to permit the printing of all symbols, including sign. Significant figures may be lost if the FORMAT specification is too small; for example, the number $+3.456892$ stored in computer memory will be truncated on some computers to $+3.45$ (with no roundings) if printed out on a FORMAT specification of F5.2. A FORMAT specification of F9.6 will be required to obtain all seven digits. On the other hand, truncation through the FORMAT specification can improve the comprehensibility of output. If the input data are precise only to three significant figures, there is nothing to be gained in printing out computer results to more than four significant figures; the fourth figure aids rounding.

Additional FORMAT Specifications

Two additional FORMAT specifications are used for inserting blanks into output. The X FORMAT inserts blanks between data items; for example,

FORMAT(' ',F10.4,30X,I10)

Table 9.14   Summary of FORMAT Specifications

I n	I designates *integer* and n designates the size of the field reserved for the integer in the input or output medium.
Fw.n	F designates a *real* number written in ordinary decimal form; w designates the size of the field reserved for the decimal in the input or output medium; n is the number of digits following the decimal point.
Ew.n	E designates a *real* number written in scientific, exponential notation; w designates the size of the field reserved for the number, including E, the exponent, and sign of the exponent; n is the number of digits following the decimal point.
A n	A designates *literal* data and n designates the number of alphanumeric symbols per field.

provides for the insertion of 30 blanks between the first real number printed and the 10-column integer field. The insertion of blanks between data items in this fashion may also be accomplished by overspecifying fields for the numbers; for example,

FORMAT(' ',F10.4,I40)

would accomplish the same job as the foregoing FORMAT using the 'X' specification. The use of the 'X' specification is, however, often more convenient than overspecifying FORMAT.

Additional lines of space may be inserted by using a slash FORMAT. One line of space is introduced for each slash; slashes may be inserted at the beginning, middle, or end of the FORMAT statement:

FORMAT(' ',///F10.3//I10)

This FORMAT statement would cause the printer to skip three lines, print a value on the specification F10.3, then skip two lines and print a value on specification I10. The final copy would end up with one line of space between the two numbers.

Summary of FORMAT Specifications

The FORMAT specifications are described briefly in Table 9.14 for convenient reference.

Arithmetic Statements

Assignment Statements

Arithmetic statements are constructed from variables, constants, and arithmetic operations. One of the most basic arithmetic operations is *assignment*, indicated by the equality sign $A = 3.0$. The equality sign has a different meaning in FORTRAN than it has in algebra. An expression involving an equality is called an *assignment statement* because it is a command to *assign* the value determined from the right-hand side of the expression to an area of computer memory bearing the *label* associated with the left-hand side of the expression. Thus in the above expression the computer is instructed to assign the value of the expression on the right (3.0) to a storage area in memory having the label A. Once a value has been assigned to a given memory location, it will remain in that location unless a new value is assigned either through another assignment statement or through a READ. Several examples will make clear the nature of the assignment statement.

Consider first the following sequence of program steps:

$$A = 3.0$$
$$B = A$$
$$A = 6.0$$

Execution of these three statements will accomplish the following: the value 3.0 is stored at memory location A. This value is copied into memory location B, an operation that leaves the content of A untouched. At this point the value 3.0 is stored at both A and B. Last, the value 6.0 is stored at A: when this is done, the previous value stored there (3.0) is first erased.

Consider next

$$A = A + B.$$

This statement shows pointedly the difference between FORTRAN and ordinary algebra. In ordinary algebra we would have to conclude that the "value of B is zero." A different conclusion is obtained in FORTRAN. This is an instruction to take the value stored at A, add to it the value stored at B, and replace the value stored at A with this new value; for example, consider the following program:

$$A = 3.0$$
$$B = 9.0$$
$$A = A + B.$$

The sum A + B is 12.0, and after execution of these three steps the value stored at B will be 9.0 and the value stored at A will be 12.0.

Arithmetic Operations

The arithmetic operations—other than assignment—are

+ addition
− subtraction
/ division
∗ multiplication
∗∗ exponentiation.

Any algebraic equation can be translated directly into FORTRAN with these operations. The quadratic $y = ax^2 + bx + c$ has the following expression in FORTRAN:

$$Y = A*X**2 + B*X + C$$

This FORTRAN expression has the following meaning: the number stored in memory location labeled X is to be squared and multiplied by A. The number stored in memory location labeled X is multiplied by the number stored in memory location labeled B and the result is added to the product previously formed. To this sum is added the number stored in memory location labeled C. The final result is transferred to a memory location labeled Y.

Shown below are examples of algebraic expressions, and their FORTRAN equivalents.

Algebraic expression	FORTRAN equivalent
$y = (a + by)x$	$Y = (A + B*Y)*X$
$g = ax^3 + t$	$G = A*X**3 + T$
$x = \dfrac{a + b}{c + d}$	$X = (A + B)/(C + D)$
$u = 3y^4 - 68t + \dfrac{dt}{r}$	$U = 3.*Y**4 - 68*T + (D*T)/R$

Note that parentheses are used in FORTRAN, as in algebra, for distributing operations. Operations of division, which occupy two lines in algebra, must be modified as shown to fit on one FORTRAN line; special attention must be paid in division to make sure that dividend and divisor are correctly expressed, using parentheses if necessary to control the sequence of operations. Note also that the operation of multiplication must be specifically indicated by an asterisk operation; it cannot be implied simply by writing two symbols together, as in algebra. The last example shows the multiplication of a real variable by a real constant (3.); the real constant appears with a decimal point. On the other hand, digits used as exponents (as in Y**4) may be written with or without decimal points: thus Y raised to the fourth power is Y**4 or Y**4.; Y raised to some nonintegral power requires that the exponent be written with a decimal point; for example, Y**2.5.

Mixed Mode Expressions: Integer Arithmetic

It is not essential that all variables and constants appearing in a FORTRAN statement be of the same type, that is, integer or real. *Mixed mode* expressions are permitted:

$$G = AA + I + B*N + J**N.$$

When only integers are involved, arithmetic remains in the integer mode; thus the sum I + J is evaluated in the integer mode. In expressions made up completely of real constants and variables arithmetic will be done in the real mode. With mixed mode expressions, however, integer arithmetic will be done with those parts of the expression that involve only integers but the integer values will be converted to real mode when they must be combined with real expressions. The product B*N therefore will be carried out in real mode, preceded by a conversion of N to a real number.

Real and integer quantities can be converted from one mode to another simply through an assignment statement; for example, to convert the real quantity stored in storage location A into an integer one simply writes

$$IA = A$$

The result of this statement will be that the real quantity A will be converted to an integer and the result stored in IA. The conversion is done by dropping all digits to the right of the decimal point in the quantity stored at A and storing the remainder minus the decimal point in IA; for example, if A contains -34.56, then IA will contain -34. This process can be reversed; thus the command

$$A = IA$$

will take the integer stored at IA and make it into a decimal number to be stored at A. Routines such as these are useful in programs for rounding off numbers to the nearest integer.

Particular attention must be paid to the operation of division involving integer quantities; the quotient I/J will not have the expected value inside the computer unless I is an exact multiple of J. This follows from the preceding assertion that arithmetic with expressions in which only integers appear will be done in integer mode and the results will be integer-form. Thus the quotient I/J will be evaluated as the largest integer, ignoring the remainder if I is not exactly divisible by J. The following examples will serve to clarify the point: the quotient I/J with J = 3 will have the value 4 for I = 12 (exactly divisible), 13, 14, and 15. If I = 11, however, I/J will then have the value 3, since 11/3 = 3 plus a fraction. The result of this kind of arithmetic is that (I/J)*J $\neq$ I unless I is an integral multiple of J.

Hierarchy of Arithmetic Operations

Arithmetic expressions are evaluated by the computer, using hierarchy rules for the arithmetic operations. Hierarchy rules are familiar to the reader from ordinary algebra; for example, in evaluating the expression $3 + 4 \times 5$, we realize that the multiplication is to be done before the addition to give the result 23. In FORTRAN the hierarchy is the following:

1. Exponentiation.
2. Unary minus.
3. Multiplication and division (left to right).
4. Addition and subtraction (left to right).

The expression D*A/B is evaluated as (D*A)/B, whereas A/B*D is evaluated as (A/B)*D. The expression A + B*D**E is evaluated as follows: the exponential D**E is calculated, the result is multiplied by B, and finally A is added to the product. The hierarchy rules are useful because they eliminate the need for excessive use of parentheses.

Arithmetic Functions

Certain standard mathematical functions are supplied to the computer in the form of subprograms as part of the compiler. These functions are automatically incorporated into any program calling for them. They include the trigonometric functions (sine, cosine, arctangent), natural logarithm, the exponential, square root and several others (Table 9.15). The functions are used by enclosing in parentheses the expression for which the function is to be found following the function name. Thus

$$Y = SIN(X)$$

is a command to obtain the sine of the value stored at location X and transfer the result to a storage location Y. The expression in parentheses may be a constant, the name of a variable, or a complicated arithmetic expression; for example, the length of a vector in three dimensions can be found as

$$VLNTH = SQRT(VX**2 + VY**2 + VZ**2)$$

which determines the square root of the sum of squares of the vector components (VX, VY, and VZ) along the x-, y-, and z-directions.

Table 9.15 FORTRAN Supplied Functions

Name	Function Performed	Argument Type
SIN	Trigonometric sine	Real
COS	Trigonometric cosine	Real
ALOG	Natural logarithm	Real
EXP	Argument power of e	Real
SQRT	Square root	Real
ATAN	Arctangent	Real
ABS	Absolute value of a real expression	Real
IABS	Absolute value of an integer expression	Integer
FLOAT	Convert integer expression to real	Integer
IFIX	Convert real expression to integer	Real
TANH	Hyperbolic tangent	Real

Any valid FORTRAN expression may appear inside the parentheses of a function, provided it agrees in mode with that required by the function—which is the real mode, unless indicated otherwise in Table 9.15. Thus FORTRAN functions may appear inside the function parentheses; for example, the log log function is

$$A = LOG(LOG(X))$$

The computer would first determine the LOG(X) value and then use this value inside the parentheses for the outer LOG.

The FORTRAN functions are supplied as series approximations by the compiler and function values are calculated from the argument as required. The functions are good out to seven significant figures. Tables of values are not used because they would require far too much memory, and look-up of values would probably require at least as much time as would be required to compute them.

A Sample Program

The following program is offered to bring together the elements of the FORTRAN language that we have considered so far and to illustrate how a program is formulated. The purpose of this program is to calculate the percentage composition and molecular weight of an organic compound that may contain carbon, hydrogen, oxygen, nitrogen, sulfur, or chlorine. The program could be extended to all of the elements of the Periodic Table, but a different approach would probably be desirable for the larger problem. The program is followed by an explanation.

```
      READ(2,1)   NC,NH,NO,NN,NS,NCL
    1 FORMAT(6I2)
      WTMOL = 12.01*NC + 1.083*NH + 16.00*NO + 14.01*NN
              + 32.01*NS + 35.5*NCL
      PCTC = 12.01*NC/WTMOL*100.
      PCTH = 1.083*NH/WTMOL*100.
      PCTO = 16.00*NO/WTMOL*100.
      PCTN = 14.01*NN/WTMOL*100.
      PCTS = 32.01*NS/WTMOL*100.
      PCTCL = 35.5*NCL/WTMOL*100.
      WRITE(3,2)   WTMOL,PCTC,PCTH,PCTO,PCTN,PCTS,PCTCL
    2 FORMAT('0',F8.2,10X,6F10.2)
      CALL   EXIT
      END
```

The READ statement calls for reading six values from a data card which gives the molecular formula of the compound. The number of carbon atoms (NC) appears in the first field of two columns, the number of hydrogen atoms appears in the next field of two columns, and so on. The number of atoms of each type (carbon, hydrogen, oxygen, nitrogen, sulfur, and chlorine) are given as integers and in the order stated. The molecular weight (WTMOL) is calculated. (We could not use the name MOLWT for molecular weight, for that would have specified an *integer* rather than a decimal number.)

The molecular weight is used in the subsequent expressions for calculating percentage carbon (PCTC), percentage hydrogen (PCTH), etc. The number stored at WTMOL is used repeatedly; this is possible because the stored value remains in memory unless that value is changed by a subsequent assignment statement or a subsequent READ. Note that use has been made of hierarchy in calculating the percentage composition; for example, for *percent carbon* the number of carbon atoms NC is first multiplied by 12.01; the product is then divided by WTMOL, and finally the result is multiplied by 100, in order of operating from left to right. Note also the mixed mode used for calculation. We could have multiplied by 100 (integer) instead of 100. (real) to obtain the percent, but this would have forced the computer to make an extra conversion of the factor 100 from integer to real mode.

The WRITE statement calls for the printing of molecular weight and percentages, all on one line. Molecular weight will be printed out to two decimal places (FORMAT F8.2) and sufficient space will be left to accommodate five digits before the decimal point. The printed value of molecular weight is separated from subsequent percentages by a space of 10 blanks. The percentages are reported to two decimal places, but FORMAT has been overspecified in relation to the expected sizes of these numbers (of the form XX.XX): overspecification of this FORMAT will leave blanks between the percentages.

The CALL EXIT statement must appear in every program as a signal to the computer that control is to pass from this program to the "monitor"; the END statement signifies the end of the FORTRAN program and must *always* be the last statement in the program.

This illustration shows the sequential nature of a computer program. Note in particular that WTMOL had to be defined and calculated before it could appear in any further statements. It is generally true that a variable that appears in a computer program must either be entered into memory by means of a READ or appear on the left side of an assignment statement before it can be used as an argument in any arithmetic or logical expression. To do otherwise is to create an undefined variable, which may not always be recognized by the error routines in the compiler.

Control Statements

We have emphasized the sequential nature of the computer program. Frequently it is necessary to depart from the serial order, and commands that effect this procedure are called *control statements*. Control statements allow us to formulate programs of great logical complexity and conciseness.

The GO TO Statement

GO TO n where n is a statement number is a command to transfer control to the statement number n. The statement numbered n may be anywhere in the program, preceding or following the GO TO n statement; for example,

$$B = 0.$$
$$A = 10.$$
$$40 \quad A = A/2.$$
$$B = B + A$$
$$GO \quad TO \quad 40$$
$$50 \quad - - - -$$

A and B are initialized to values of 10. and 0., respectively. In statement 40 the value currently in A is divided by 2 and the new value is stored in A. The value of A is added to the content of B, and the program branches back to statement 40. At statement number 40 the value of A is halved again and the result is added to the quantity stored in B, and so on. Thus through n-cycles of the program the value stored at A will become $10(\frac{1}{2})^n$ and the value stored at B will be $\sum_{i=1}^{n} 10(\frac{1}{2})^i$.

One obvious problem in this program, of course, is how to terminate the process. Ultimately the number in A will be too small for the computer to handle; an error message may appear and processing may terminate. There are, however, more elegant ways of terminating the program—ways that may waste far less computer time. This example, and the problem it creates, illustrates the point that the GO TO is unlikely to appear in a computer program without some other logic to supplement control. A lone GO TO, if it is the only control statement in a computer program, will generate an endless loop if it refers to a previous statement and will result in the skipping of segments of the program (which might just as well not be there) if it refers to a statement further along in the program. It is required by the FORTRAN language that the next statement after a GO TO statement *must* have a statement number (here, 50).

The IF Statement

The IF statement allows us to introduce decision making into a computer program. It has the form

$$IF(a) \quad n_1, n_2, n_3$$

where **a** is any FORTRAN expression and n_1, n_2, and n_3 are statement numbers. Control is transferred to statements numbered n_1, n_2, or n_3, depending on whether the value of a is less than, equal to, or greater than zero. The statement following an IF statement also *must* have a statement number.

Incorporation of an IF statement in the program segment described immediately above will insert the desired control and prevent the endless loop. We may decide, for example, that the loop is to terminate when the value stored at A is less than 10^{-10}:

```
        B = 0.
        A = 10.
40 A = A/2.
        B = B + A
        IF(A-1.E-10)   50,50,40
50 WRITE(2,3)   A,B
```

. . . .

After initialization A and B are computed; A is tested against the value 1.E-10 by forming the difference A-1.0E-10. If the value of this difference is greater than zero (because A is larger than 1.E-10), control is transferred back to statement 40, where A is again divided by two and B is incremented by the current value of A. Then this new value of A is tested, and so on. When the value of A becomes equal to 1.E-10, or less than this value (i.e., when the difference $A-10^{-10}$ is equal to or less than zero), control is transferred to the WRITE statement numbered 50. Thus the loop originally formed through the GO TO terminates whenever A is less than or equal to 1.E-10.

The expression a may be any FORTRAN expression that has a definite numerical value at the point at which the IF statement is executed. In solving a quadratic equation, we check the discriminant $b^2 - 4ac$ to see whether it is less than zero, which would give an imaginary root. Since the standard FORTRAN square root routine cannot properly take the square root of a negative quantity, the discriminant may be checked against zero through the statement

$$\text{IF} \quad (\text{B}**2 - 4.*\text{A}*\text{C}) \quad 20,30,30$$

If the quantity in parentheses—the discriminant—is less than zero, control passes to statement 20, which could be a routine to announce the presence of the imaginary root and which might also reverse the sign of the discriminant and go on to calculate the root. On the other hand, if the discriminant is greater than or equal to zero, control passes to statement 30, where the roots will be computed normally.

The Computed GO TO Statement

The logic of an IF statement is combined with the GO TO in a computed GO TO, which has the form

$$GO \quad TO \quad (n_1, n_2, \ldots, n_m), \quad i$$

where $n_1, n_2, \ldots, n_m$ are statement numbers and i is an integer variable whose value indexes one of the subscripts $1, 2, \ldots, m$. This statement transfers control to statement n_1, n_2, or $n_3, \ldots, n_m$, depending on the current value of i $= 1, 2, 3,$ or m; for example,

$$I = 3$$
$$GO \quad TO \quad (30,40,50,60,20), \quad I$$

would transfer control to statement number 50, which is the *third* statement number contained in the parentheses. If I had the value 5, control would be transferred to statement number 20, which is the *fifth* number appearing in parentheses.

The computed GO TO is useful for selecting different program blocks for execution according to the value of some input parameter. It is also useful when a given program block may have to be used repeatedly but with intervention of other program steps between each use. Rather than having the

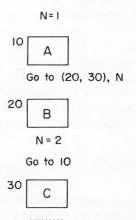

Fig. 9.32 Block diagram showing programming use of the computed GO TO.

repeated program block appear several times as part of the program, we could route to it with a computed GO TO.

This use is illustrated in the following example (Fig. 9.32); the blocks A, B, and C represent program blocks, each composed of a number of steps. Initially an indicator N is set equal to 1, and the program block labeled A is executed, commencing with statement number 10, which is the first statement in this block. The computed GO TO routes the program to statement number 20 (N = 1), which is the first statement in block B. After B has been executed, the indicator N is changed to 2 and the program is routed back to statement 10 with the GO TO 10. Block A, of which statement 10 is the leading statement, is then executed. The second time around the computed GO TO is entered with N = 2, and the program is routed to statement 30, which is the first statement of block C. This permits the use of block A twice with only one compilation of block A. This use of the computed GO TO is particularly important if block A is a very large block of FORTRAN statements.

The DO Statement

One of the most useful control statements is the DO command, which has the following form:

$$DO \quad n \quad i = m_1, m_2$$

where n is a statement number of the *last* statement in the DO loop (see example below), i is the integer name assigned to an index that controls the operation of the DO, m_1 is the *initial* value of the index, and m_2 is the *test* value. The DO statement is a command to execute repeatedly the statements that follow up to and including the statement numbered n. The index i is incremented by one each time the statements are executed; when the index i attains a value that exceeds the test value m_2, control passes to the statement following the statement numbered n; for example,

$$DO \quad 100 \quad I = 1, 10$$

. . . .

. . . .

. . . .

100 . . . .

. . . .

Each line of dots represents a FORTRAN statement. When the DO statement is executed, the index I is set to its initial value of unity; the subsequent program steps are executed up to and including statement number 100. Control returns to the DO statement, with the value of I incremented by unity. The new value of I (which is now 2) is compared against the test value (10); if I is less than or equal to the test value, the steps following DO 100 are again executed. This process continues until the index I exceeds the test value, after which the program leaves the DO loop and control is passed to the statement following statement number 100. Therefore the steps following the DO command will be executed 10 times (I = 1 through 10) and control will pass out of the DO. At this point in the program the value of the index I is no longer defined.

The commands inside the DO may be any valid FORTRAN commands, with the restriction that the last statement in a DO loop (the one bearing the statement number n) cannot be another control statement (an IF, GO TO, computed GO TO, or another DO). Moreover, any commands inside the DO loop that transfer control outside the loop will, of course, terminate operation of the loop; the index I will retain its current value under this circumstance.

The uses of the DO loop are manifold. We illustrate one for the calculation of the mean and variance for a set of N pieces of data. If we let X represent each of the data items, we must form SUM = Σ X and SUMSQ = Σ X², the sum of the X's and the sum of the squares of the X's, for calculation of the mean and variance from the formulas

XMEAN = SUM/N   and   XVAR = (SUMSQ − SUM**2/N)/(N − 1)

which are FORTRAN translations of the well-known formulas for mean and variance:

$$\bar{X} = \frac{\Sigma\, X}{N}, \qquad S^2 = \frac{\Sigma\, X^2 - (\Sigma\, X)^2/N}{N-1}. \tag{9.40}$$

The computer program to accomplish this task is organized around the following steps:

1. The size of the data set is first specified by reading a card containing the value of N.
2. The value of N is used to control a DO loop, in which a card bearing a value of X is read. A running sum and sum of squares is generated inside the loop (SUM and SUMSQ).
3. Finally, the mean and variance are calculated from the sums, and reported out of memory through a WRITE command.

The program follows.

```
1  FORMAT(I3)

2  FORMAT(F10.3)

3  FORMAT('0',F10.3,30X,F10.3)

   SUM = 0.

   SUMSQ = 0.

   READ(2,1)  N

        DO   100   I = 1,N

   READ(2,2)   X

   SUM = SUM + X

100  SUMSQ = SUMSQ + X**2

   XMEAN = SUM/N

   XVAR = (SUMSQ − SUM**2/N)/(N − 1)

   WRITE(3,3)   XMEAN,XVAR

   CALL   EXIT

   END
```

In this example we have placed all the FORMAT statements at the beginning of the program. SUM and SUMSQ accumulate sums by adding the current value of X or X^2 to the previous value stored in memory locations labeled SUM and SUMSQ; these memory locations must contain initial values of zero, which must be *assigned*, because computer memory is not normally cleared when a new program is entered into memory; that is, we cannot assume that zeros will exist initially at memory locations SUM and SUMSQ. Inside the DO loop a data card is read to obtain a current value of X. Note that the FORMAT statement for the READ does not have to be inside the loop. The loop terminates when N data cards have been read; one piece of data is entered from the first 10 positions of each card. After the loop has been executed N-times through statement number 100 the sums generated in the loop are used to compute XMEAN and XVAR, which are written out on FORMAT statement number 3. Note also that the DO command is indented on the line. Although neither required nor prohibited in FORTRAN, this is a useful means of locating the DO loops and "paragraphing" the program for easy comprehension.

A general form of the DO loop allows the increment in the index of the loop to be a value other than unity; for example,

$$DO \quad 100 \quad IND = 1,20,2$$

where the additional digit 2 following the test value for IND is an instruction that IND is to be incremented by 2 (rather than by unity) on every cycle of the loop. Thus IND takes the values 1, 3, 5, 7, ..., 19. The loop is discontinued after 19 because the next value of IND becomes 21, which exceeds the test value 20.

As mentioned earlier, the last statement in a DO loop cannot be another control statement; for example, it may be necessary to run a loop to build up a sum to a certain value, but once that sum is achieved the loop is to terminate. Such a situation calls for a test on the sum with an IF statement and a transfer out of the loop when SUM is sufficiently large. To avoid ending the loop with a control statement, such as an IF, we can employ a CONTINUE statement, which does essentially nothing except to supply a statement number with which to end the loop; for example,

$$DO \quad 3000 \quad JJJ = 1,100$$

$$SUM = SUM + DRT*JJJ$$

$$IF(SUM - 1089.)3000,3000,3050$$

3000 CONTINUE

3050 ....

Inside the loop SUM is determined as a function of the loop index JJJ multiplied by some quantity DRT (supplied previously from outside the loop). If SUM is less than or equal to 1089., control is passed to the CONTINUE statement, which simply supplies the statement number required by DO   3000, and the loop continues. If SUM exceeds 1089., transfer is made to statement 3050, the next statement after the loop. The CONTINUE statement avoids terminating the loop in an IF statement and provides a statement number to which control can be transferred by the IF so that the DO loop can continue. CONTINUE statements give rise to no executable machine-language commands and may be inserted anywhere within the program as needed. Some programmers terminate every DO loop with a CONTINUE statement so that they can alter executable statements within the loops freely without inadvertently omitting a statement number while such changes are being made.

Subscripting, Arrays, and Specification Statements

Subscripts and Arrays

Subscripts provide a powerful aid to programming and to handling large volumes of data. Parenthesized integers or integer names indicate the subscripted quantities; for example, the subscript variable $a_1, a_2, a_3, \ldots, a_i, \ldots, a_n$ is represented as A(1), A(2), A(3), ..., A(I), ..., A(N) in FORTRAN. A subscripted variable such as A(I) is called an *array*. The variable type (real or integer) is determined by the array name; the subscript itself must always be integer. Thus REAL(I) is the name of a real array, whereas INT(I) is the name of an integer array.

The DIMENSION Statement

When the computer encounters an array, it reserves a number of adjacent memory addresses for storing the values associated with that array. The information the computer requires to reserve such storage is contained in a DIMENSION statement. This specification statement must be the first statement in the program and has the form

$$\text{DIMENSION} \quad A(n), B(m), \ldots, I(k), J(l), \ldots, \text{etc.,}$$

where A, B, ..., I, J, ... are the names of any arrays appearing in the program and n, m, ..., k, l, ... are integers giving the *maximum* size of the arrays to which they refer; for example,

$$\text{DIMENSION} \quad A(50), JJY(100)$$

instructs the computer that the program will contain two arrays, one of them to contain real numbers and to occupy not more than 50 storage locations, the other to contain integers and to occupy not more than 100 storage locations. During compilation the computer will reserve an adequate number of consecutive storage locations to hold all of the elements of each of these arrays. *Any subscripted variable appearing in a program must appear in a DIMENSION statement* or the program will not compile. This omission is a common programming error. More than one DIMENSION statement may appear in a program; in such a case all of the DIMENSION statements appear together at the beginning of the program.

Algebraic Manipulation of Subscripts

The algebraic operations that can be carried out on subscripts are restricted to a few algebraic forms as follows:

$$v \text{ (variable; e.g., I, IND, JKL)}$$
$$c \text{ (integer constant; e.g., 1, 6, 999)}$$
$$v + c$$
$$v - c$$
$$c*v$$
$$c*v + c'$$
$$c*v - c'$$

For example, if we wished to refer to all elements of an array A having even values of the index, we could refer to them as A(2*IND).

Manipulation of Arrays in DO Loops

A great usefulness of arrays resides in the fact that the index of an array can be referred to in a DO loop and that arithmetic on elements of an array is easily accomplished. Suppose, for example, that we wished to sum all of the elements of an array:

$$\text{SUM} = 0.$$
$$\text{DO} \quad 300 \quad \text{I} = 1, \text{N}$$
$$300 \quad \text{SUM} = \text{SUM} + \text{A(I)}$$

. . . .

In executing this loop the computer will select array elements A(1), A(2), A(3), . . . as I is incremented in the loop and add each of these elements to the quantity SUM; SUM accumulates the sum of all of the elements A(I); for example, the following program generates the factorial of the first 10 positive integers, and stores them in an array IFACT. The iterative program requires an initial value for the first factorial IFACT(1) = 1. This value initializes the loop, which then continues from an index value of 2:

$$\text{DIMENSION} \quad \text{IFACT(10)}$$
$$\text{IFACT(1)} = 1$$
$$\text{DO} \quad 400 \quad \text{J} = 2, 10$$
$$400 \quad \text{IFACT(J)} = \text{J*IFACT(J} - 1)$$

The generation of the factorials requires multiplication of the *previous* factorial IFACT(J − 1) (note, subscript J − 1 refers to the *previous* IFACT) by the current value of J. The loop must start with 2, so that J − 1 = 1 for the first round. Had the loop started with unity $J - 1$ would have taken the value of zero and zero subscripts are not allowed in FORTRAN.

Subscripted data may be read into the computer through a DO loop; for example, in the following set of instructions the value of each element of the array named GRIT is read into storage, one value from each data card. It is assumed that the number of values to be read, NVAL, has been previously entered into the computer:

$$DO \quad 800 \quad I = 1,NVAL$$
$$800 \quad READ(2,5) \quad GRIT(I)$$
$$5 \quad FORMAT(F10.4)$$

Every time the READ statement is executed in the DO loop a new card will be read.

Implied DO Loops

The operation of reading an array, as in the preceding example, could also be carried out with the following statements:

$$READ(2,5) \quad (GRIT(I),I = 1,NVAL)$$
$$5 \quad FORMAT(F10.4)$$

In a READ of this form the DO loop is said to be *implied*. The READ instruction covers variation of the index I from unity to NVAL.

The READ with the implied DO, however, differs from the ordinary READ in one important respect: the number of items read from one data card is determined by the FORMAT specification as well as by the READ list in the implied DO. In the preceding example one data item per card on a FORMAT of F10.4 is read. In the following READ four data items are read from the first four 10-column fields of a data card; any remaining elements of the list are read from succeeding cards, four from each card:

$$READ(2,6) \quad (GRIT(I),I = 1,NVAL)$$
$$6 \quad FORMAT(4F10.4)$$

The difference between this example and the preceding is in the FORMAT specification; the second example carries a FORMAT of 4F10.4, which causes the computer to read *four* fields on a data card, rather than one, as in the previous case. Thus the FORMAT and the list to be read work together to determine how the data cards are read.

Implied DO loops can also be built into WRITE statements. Thus

$$WRITE(3,10) \quad (BRT(I), I = 1,M)$$
$$10 \quad FORMAT('0',10F10.4)$$

will cause the array BRT(I) to be printed out as ten 10-digit numbers in a line across the page (FORMAT 10F10.4), with a space between each line. Depending on the value of M in the WRITE statement, one or more lines will be printed out; for example, if M = 4, one line will be printed out with four items. The remaining six items specified in the FORMAT will be unprinted, since they are not called for. If M = 36, three lines containing 10 data items will be printed, followed by a fourth line containing six data items.

Multidimensional Arrays, Nested DO Loops

So far we have considered arrays carrying a single index. Such arrays are called one-dimensional. Arrays of higher dimension are possible in FORTRAN; A(I,J) is an example of a two-dimensional or doubly subscripted array. A typical example is shown in (a) and a general form of the same array is given in (b), with a_{ij} a general element of the array. The subscript i indexes the *rows* of the array and the subscript j indexes the *columns*. In FORTRAN the subscripts I and J in A(I,J) may have the same relationship to rows and columns.

1.10	1.10	3.06	4.11
1.00	1.00	1.00	10.06
10.10	1.13	36.11	9.30
8.60	7.60	14.50	6.70

a_{11}	a_{12}	a_{13}	a_{14}
a_{21}	a_{22}	a_{23}	a_{24}
a_{31}	a_{32}	a_{33}	a_{34}
a_{41}	a_{42}	a_{43}	a_{44}

(a)   (b)

Arrays, as exemplified above, are also called *matrices*, and a special branch of algebra, with its own rules of manipulation, has been developed to handle them. We can illustrate a very simple matrix operation and how it may be programmed on a computer; we shall consider the operation of matrix addition. If a_{ij} and b_{ij} are corresponding elements of two matrices A and B, both of the same dimension, the sum of the two matrices A and B, written

$$C = A + B \tag{9.41}$$

is a new matrix C, each of whose elements (indicated by a lower-case letter with subscripts) is the sum of the corresponding elements of A and B; that is,

$$c_{ij} = a_{ij} + b_{ij} \tag{9.42}$$

where c_{ij} is the element in the ith row and jth column of C.

To add matrices on the computer we must refer to both sets of indices, I and J, since matrix addition is done for all possible combinations of values of I and J. For each value of I, therefore, the program must sweep through the whole range of values of J. A programming problem like this is handled as a set of *nested* DO's as shown in the following program segment:

DIMENSION   A(50,50), B(50,50), C(50,50)

. . . .

DO   100   I = 1,N
DO   100   J = 1,N
100   C(I,J) = A(I,J) + B(I,J)

. . . .

The DIMENSION statement is shown extended to two-dimensional arrays; the program provides for storage of arrays in areas labeled A, B, and C, each with up to 50 × 50 = 2500 elements. Too generous dimensioning may allocate the whole of memory to array storage, leaving no room for the program; for example, in the present example the program requires reservation of storage for 7500 numbers; this would be more than enough to swamp the memory of an IBM 1130 computer with a core memory of 8192 words.

The DO loops in this program operate in the following fashion: the index I of the outer loop is first set at unity; the inner loop, indexed by J, then sweeps through the values of J from unity to N. The addition operation (statement 100) is therefore carried out for elements C(I,J): C(1,1), C(1,2), C(1,3), . . . , C(1,N). After the inner loop has been completed control is transferred to the outer loop, indexed by I, the index I is moved to its next value 2, and the inner loop, indexed by J, again runs through the whole range of J to generate elements C(2,1), C(2,2), C(2,3), . . . , C(2,N). Thus the inner loop carries through its complete cycle before the outer loop index is advanced, and once the outer loop index has advanced the inner loop will start from the beginning for another complete cycle, and so on. This process continues through the value of the index I = N and terminates after this cycle. Control then passes to the statement following statement number 100.

In similar fashion we can operate with multidimensional arrays, A(I,J,K . . .). The number of allowed subscripts depends on the particular computer. On the IBM 1130 three subscripts is the maximum number, but the number may be much larger on a larger computer. The particular way in which the DO loops are nested is entirely under the control of the programmer; in the preceding example the I- and J-loops could have been interchanged so that the I-controlled loop would have been the inner loop. The only consequence in this case would have been generation of the C(I,J) in a different sequence. The inner loop, however, must go through its cycle completely inside the outer loop.

Nested DO loops occur frequently in applications other than in the handling of multiply subscripted quantities. Let us reconsider the problem of computing the mean and variance for a set of data (Section 5) and generalize the program to cover the case in which we have a large number of data sets, NSETS, for which the statistics must be computed. Rather than recompiling the program NSETS times, we may run the program under control of a DO loop, with NSETS as the test value on the DO loop:

```
 1 FORMAT(I3)
 2 FORMAT(F10.3)
 3 FORMAT('0',F10.3,30X,F10.3)
   READ(2,1)  NSETS
           DO  1000  ISETS = 1,NSETS
   SUM = 0.
   SUMSQ = 0.
   READ(2,1)  N
           DO  100  I = 1,N
   READ(2,2)  X
   SUM = SUM + X
100 SUMSQ = SUMSQ + X**2
   XMEAN = SUM/N
   XVAR = (SUMSQ – SUM**2/N)/(N – 1)
1000 WRITE(3,3)  XMEAN,XVAR
   CALL  EXIT
   END
```

The outer loop, controlled by DO 1000, operates the program NSETS times; the value of NSETS is read in at the head of the program. Note that care must be taken to initialize all quantities (SUM and SUMSQ) on each problem cycle. The DO 100, in which the sums and sums of squares are generated, is nested inside the main DO that controls the number of problems. For each problem, therefore, the sum and sum-of-squares are generated and the mean and variance are calculated. The loop for one problem terminates when results XMEAN and XVAR are printed out. Control is transferred back to DO 1000, initializations are re-established, and a new value of N and a new data set (READ(2,2) X) are read in for the next problem.

If statistics were to be calculated for five different data sets, the data cards for all five sets would be stacked up, each set separated by a card bearing the number of items (N) in the set, and a card bearing the number 005 (value of NSETS) would head the whole stack. Under control of the program the computer would first read the first card to determine how many problems would be run; it would then read the next card to determine the size of the first data set; thereafter it would read the next N cards as data cards for the calculation. After results of the first calculation were printed out, the computer would read the next card to find out how many data cards were contained in the next data set and then proceed to read that number of data cards. It would continue in this fashion until NSETS of data had been read and processed.

Alphabetic Data

It is highly desirable to be able to incorporate alphabetic data into a program. Such data are required for identification of output by means of table headings, titles on pages, and designation of units. It is also possible, in FORTRAN, to manipulate alphabetic data for alphabetizing and printing out lists, although business languages and PL/I are better adapted for character manipulation.

Literal Data in FORMAT Statements

Literal data may be entered into computer memory with FORMAT statements. Alphabetic information enclosed in apostrophes in a FORMAT statement can be written out by using a WRITE indexed to that FORMAT; for example,

> WRITE(3,4)
>
> 4 FORMAT(' ','MERRY CHRISTMAS')

will cause the message MERRY CHRISTMAS to appear at the beginning of the printed line when the statement WRITE(3,4) is executed by the computer.

Mixed literal and numerical FORMATS can be used to provide for the output of numerical data along with literal labels. The following output statements allow for the printing of a problem number called IPRB in the program, which indexes a DO loop:

> . . . .
>
> . . . .
>
> DO   100   IPRB = 1,NPRB
>
> WRITE(3,5)   IPRB
>
> . . . .
>
> 100 . . . .
>
> 5 FORMAT('0',30X,'PROBLEM NO.',I3)

When the computer encounters the WRITE statement, it will print out the value of the index IPRB on each cycle of the DO loop, using FORMAT statement number 5. The FORMAT requires that a title, 'PROBLEM NO.', also be printed out, followed by a number (IPRB) on a FORMAT 13. The FORMAT 30X which precedes the literal data causes the title to be indented 30 spaces (3 inches) on the line. Thus during the first execution of the loop a title will appear, indented 30 spaces,

PROBLEM   NO.   1

and during second execution of the loop a second title will appear, indented 30 spaces,

PROBLEM   NO.   2

The problem number will appear during each execution of the loop up to and including NPRB.

The values of variables that appear in a WRITE statement must be in one-to-one correspondence with the sequence of proper numerical FORMATS, regardless of the interspersal of alphabetic information: for example, we may wish to print out the following title

PROBLEM   NO.   1   AREA = 383.678   SQ.   METERS

where the problem number appears in the program as a variable NPRB and area appears in the problem as a variable AREA. We note that the computer is being asked to print out the value of an integer variable and a real variable:

WRITE(3,11)   NPRB,AREA

11 FORMAT('0','PROBLEM   NO.',I3,5X,'AREA = ',F8.3,' SQ.

METERS')

The FORMATS for NPRB and AREA appear in the FORMAT statement in the sequence I3 and F8.3, that is, in the sequence required by the WRITE statement. It will be useful to examine this FORMAT in detail to make clear all that is required by the FORMAT on output:

1. The carriage control ('0') instructs the computer to turn up two lines before it starts to print so that one additional line of space will appear between the last output and the present.

2. The phrase PROBLEM NO. is printed out with no indentation and is followed by an integer value on FORMAT I3.

3. Five blank spaces are provided between the value of PROBLEM NO. and the word AREA which follows it.

4. The value of AREA is a real number, printed out on FORMAT F8.3, and immediately following the label AREA = . A label SQ. METERS follows the value of AREA. Note that the blanks separating the value of

AREA and the label SQ. METERS is programmed as part of the label and appears as the blank spaces immediately following the apostrophe in ' SQ. METERS'.

There are three different ways of inserting blanks into a printed line, and all three are exemplified in the preceding illustration:

1. Blanks may be inserted by using the X-FORMAT.

2. Blanks may be inserted by incorporating them between apostrophes in a FORMAT statement controlling output.

3. Blanks may be inserted by overspecifying FORMAT for writing out the values of variables. Thus, if the value of NPRB is written out on a FORMAT I3, and NPRB is never larger than a two-digit number, the left-most digit(s) will appear as blanks because the integer is right-justified on the output field. The same is true for real numbers. The number 8.36 printed out on FORMAT F5.2 would appear as b8.36, where "b" stands for blank. Note, however, that we must be cautious about sign on output. The value 8.36 appears with a left-most blank because the number is positive; this space would disappear and be occupied by a sign ($-$) if this number were negative; in such a case we would specify a FORMAT F6.2 to leave a left-most blank and allow room for sign.

Variable Literal Data, A-FORMAT

Literal data specified on FORMAT will appear in invariant form from one execution of the program to another, since the FORMAT statements are invariant. It is frequently necessary to change literal data from one program execution to another; for example, we might do calculations for different molecules and wish to print out the names of the molecules to identify the calculations. We therefore wish to be able to read a name from an input card and print this name during output. FORTRAN provides for reading *literal* data and storing such data in an area of memory bearing the name of a variable, just as *numerical* data are stored in labeled areas of memory. The number of alphabetic symbols that can be stored at one storage location is limited: the maximum number is four alphabetic symbols per storage location in a small computer such as the IBM 1130. To store a whole line of alphabetic data requires the use of an *array* of memory locations; if the maximum number of alphabetic symbols that can be stored in one memory location is 4, an array of 20 subscripts will be required to store the alphabetic symbols that can be fitted onto an 80-column punched card.

Literal data can be read into the computer with an A-FORMAT:

An where A specifies that the variable has alphabetic "values" and n specifies the number of alphabetic symbols to be stored per memory location (any number from unity up to the maximum possible for the given computer).

For example, to read a title from an 80-column punched card with an A-FORMAT requires the following statements:

DIMENSION   TITLE(20)

READ(2,3)   (TITLE(I),I = 1,20)

3 FORMAT(20A4)

On execution of the READ command, the computer will transfer the symbols it finds on an input punched card into an array called TITLE; the first four symbols on the card will be transferred into TITLE(1), the next four symbols will be transferred into TITLE(2), and so on. The number of symbols transferred per address is specified by A4 in the FORMAT statement.

FORTRAN permits the simplification of READ and WRITE statements involving arrays by omission of the index specification; thus the above READ may appear as

READ(2,3)   TITLE

with the same DIMENSION and FORMAT statements as in the preceding example. The shortened form of the READ may be used with arrays that have numerical values as well as those that are used to store literal data, but the shortened READ is not recommended for the novice programmer except for alphabetic input and output.*

A program almost equivalent to the above is the following:

DIMENSION   TITLE(40)

READ(2,3)   TITLE

3 FORMAT(40A2)

This program stores *two* alphabetic symbols per storage location (instead of *four* as in the preceding example); therefore to store the content of an 80-column card requires the use of 40 memory locations. Obviously this program wastes computer storage because fewer symbols are stored per storage address. There are, however, cases in which such smaller A-FORMATS are required, as discussed later. It is not necessary, of course, to use a whole punched card for reading a title. If the title can be restricted to the first 40 spaces of a punched card, it may be read into memory with the

---

* Use of the simplified READ or WRITE implies certain conventions made by the computer manufacturer in storing arrays, and the user must be aware of these conventions in manipulating data arrays. Particular problems are encountered with two-dimensional arrays, which, like one-dimensional arrays, can be entered into computer memory with a simplified READ. In such cases it is much easier to control the indices by having them explicit in the READ (or WRITE) than it is to remember the storage conventions used by the computer manufacturer. When data are not to be manipulated, as is the case with literal data that are simply read in and written out, there are no problems in using the simplified READ and WRITE statements.

following program:

DIMENSION   A(10)

READ(2,7)   A

7 FORMAT(10A4)

Here the array which is to hold the alphabetic data is called A. A smaller array is required than in the preceding examples because only 40 spaces on the punched card are to be used for recording the alphabetic data. If a FORMAT(40X,10A4) had been used in place of statement 7, the *last* 40 spaces on the punched card would be used for recording the alphabetic data, the X-format serving to divert the READ from the first 40 spaces.

Alphabetic data stored in memory by means of a READ can also be reported out by means of a WRITE statement, using the same FORMAT as that employed with the READ, with the addition of carriage control: thus the content of array A considered above can be printed out:

WRITE(3,8)   A

8 FORMAT(' ',30X,10A4)

The printed line is indented 30 spaces and the content of A is written out, requiring 40 spaces on the line corresponding to the total of 10A4. It is not possible to insert blanks into the literal output, which is entirely determined by the data contained in the memory locations assigned to A.

Data read into memory on an A-FORMAT are handled quite differently from numerical data and may not be manipulated in the same way. This is particularly evident when we consider the reading in of *numerical* data on F-FORMAT versus A-FORMAT. The *number* 3.0 read into computer memory on an F-FORMAT to be stored at a memory location named X assigns this *value* to that memory position; the *symbols* 3.0 read into computer memory on an A-FORMAT to be stored at a memory location X constitutes a numeral three followed by a decimal point followed by a numeral zero. In the first case we store 3.0 at X location; in the second case we store '3.0' at location X. For this reason the *symbols* 3.0 cannot be meaningfully manipulated with arithmetic operations; we cannot, for example, add the number 2.0 to a set of *symbols*; the addition can be done only with another *value*. This, of course, becomes even clearer when we consider the manipulation of data that are more obviously alphabetical than the set of symbols 3.0: there is no meaningful way of adding 2.0 to a symbol A.

Manipulation of Alphabetic Data

Alphabetic data read into memory on A-FORMAT are stored as bits. These bits can be interpreted as numbers. Only two meaningful logical operations can be carried out on such data: the data may be transferred or copied from one memory location to another (by an assignment statement such as A = B), and two codes, stored at different memory locations, may be *compared* to determine whether they are the same. Suppose, for example, that storage locations A and B each contained alphabetic data entered through A-FORMAT; the following IF statement would allow one to determine whether the same alphabetic data were stored at A and B:

$$IF(A - B) \quad 20,30,20$$

If the contents of A and B are the same (i.e., the coded representations of alphabetical data stored at A and B are the same), control will pass to statement number 30; on the other hand, if the coded values stored at A and B are *different*, control will pass to statement number 20.

Example: Alphabetizing a List

We consider now a simple program for alphabetizing an arbitrary list containing NLIST single letters. The reader might find it challenging to modify this program so that a frequency count of each letter can be made as alphabetization proceeds and reported out along with the alphabetized list. A comment about the program, to be ignored by the computer when compiling the program, is punched with a "C" in column 1.

```
C   PROGRAM  TO  ALPHABETIZE  A  LIST
    DIMENSION   ALFBT(26),ALIST(1000),BLIST(1000)
  1 FORMAT(26A1)
  2 FORMAT(I4)
  3 FORMAT(80A1)
  4 FORMAT(' ',120A1)
    READ(2,1)(ALFBT(I),I = 1,26)
    READ(2,2)  NLIST
    READ(2,3)(ALIST(I),I = 1,NLIST)
    L = 1
        DO  30  K = 1,26
        DO  30  M = 1,NLIST
    IF(ALFBT(K) − ALIST(M))30,20,30
 20 BLIST(L) = ALIST(M)
    L = L + 1
 30 CONTINUE
    WRITE(3,4)(BLIST(I),I = 1,NLIST)
    CALL  EXIT
    END
```

Before discussing this program in detail, the general procedure for alphabetization will be described. A reference alphabet (the letters A, B, ... , Z) is first read from a card and stored in memory as the 26-element array ALFBT(I). This is a way in which the reference alphabet can be entered and referred to in the program. Although this reference alphabet is, in a sense, a constant required for each execution of the program, there is no other way of referring to it in the program than to read it in as an array, for if it were read in as a FORMAT containing literal data there would be no way in FORTRAN of assigning such data to the array ALFBT for subsequent use.

The list to be alphabetized is stored in an array called ALIST; the ultimate alphabetized copy of this list will eventually appear in another array called BLIST. The logic behind the program is to take each letter in sequence from the reference alphabet, starting with the letter A, and compare that letter with each letter of the input list contained in ALIST. If a match occurs between the reference letter and the list letter, the list letter is copied into the alphabetized array BLIST; if there is no match, the program simply moves to the next letter in the input list and makes the comparison again. Thus, starting with the letter A in the reference alphabet, the letter A is transferred into BLIST each time the A from the reference alphabet matches a letter (A) in the unalphabetized input list. When all elements of the input list have been scanned against the A in the reference alphabet, the process is repeated with the next letter (B) in the reference alphabet, and so on.

The arrays ALIST and BLIST are each dimensioned to hold as many as 1000 characters. The reference alphabet ALFBT(I) is read from a card on FORMAT 26A1, and the number of letters NLIST to be alphabetized is then read under FORMAT I4, followed by the unalphabetized input list. A running index L is used subsequently for addressing the alphabetized list BLIST and must be initialized to unity. The alphabetization occurs in the two nested DO loops. The outer DO loop (index K) selects an element from the reference alphabet in array ALFBT(I); the next, the internal loop indexed by M, compares the selected reference element ALFBT(K) against each element in the unalphabetized input list ALIST(M). If the two elements do not match, control is transferred to the CONTINUE statement and the index on the inner loop M is advanced by unity; that is, the next element in ALIST(I) is selected for comparison. On the other hand, if the two elements ALFBT(K) and ALIST(M) *do* match, control is transferred to statement 20, where the matching element is copied from ALIST into BLIST. The index L which refers to the elements of BLIST starts at unity (because of initialization) and is incremented (L = L + 1) each time a new element is added to BLIST; this simple trick often used by programmers saves elaborate indexing of the array BLIST. The DO 30 loops terminate when all letters A $\cdots$ Z from the reference alphabet have been used for comparisons against the input list ALIST.

This program for alphabetization is notably deficient in one respect: letters that have been matched in ALIST remain on the list and must undergo further comparisons with the rest of the letters in the reference alphabet. A more efficient routine would contract the number of elements of ALIST to be scanned each time a successful copy to BLIST occurs; this modification markedly reduces the number of processing operations. Another modification which permits elimination of the auxiliary array BLIST by doing all alphabetization within ALIST, and which also avoids redundant scans, is shown below. This program scans ALIST for the first occurrence of the letter A and interchanges this A with the first element in ALIST; it continues the scan for the second occurrence of the letter A in ALIST and makes an interchange with the second element of ALIST, and so on. Such a modification both obviates the need to reserve space in memory for BLIST and the need to retest elements once they have been alphabetized.

```
C MORE EFFICIENT PROGRAM TO ALPHABETIZE A LIST
      DIMENSION   ALFBT(26),ALIST(1000)
    1 FORMAT(26A1)
    2 FORMAT(I4)
    3 FORMAT(80A1)
    4 FORMAT(' ',120A1)
      READ(2,1)ALFBT
      READ(2,2)
      READ(2,3)(ALIST(I),I = 1,NLIST)
      NEWL = 1
         DO   30   K = 1,26
      L = NEWL
         DO   30   M = L,NLIST
      IF(ALFBT(K) − ALIST(M))30,20,30
   20 TEMP = ALIST(NEWL)
      ALIST(NEWL) = ALIST(M)
      ALIST(M) = TEMP
      NEWL = NEWL + 1
   30 CONTINUE
      WRITE(3,4)(ALIST(I),I = 1,NLIST)
      CALL   EXIT
      END
```

We have discussed the use of real variable names of arrays to store alphabetic data. Integer *names* of arrays may also be used, but because integer storage uses less space per number than real variable storage the number of allowed alphabetic symbols that can be stored at one memory location is reduced; thus for a small computer such as the IBM 1130 no more than two literal symbols can be stored at one integer memory location and therefore A2 is the maximum FORMAT usable with an integer name.

H-Format

We have described the use of apostrophes within a FORMAT statement for entering literal data into memory. The reader should be aware of another convention for entering literal data into memory and for writing out such data; this is the use of H-FORMAT, as exemplified in the following statement:

4 FORMAT(' ',12H   PROBLEM NO.)

The letter H indicates that the information following is to be considered as literal data; the number 12 preceding H specifies the number of symbols (including the blank immediately preceding the word PROBLEM) which constitute the literal data. The use of H-FORMAT is less convenient than the use of apostrophes because H-FORMAT requires a symbol count. H-FORMAT, however, may appear in older computer programs and so was considered worthy of mention.

9   USING FORTRAN

Control Cards: Comments Cards

Programs are usually run on a digital computer under the control of a master program called a *monitor*. *Control cards*, which control the action of the monitor, give the monitor such basic information as the kind of programming language that will appear in the source deck and whether the program is to be compiled or whether it is to be both compiled and executed. It is also possible to change the *precision* (word length) of the computer by means of a control card so that a larger number of significant digits can be handled. A control card also makes it possible to print out a listing of the source program for debugging or record purposes; the listing can be suppressed by omitting the listing control card. Program listing occurs during compilation; on some computers it is extremely slow and is therefore often omitted in standard programs that have been thoroughly debugged and tested. Suitable control cards for a given installation are generally supplied by computer center personnel.

It is possible to include expository comments in the listing by punching a letter 'C' into column 1 of the card carrying the comments. Such usage is illustrated on the first line of the preceding program. Comments are useful for identification of variables, to outline the various phases of a complex program, and to report information concerning details of input and output and instructions for using the program. Comments are particularly useful when a program is to be implemented on a computer other than the one for which it was originally written.

Subroutines

A subroutine is a program subunit (Section 7) that can be called into a main program (sometimes called "the mainline"); for example, we may provide for reading two matrices A and B into memory and then call a subroutine (already compiled and stored in memory) to perform a matrix addition between matrices A and B. A program of this type would be the following:

```
        DIMENSION   A(50,50),B(50,50),C(50,50)
      1 FORMAT(8F10.0)
      2 FORMAT(2I2)
C  NROW  AND  NCOL  ARE  THE  NUMBER  OF  ROWS
C  AND  COLUMNS  IN  A  AND  B
        READ(2,2)   NROW,NCOL
        READ(2,1)((A(I,J),B(I,J),I = 1,NROW),J = 1,NCOL)
        CALL   MADD(A,B,C,NROW,NCOL)
        WRITE(3,3)((C(I,J),I = 1,NROW),J = 1,NCOL)
        CALL   EXIT
        END
```

After reading in the input data—the sizes of the arrays A and B and the elements of those arrays—a subroutine MADD(A,B,C,NROW,NCOL) is called. The argument list (A,B,C) in the name MADD provides for transferring input data in matrices A and B into the subroutine and calculated results into matrix C. NROW and NCOL are the number of rows and columns in A, B, and C.

The subroutine is used in a program by means of a CALL statement. Generally the subroutines available in a given computer installation are contained in a catalog that describes the purpose of the subroutine, defines the input and output variables and other parameters that appear in the argument list, and gives information about dimensioning requirements. In particular, IBM has available as part of the "software" for IBM computers a Scientific Subroutine Package that contains a large number of routines for carrying out a number of procedures. Matrix operations provided for in this package include matrix addition, subtraction, and multiplication and the more complicated processes of diagonalization, inversion, and rank determination. There are many statistical routines such as analysis of variance, multiple regression, and correlation and analysis of factorial experiments. The package also includes accurate routines for numerical integration and the fitting of various kinds of polynomials to data. The reader is referred to IBM literature for a complete summary of these routines.

Frequently particular computing sequences must be done repetitively in a number of more complex, one-shot calculations; for instance, suppose data from a particular laboratory instrument must be read from cards, normalized, and stored in an array as the first step of an analysis. Subsequent steps might include comparison to a standard and statistical studies. A subroutine could be written to read the data cards with a correct FORMAT, normalize the data, and store it in an array. Subsequently this sequence of operations would be performed by calling that subroutine.

The construction of specialized computing elements with individualized subroutines can be extended so that many difficult sections of mainline programs can be done without further programming time and errors. This really amounts to constructing an individualized programming language.

Other FORTRAN Features

This account of FORTRAN does not exhaust its possibilities. In keeping with our purpose of providing the elements of the language, we have considered only its basic features. Other variables may be used with the complete version of FORTRAN IV; for example, complex variables and "logical" variables (variables that can have the values of "true" or "false"). There are elegant techniques for data initialization as well as more sophisticated IF statements that may simplify some programming considerably. We have also omitted discussion of direct-access devices, such as tapes and disks, which can serve to augment the limited capacity of most computer memories and provide almost unlimited data storage.

10   SAMPLE PROGRAMS

Polymer Analysis

The sample program presented in Fig. 9.33a was written for the purpose of calculating the percentage composition of organic polymers from the composition of the feed, which is specified by giving the number n_1 moles of monomer M_1, the number n_2 moles of monomer M_2 ... etc., that appear in it. Knowing the molecular formulas of the monomers, we can calculate the percentage composition of the polymer, assuming 100% conversion.

This computation can be tedious, particularly when monomers appear in fractional amounts. The program that follows [11] is based on the calculation of percentage composition of simple compounds considered earlier; the program was compiled and executed on an IBM 1130 digital computer.

The program listing contains innovations not previously explained. Besides FORTRAN statements, other statements starting with // or * are monitor controls (Section 9). The mode of a variable (real or integer) normally depends on the initial letter of the variable's name, those with I through N

Fig. 9.33a   Program listing, composition of polymers.

```
// FOR
*IOCS(2501 READER,1132 PRINTER)
*LIST SOURCE PROGRAM
*ONE WORD INTEGERS
C
C CALCULATION OF PERCENT COMPOSITION OF POLYMERS
C
      INTEGER C,H,CL,O,S,F
      REAL MOLE,NT,NAT,MOLWT,MW
      DIMENSION TITLE(5)
    1 FORMAT(I2,5A2)
    2 FORMAT('1',38X,'PROBLEM NO.',I2)
    3 FORMAT('0',40X,5A2/)
    4 FORMAT(F10.2,8I2)
    5 FORMAT(' ','NO. OF MOLES OF MONOMER ',I2,' =',F5.2,5X,'MOLECULAR F
     1ORMULA  C-',I2,' H-',I2,' N-',I2,' O-',I2,' S-',I2,' F-',I2,' CL-'
     2,I2,' NA-',I2)
    6 FORMAT(/'0',30X,'NO. OF ATOMS',19X,'PERCENT COMPOSITION'//10X,
     1' C',18X,F10.2,26X,F10.2/10X,' H',18X,F10.2,26X,F10.2/10X, ' N',18
     2X,F10.2, 26X,F10.2/10X,' O',18X,F10.2,26X,F10.2/10X,' S',18X,F10.2
     3,26X,F10.2/10X,' F',18X,F10.2,26X,F10.2/10X,' CL',17X,F10.2,26X,F1
     40.2/10X,' NA',17X,F10.2,26X,F10.2//' MOLECULAR WEIGHT=',F10.3)
C READ TOTAL NUMBER OF PROBLEMS
      READ(8,1)NPROB
         DO 51 J=1,NPROB
      WRITE(3,2)J
C ENTER IDENTIFYING LITERAL DATA
      READ(8,1)NCOMP,TITLE
      WRITE(3,3) TITLE
      MOLE=0.0
      CT=0.0
      HT=0.0
      CLT=0.0
      FT=0.0
      NT=0.0
      OT=0.0
      ST=0.0
      NAT=0.0
      MOLWT=0.0
         DO 50 I=1,NCOMP
      C=0
      H=0
      N=0
      O=0
      S=0
      F=0
      CL=0
      NA=0
C READ NO. OF MOLES OF A MONOMER AND MOLECULAR FORMULA. LIST ELEMENTS OF
C MOLECULAR FORMULA IN THE ORDER C,H,N,O,S,F,CL,NA
      READ(8,4) MOLE,C,H,N,O,S,F,CL,NA
C WRITE INPUT DATA
```

```
     WRITE(3,5) I,MOLE,C,H,N,O,S,F,CL,NA
     MOLWT=MOLWT+MOLE*(12.01*C+1.008*H+35.45*CL+19.00*F+14.01*N
    1+16.00*O+32.06*S+22.99*NA)
     CT=CT+MOLE*C
     HT=HT+MOLE*H
     CLT=CLT+MOLE*CL
     FT=FT+MOLE*F
     NT=NT+MOLE*N
     OT=OT+MOLE*O
     ST=ST+MOLE*S
  50 NAT=NAT+MOLE*NA
     MW=MOLWT*1.0E-2
     PCC=CT*12.01/MW
     PCH=HT*1.008/MW
     PCCL=CLT*35.45/MW
     PCF=FT*19.00/MW
     PCN=NT*14.01/MW
     PCO=OT*16.00/MW
     PCS=ST*32.06/MW
     PCNA=NAT*22.99/MW
  51 WRITE(3,6)CT,PCC,HT,PCH,NT,PCN,OT,PCO,ST,PCS,FT,PCF,CLT,PCCL,
    1NAT,PCNA,MOLWT
     CALL EXIT
     END

FEATURES SUPPORTED
 ONE WORD INTEGERS
 IOCS

CORE REQUIREMENTS FOR
 COMMON        0  VARIABLES     74  PROGRAM     664

 END OF COMPILATION

 // XEQ
```

being integer, the others real. However, any variable may be made to take either mode by *explicitly* stating it to be REAL or INTEGER; these replace any mention of the variable in the DIMENSION statement. Note that variable names have been chosen to be suggestive of the kind of quantity appearing in the problem; for example, 'C' for the number of carbon atoms, 'PCC' for percentage carbon, and 'MOLWT' for molecular weight.

The program permits calculation of compositions for several polymers; NPROB is the number of polymers, and this is the first datum read into the computer.* A DO loop (DO 51) is set up to handle each polymer. We consider the computation for one polymer, which starts immediately after the DO 51. A WRITE statement on FORMAT 2 reports the problem number. This is followed by READ(8,1) to read a data card containing the number of monomers appearing in the polymer (NCOMP) and an identifying title (in this case, a notebook reference number). The identifying title is printed.

* The reader may note that the card reader on the particular computer for which this program was written bears the unit designation number 8, so all read statements are of the form READ(8, . . .).

Fig. 9.33b Program listing composition of polymers.

PROBLEM NO. 1

P436-03

NO. OF MOLES OF MONOMER 1 = 1.00   MOLECULAR FORMULA C- 8 H- 8 N- 0 O- 0 S- 0 F- 0 CL- 0 NA- 0
NO. OF MOLES OF MONOMER 2 = 2.00   MOLECULAR FORMULA C- 4 H- 2 N- 0 O- 3 S- 0 F- 0 CL- 0 NA- 0

NO. OF ATOMS   PERCENT COMPOSITION

C   16.00   63.99
H   12.00   4.02
N   0.00   0.00
O   6.00   31.97
S   0.00   0.00
F   0.00   0.00
CL   0.00   0.00
NA   0.00   0.00

MOLECULAR WEIGHT=   300.255

PROBLEM NO. 2

P436-04

NO. OF MOLES OF MONOMER 1 = 1.00   MOLECULAR FORMULA C- 8 H- 8 N- 0 O- 0 S- 0 F- 0 CL- 0 NA- 0
NO. OF MOLES OF MONOMER 2 = 2.00   MOLECULAR FORMULA C- 4 H- 2 N- 0 O- 3 S- 0 F- 0 CL- 0 NA- 0
NO. OF MOLES OF MONOMER 3 = 1.00   MOLECULAR FORMULA C- 6 H-12 N- 0 O- 1 S- 0 F- 0 CL- 0 NA- 0

NO. OF ATOMS   PERCENT COMPOSITION

C   22.00   65.98
H   24.00   6.04
N   0.00   0.00
O   7.00   27.97
S   0.00   0.00
F   0.00   0.00
CL   0.00   0.00
NA   0.00   0.00

MOLECULAR WEIGHT=   400.411

PROBLEM NO. 3

P436-05

NO. OF MOLES OF MONOMER 1 = 1.00   MOLECULAR FORMULA   C- 3 H- 4 N- 0 O- 2 S- 0 F- 0 CL- 0 NA- 0
NO. OF MOLES OF MONOMER 2 = 3.00   MOLECULAR FORMULA   C- 5 H- 8 N- 0 O- 2 S- 0 F- 0 CL- 0 NA- 0
NO. OF MOLES OF MONOMER 3 = 0.50   MOLECULAR FORMULA   C- 3 H- 5 N- 1 O- 1 S- 0 F- 0 CL- 0 NA- 0

NO. OF ATOMS   PERCENT COMPOSITION

C   19.50   57.40
H   30.50   7.53
N   0.50   1.71
O   8.50   33.33
S   0.00   0.00
F   0.00   0.00
CL   0.00   0.00
NA   0.00   0.00

MOLECULAR WEIGHT=   407.943

305

A series of variables is initialized to zero; then the program enters a loop (DO 50) in which the percentage composition of the polymer is calculated. This loop is indexed to the number of components appearing in the polymer. The storage areas which will contain the molecular formula of the monomers (C, H, N, . . . , etc.) are initialized to zero. Then a data card containing the number of moles of the first monomer (MOLE) and the molecular formula of the first monomer is read. The molecular formula is a series of numbers (integers) giving the number of atoms of carbon, hydrogen, oxygen, . . . , etc., per molecule of monomer; these integers are stored at locations labeled C, H, N, O, . . . , etc. Note that some of these variable names were declared as integer names in the INTEGER statement at the head of the program and that actual atom names could be used for representing the molecular formula. The initialization of these storage areas to zero (done just after the opening of the DO 50 loop) is a precaution to ensure that any blanks left on the input molecular formula card are properly entered as zero; for example, the monomer styrene has the molecular formula C_8H_8; the numbers punched into the molecular formula card (following the specification of the number of moles of styrene) may then be 0808, and all spaces representing succeeding elements (N, O, S, F, CL, NA) may be left blank because initialization will have already made them zero. It is generally necessary to zero those portions of memory that must be zero before commencing calculation because computer memory is *not* cleared when a new program enters; unless initialization is carried out spurious numbers left over from a previous program may appear in the current program.

After the quantities MOLE, C, H, . . . , etc. are read in, the input data are listed in the output. It is wise to make provision for printing out all input data to make sure that the correct numbers were fed into the computer. The next step is the calculation of the total molecular weight of the monomer; this molecular weight is calculated in the usual fashion from the molecular formula and is then weighted by the number of moles of monomer appearing in the polymer feed. Similarly, the total number of atoms of carbon, hydrogen, nitrogen, etc. are calculated from the number of atoms of each of the elements per molecule, multiplied by the number of moles of monomer.

When the program reaches statement number 50, it cycles back to DO 50, where storage locations C, H, N, . . . , etc. are reinitialized to zero in preparation for reading the next data card which bears the number of moles of the second monomer appearing in the polymer feed along with its molecular formula. These input data are written out; the molecular weight contributed by the second monomer is calculated and added to MOLWT which already contains the molecular weight contributed by the first monomer. Similarly, the number of atoms of carbon, hydrogen, nitrogen are calculated and added to the numbers of such atoms already calculated for the preceding monomer. The DO 50 loop continues for all monomers in the polymer so that finally MOLWT contains the total molecular weight contributed by the monomers and CT, HT, NT, etc. contain the total numbers of atoms of carbon, hydrogen, and nitrogen contributed by the monomers. The calculation of the percentage compositon from these numbers follows statement 50. At statement 51 the results are written out.

Examples of output from this program are shown in Fig. 9.33b. Monomer compositions in the output are printed out on FORMAT statement number 5, using the statement WRITE(3,5) I,MOLE,C,H,N,O,S,F,CL,NA. The first variable (I) indexes the monomer, taking values from unity through NCOMP. MOLE is the number of moles of the monomer and is declared to be REAL at the head of the program; it is printed out on FORMAT F5.2 as in statement 5. The rest of the variables which give the molecular formula is printed on FORMATS I2.

The main body of the calculated results is printed out on a rather complex FORMAT, statement number 6. This FORMAT is responsible for printing the table headings "NO. OF ATOMS" and "PERCENT COMPOSITION." There follow eight sections of FORMAT separated by slashes for printing the lines, starting with the element names C, H, N, . . . , etc. Two variables are written on each of these lines: the first variable is the total number of atoms of a given type represented in the mixture of monomers; the second variable is the percent composition represented by the given atom. The quantity MOLECULAR WEIGHT represents the total (weighted) molecular weight of the monomers in the polymer feed; the FORMAT for this line is preceded by two slashes to put a line of space into the output separating MOLECULAR WEIGHT from the body of the table. The reader should note that FORMAT 6 required four continuation cards, punched with numerals 1–4 on column 6. Although any single digit may be used in this column to designate continuation, it is convenient to use sequential numbering as shown, in case someone drops the deck.

Debugging

The process of ensuring a computer program free from error is called *debugging*. There are two phases of debugging; the first is accomplished when the program is successfully compiled, that is, when all syntax errors have been eliminated. This phase of debugging depends heavily on the diagnostics supplied by the computer manufacturer. However, a computer program which can be compiled may still contain *logical* errors. Such errors can often be detected by running sample problems with known answers. It is wise to run several problems, since an incorrect program may give the correct answer because of fortuitous choice of problem. Logical errors are frequently difficult to uncover. The following techniques are helpful in locating such errors:

1. The nature of the output (i.e., the kinds of numbers produced) is sometimes a key to the error; for example, numbers that become unreasonably large during processing may reflect failure to perform a correct initialization before going into a DO loop. This is a common error.

2. It is often useful to take a set of simple numbers as input and carry it through the program step-by-step manually, processing the numbers as required by the program.

3. Temporary WRITE statements (using simple FORMATS to avoid introducing more error) may be inserted at strategic points in the program for writing out intermediate results. This may help to locate the section in which the error occurs, a technique particularly important in large complex programs.

4. If you can persuade a patient friend to look at your program, he may be able to find your error very rapidly after you have given him a brief rundown on how the program operates. Most of us develop mental blocks to seeing rather obvious programming errors.

5. In the last resort you can enlist the help of a professional programmer who has advanced debugging techniques at his disposal. He may, for example, obtain a "dump" of the content of computer memory and be able to analyze the coded data to find the trouble.

Other Examples

Chemists have found a wide variety of applications of the digital computer, and the number reported in the literature has grown steadily each year since about 1955. References to existing computer programs indexed in Chemical Abstracts are frequently available on request from the authors. Programs reported in Chemical Abstracts cover an unimaginably large range of applications: NMR spectral calculations, X-ray crystallographic structure determinations, infrared band shape analysis, analysis of ultracentrifugation data, interpretation of mass spectral data, theoretical calculation of reaction velocities, and fitting of kinetic equations, to mention a few. Quantum mechanical calculations beyond the very simplest variety cannot be done except by computer, and programs for these calculations may be obtained on request, and for a very modest fee, from the Quantum Chemistry Program Exchange at Purdue University. Many equipment manufacturers supply small computers to be used in conjunction with analytical equipment such as gas chromatographs, and programs are supplied for doing a variety of on-line computations such as base-line correction, resolution of bands, integration of peak areas and calculations of concentrations of components appearing in the effluent. Because of the bulk of the literature, it is possible to present only representative examples of the problem types that have been programmed.

Analysis from Spectral Data of an Equilibrium Mixture Containing Several Components [12]

Pyridoxal (**1**) is present in solution only in small amounts as the aldehyde structure shown and exists largely as the hemiacetal H_2P (**2**). The hemiacetal is an equilibrium with the dissociated structures HP (**3**) and P (**4**). At high pH a new structure appears as a result of further dissociation; it is conjectured to be POH (**5**). Ignoring the free aldehyde form (**1**), we find that an equilibrium exists among four structures:

$$H_2P \xrightleftharpoons{K_1} HP \xrightleftharpoons{K_2} P \xrightleftharpoons{K_3} POH$$

The absorption spectra of pyridoxal in solutions at 19 different pH's were determined. Since the composition of the equilibrium mixture is a function of pH, the spectra varied with pH as the relative amounts of H_2P, HP, P, and POH changed. Computer analysis of the spectral data for the 19 different solutions allowed computation of the three equilibrium constants K_1, K_2, K_3, and determination of the absorption spectra of the individual components in solution at any given pH. To start the determination the pK_a's for the three dissociation steps were estimated within a few tenths of a pK unit by inspection of the set of spectra. These initial estimates of the pK_a's were used to calculate estimated concentrations of the four absorbing components. From the expressions for the equilibrium constants,

$$\frac{C_{POH}}{C_P} = \frac{K_3}{a_H},$$

$$\frac{C_{HP}}{C_P} = \frac{a_H}{K_2}, \tag{9.43}$$

$$\frac{C_{H_2P}}{C_P} = \frac{a_H{}^2}{K_1 \cdot K_2},$$

where $a_H = 10^{-PH}$ is the hydrogen ion activity. Letting C_{tP} be the total (measured) pyridoxal concentration,

$$
\begin{aligned}
C_{tP} &= C_{H_2P} + C_{HP} + C_P + C_{POH} \\
&= \left(\frac{C_{H_2P}}{C_P} + \frac{C_{HP}}{C_P} + \frac{C_{POH}}{C_P} + 1 \right) \cdot C_P. \tag{9.44}
\end{aligned}
$$

Since C_{tP} is known and the ratios in parentheses in the last expression can be obtained from estimates of the pK_a's, the quantity C_P can be estimated. Once C_P is estimated, estimates of the concentrations of the rest of the components can be found from the above equations. This estimate of composition is done on the computer for all 19 solution pH's. The *absorbance* at each pH, at a given wavelength, is given by

$$A = \sum_{i=1}^{4} C_i \epsilon_i l, \tag{9.45}$$

where C_i is the (estimated) concentration of the ith component, ϵ_i is its molar extinction coefficient, and l is path length. At the given wavelength the observed absorbance A and the estimated compositions C_i for all 19 solutions may be used in a least squares regression calculation to estimate the extinction coefficients ϵ_i. The calculation of the set of extinction coefficients was done for about 100 values of the wavelength from 240 nm to 500 nm.

Provided that correct estimates of the concentrations C_i are used in the regression analysis, "good" values of the extinction coefficients will be obtained, and the calculated values of the absorbance, $\hat{A} = \sum C_i \hat{\epsilon_i} l$ will be in good agreement with the observed values at all wavelengths and all pH's. A measure of the total deviation of the calculated absorbances from the observed absorbances is given by the sum of squares

$$U = \sum_{ik} \left(A_{ik} - \sum_{j=1}^{4} C_{ji} \epsilon_{jk} \right)^2, \tag{9.46}$$

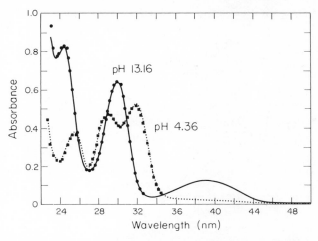

Fig. 9.34 Observed and calculated spectra of solutions of pyridoxal at high and low pH.

where subscript i refers to pH and subscript k refers to wavelength. The best set of C_i's will be the set that makes U a minimum. However, the sum of squares must be a minimum subject to the constraint that all of the ϵ_{jk} remain positive; this constraint was introduced by introducing a new error index:

$$U_a = U + \sum (C_{iP}\epsilon_{neg})^2, \tag{9.47}$$

where the summation represents the sum of squares of the deviations for all negative values of ϵ.

The original choice of pK_a's, which determine the values of C_i, will determine the size of the sum of squares U_a. Once U_a has been calculated for the initially assumed pK_a's, the first pK_a is altered by a small increment and the computations are repeated to determine a new value of U_a. The first pK_a is then varied again in the same or the opposite direction, depending on whether U_a decreased or increased after the first variation. The variation in the first pK_a is made smaller as the sum of squares converges to a minimum. When the variation in the first pK_a becomes sufficiently small, the next pK_a is varied, and so on. In this way the set of four pK_a's is determined which makes U_a a minimum. Special methods, discussed in the original paper, are used if two pK_a's are quite close in value. Figure 9.34 shows a comparison of the observed and calculated absorption spectra of solutions of pyridoxal at low and high pH. Figure 9.35 shows the calculated absorption spectra of the four components. These spectra are available, of course, from the fact that the calculation yields the extinction coefficients of each of the four components at a large number of wavelengths. This analysis, involving

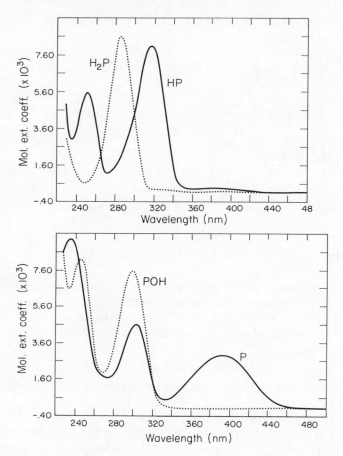

Fig. 9.35 Absorption spectra of four components.

100 different wavelengths, 19 pH's, and the repetitive variation of four parameters, is well suited to solutions formed on a digital computer. Programming for execution on a particular machine is straightforward once the logical scheme is in hand.

Determination of All Possible Molecular Formulas Consistent With a Given Set of Analytical and Molecular Weight Data [13]

Specification of an accurate molecular weight and an accurate percentage composition is generally sufficient to determine a unique molecular formula for a compound. Because of experimental error, however, both molecular-weight and percentage-composition determinations can be stated only within a certain range. Consequently there may be several molecular formulas for a given compound consistent with the analytical data. The calculation of the set of such molecular formulas is well-adapted to computer solution.

We illustrate the computation of a compound with molecular formula $C_{I_C}H_{I_H}N_{I_N}O_{I_O}S_{I_S}$ where $I_C, I_H, \ldots$, etc. are the number of atoms of C, H, $\ldots$, etc., per molecule. We suppose that a molecular weight determination is available with upper and lower bounds M_U and M_L. The restrictions imposed by the molecular-weight limits are

$$M_L < \sum W_X I_X < M_U, \tag{9.48}$$

where X represents an atom name (C, H, N, $\ldots$), W_X is the atomic weight of atom X, I_X is the number of atoms of atom A present in one molecule of the compound, and the sum is taken over all atom types in the molecule.

The restrictions imposed by the elemental analysis limits are

$$P_A - E_A < \frac{100 W_A I_A}{\sum W_X I_X} < P_A + E_A, \tag{9.49}$$

where P_A is the observed percentage by weight of element A, and $\pm E_A$ is the error attached to the analysis for A. The inequalities in (9.10) may be solved for I_A to establish the limits on the possible number of atoms A present in the molecule:

$$\frac{(P_A - E_A) \sum W_X I_X}{100 W_A} < I_A < \frac{(P_A + E_A) \sum W_X I_X}{100 W_A}. \tag{9.50}$$

Taking the restrictions of inequalities (9.48) along with those in the preceding inequalities (9.50) establishes the bounds on the number of atoms I_A in terms of the error limits on both molecular weight and elemental analysis:

$$\frac{(P_A - E_A) M_L}{100 W_A} < I_A < \frac{(P_A + E_A) M_U}{100 W_A}. \tag{9.51}$$

Possible values for each I_A are the integers that fall within the limits set by inequalities (9.51). The *calculated* percentage weight C_A for each element A is determined for all possible sets of integer values I_A within the above limits, and I_A is accepted provided that

$$P_A - E_A < C_A < P_A + E_A, \tag{9.52}$$

that is, provided the elemental analysis calculated for A agrees with the observed value within experimental error.

Table 9.16 Input Data for Molecular-Formula Determination

Element	Atomic Weight	Lower Limit (%)	Upper Limit (%)
Carbon	12.010	58.0	58.8
Hydrogen	1.008	5.3	6.1
Nitrogen	14.010	1.8	2.2
Sulfur	32.060	4.0	4.9
Oxygen	16.000	28.0	30.9
Molecular weight	680 lower limit		750 upper limit

A numerical measure of the nearness of analytical fit is calculated as the weighted sum of squares of the deviations of the calculated from the observed percentage weights:

$$S_E = \sum \left(\frac{C_A - P_A}{E_A} \right)^2, \qquad (9.53)$$

where the sum is taken over all of the atoms A in the molecule. S_E will vary from zero (when the solution coincides with the analytical results) to n, where n is the number of different elements present in the molecule. The value n will be achieved when each elemental analysis is at its limit of error.

A sample calculation taken from the original paper is shown in Table 9.16 for the analytical and molecular weight data contained in Table 9.17. In terms of minimum sum of squares, molecular formula number 3 gives the best fit. Formulas 2, 4, 7, 9, and 11, with even hydrogen integers, can be excluded as possible molecular formulas.

Table 9.17 Output of All Molecular Formulas Consistent With Input of Table

	Formula	Mol. Wt.	S_E
1	$C_{34}H_{37}N_1S_1O_{13}$	699.706	0.9876
2	$C_{34}H_{38}N_1S_1O_{13}$	700.714	0.5425
3	$C_{34}H_{39}N_1S_1O_{13}$	701.722	0.4198
4	$C_{34}H_{40}N_1S_1O_{13}$	702.730	0.6167
5	$C_{34}H_{41}N_1S_1O_{13}$	703.738	1.1305
6	$C_{35}H_{41}N_1S_1O_{13}$	715.748	0.8316
7	$C_{35}H_{42}N_1S_1O_{13}$	716.756	0.7877
8	$C_{35}H_{43}N_1S_1O_{13}$	717.764	1.0497
9	$C_{36}H_{40}N_1S_1O_{14}$	742.750	1.3350
10	$C_{36}H_{41}N_1S_1O_{14}$	743.758	1.2241
11	$C_{36}H_{42}N_1S_1O_{14}$	744.766	1.3977

The original paper [13] shows how group analyses (e.g., a methoxyl determination) can be included in the calculation. It is apparent from Table 9.17 that a very accurate molecular weight determination, such as that provided by high resolution mass spectrometry, would be sufficient to pinpoint the true molecular formula among the 11 possibilities shown.

Again, the tedious repetitive calculations required to select the 11 possible formulas are best done on a digital computer. The actual program can be written fairly easily at any installation, once an effective system of calculation has been selected. Efficient programming is important only when a program is used routinely, when the program will not fit in a computer's memory, or when computing times become very long. Most jobs are short and are completed in a few minutes; for them the cost of writing the program is higher than the cost of computing one time, and the programmer should not be much concerned with efficient machine use.

11 COMPUTING TERMINALS

Large computers are expensive to buy or rent, and in recent years there has been a trend toward time-sharing of facilities. Relatively inexpensive devices such as a teletype machine or a small computer may be used as *terminals*, connected by telephone lines to a remote large computer equipped for both input and output. In this way small users may gain the advantages inherent in a large computer, and the overhead of the large installation is shared by the subscribers. At any one time the computer cycles through each of the problems currently being worked on, and does this so rapidly that each subscriber may view the computer as if he were the only one using its facilities. Occasionally, the computer may be tied up on one problem; if so, it will signal a message "WAIT" to other users demanding its service.

The FORTRAN language, and other similar languages, are not well adapted to terminal use, and several special languages [BASIC, APL (14)] have been developed for this purpose. These special languages are *interactive*: that is, the user receives instructions from the computer in the formulation of his problem. Debugging is done on a line-by-line basis, so that corrections of syntax errors may be made immediately, and provision is made for canceling or altering lines while the program is being entered.

An example of a simple program run on a GE time-sharing computer [15] is shown in Fig. 9.36. After the teletype machine is turned on the computing service is dialed from the console of the teletype. The computer requests the USER NUMBER. This number identifies the user, confirms that he is an allowed user, and permits billing for computer time. The user types in his number. The computer asks SYSTEM, that is, the programming language.

In the example this was BASIC, and the user responds with BAS. The computer asks whether the program to follow is NEW or OLD; that is, is the program one already in storage or is it to be entered from the teletype keyboard? The user signals NEW; the program will be entered from the keyboard of the teletype. A name is assigned to the new program: NEW FILE NAME—JFF. Then the computer signals READY.

Each statement in the program is assigned a number. These numbers index the line and are used sequentially in order of magnitude by the computer. In line 10 three values for A, B, and C are to be read in. Note that the READ statement is FORMAT free. In statement 20 a value of $X = 3*A + B + 3 + C$ is calculated; the results are printed out in statement 30. The expressions in quotation marks will appear in the output. No FORMAT is required to specify how A, B, and C are to be printed. On line 40 values of A, B, and C are entered by a DATA statement. This statement assigns values (1, 2, 3 in the example) to the variables in the same order in which they appear in the READ statement. At line 50 the end of the program is signaled. With

```
GE TIME-SHARING SERVICE


ØN AT    9:23    B SAT 10/25/69    TTY 31

USER NUMBER--BXX000
SYSTEM--BAS
NEW ØR OLD--NEW
NEW FILE NAME--JFF
READY.

10 READ A,B,C
20 LET X=3*A+B↑3+C
30 PRINT "A=",A,"B=",B,"C=",C,"X=",X
40 DATA 1,2,3
50 END
RUN



JFF          9:26     B SAT 10/25/69

A =            1              B=            2           C=
   3           X=              14



USED      1.33 UNITS
BYE

*** ØFF AT  9:26    ELAPSED TERMINAL TIME =      2 MIN.
```

Fig. 9.36 Example of time-sharing program.

the instruction RUN the computer executes the program, using the values provided in line 40. The output appears below the program. Note that the output is in integer form because all the input data were expressed as integers.

This simple example by no means exhausts the possibilities of BASIC. Instead of using a DATA statement in the program, a general program can be compiled, with data entered later. A large library of mathematical routines is available and may be simply used. No extensive knowledge of programming is required: when a routine is called out of the library, the computer issues instructions for its use and leads the user on line-by-line.

12   ACKNOWLEDGMENTS

The authors received help and encouragement from many sources, though they must take the exclusive responsibility for the choice of material in this chapter. Valuable criticism and comment was offered, particularly by Mr. David Barton, who read the manuscript with great care.

APPENDIX

Conversions Between Number Systems

A four-part table will help you to convert small numbers from one common number system to another. Table A.1 shows the four number systems treated and the maximum entry of each part of the table for each number system. The concepts of the table can be extended to larger numbers.

To make conversions between any two of these numbering systems you must be able to add and subtract in any of the numbering systems. Addition and subtraction require carrying and borrowing when the results overflow or underflow any one position; for example, in decimal arithmetic, using symbols 0, 1, 2, 3, 4, 5, 6, 7, 8, and 9, when you add 1 to 9 you replace the 9 with a 0 and "carry" (add) 1 to the next position to the left. Conversely, in subtracting 1 from 10, you replace the 0 with a 9 and "borrow" (subtract) 1 from the column to the left.

Similarly, in binary arithmetic, using the numbers 0 and 1,

$$\begin{array}{r} 10 \\ +11 \\ \hline 101 \end{array}$$

(The decimal equivalent is $2 + 3 = 5$.)

In octal notation the symbols 0, 1, 2, 3, 4, 5, 6, and 7 are used. Here

$$\begin{array}{r} 10 \\ -1 \\ \hline 7 \end{array}$$

The decimal equivalent is $8 - 1 = 7$. Octal numbers replace three binary digits with a single symbol; for example, a binary 111 is an octal 7. This coding can be done in your head with a little practice. Binary registers are often displayed in successive groups of three binary digits so that the viewer can copy the contents of the register in octal notation, which is more compact than pure binary.

Hexadecimal notation is similar to octal notation but uses 16 symbols to represent the decimal numbers 0 to 15, which are represented by a group of four binary digits. Many third-generation computers present their binary data in groups of four binary digits. Here again the user can write down the contents of the registers in this compact notation, translating from the four binary digits in his head after a little practice. The hexadecimal symbols are 0, 1, 2, 3, 4, 5, 6, 7, 8, 9, A, B, C, D, E, F. Here

$$
\begin{array}{r}
8 \\
+3 \\
\hline
B
\end{array}
$$

since $B = 11$ in the decimal system. Also

$$
\begin{array}{r}
F0 \\
-1 \\
\hline
EF
\end{array}
$$

The decimal equivalent of EF is $240 - 1 = 239$, or $14 \times 16^1 + 15 \times 16^0$. Mental translations of coding to and from the hexadecimal system is more difficult than translations to and from the octal system.

To convert from one number system to another lay out a work sheet with two columns on it. Write the given number in the left-hand column. Enter the table that brackets this number; write the next smaller table entry below the number in the left column and its conversion equivalent in the right-hand column. Subtract the numbers in the left-hand column; the difference will be bracketed in one of the following sheets of the table. Repeat the operation, adding the entries in the right-hand column as you

Table A.1

	Decimal			Binary				Octal		Hexa-decimal	
Table A.2a	65,536	1	0000	0000	0000.	0000	1	000	000	10	000
A.2b	3,840			1111	0000	0000		7	400		F00
A.2c	240				1111	0000			360		F0
A.2d	15					1111			17		F

Table A.2a
4096₁₀ to 65536₁₀

4096_{10} to 65536_{10}

1 0000 0000 0000₂ to 1 0000 0000 0000 0000₂
10000₈ to 100 0000₈
1000₁₆ to 10000₁₆

Decimal	Binary				Octal		Hexadecimal
4,096	1	0000	0000	0000	1	0000	1000
8,192	10	0000	0000	0000	2	0000	2000
12,288	11	0000	0000	0000	3	0000	3000
16,384	100	0000	0000	0000	4	0000	4000
20,480	101	0000	0000	0000	5	0000	5000
24,576	110	0000	0000	0000	6	0000	6000
28,672	111	0000	0000	0000	7	0000	7000
32,768	1000	0000	0000	0000	10	0000	8000
36,864	1001	0000	0000	0000	11	0000	9000
40,960	1010	0000	0000	0000	12	0000	A000
45,056	1011	0000	0000	0000	13	0000	B000
49,152	1100	0000	0000	0000	14	0000	C000
53,248	1101	0000	0000	0000	15	0000	D000
57,344	1110	0000	0000	0000	16	0000	E000
61,440	1111	0000	0000	0000	17	0000	F000
65,536	1 0000	0000	0000	0000	100	0000	10000

Table A.2b
256₁₀ to 4096₁₀

256_{10} to 4096_{10}

1 0000 0000₂ to 1 0000 0000 0000₂
400₈ to 10000₈
100₁₆ to 1000₁₆

Decimal	Binary			Octal	Hexadecimal
256	1	0000	0000	400	100
512	10	0000	0000	1000	200
768	11	0000	0000	1400	300
1024	100	0000	0000	2000	400
1280	101	0000	0000	2400	500
1536	110	0000	0000	3000	600
1792	111	0000	0000	3400	700
2048	1000	0000	0000	4000	800
2304	1001	0000	0000	4400	900
2560	1010	0000	0000	5000	A00
2816	1011	0000	0000	5400	B00
3072	1100	0000	0000	6000	C00
3328	1101	0000	0000	6400	D00
3584	1110	0000	0000	7000	E00
3840	1111	0000	0000	7400	F00

Decimal	Binary	Octal	Hexadecimal
16	1 0000	20	10
32	10 0000	40	20
48	11 0000	60	30
64	100 0000	100	40
80	101 0000	120	50
96	110 0000	140	60
112	111 0000	160	70
128	1000 0000	200	80
144	1001 0000	220	90
160	1010 0000	240	A0
176	1011 0000	260	B0
192	1100 0000	300	C0
208	1101 0000	320	D0
224	1110 0000	340	E0
240	1111 0000	360	F0

Table A.2d
0_{10} to 16_{10}
0_2 to 1 0000_2
0_8 to 20_8
0_{16} to 10_{16}

Decimal	Binary	Octal	Hexadecimal
0	0000	0	0
1	1	1	1
2	10	2	2
3	11	3	3
4	100	4	4
5	101	5	5
6	110	6	6
7	111	7	7
8	1000	10	8
9	1001	11	9
10	1010	12	A
11	1011	13	B
12	1100	14	C
13	1101	15	D
14	1110	16	E
15	1111	17	F

subtract the numbers in the left-hand column; for example, convert decimal 23,173 to binary, octal, and hexadecimal numbers.

Decimal	Binary	Octal	Hexadecimal
23,173			
−20,480	101000000000000	50000	5000
2,693			
−2,560	+101000000000	+5000	+A00
133	101101000000000	55000	5A00
−128	+10000000	+200	+80
5	101101010000000	55200	5A80
−5	+101	+5	+5
0	101101010000101	55205	5A85

For an inverse example convert the hexadecimal number F0A9 to decimal, binary, and octal.

Hexadecimal	Binary	Octal	Decimal
F0A9			
−F000	1111000000000000	170000	61,440
A9			
−A0	+10100000	+240	+160
9	1111000010100000	170240	61,600
−9	+1001	+11	+9
0	1111000010101001	170251	61,609

Such conversions from one number system to another can best be done by a computer; the user will perform these conversions only when trying to find a "bug" or error in a program. The conversions are not difficult, particularly with the tables furnished, provided the user remembers to carry or borrow when going from place position to place position. The same problem exists when manipulating minutes and seconds, which use a base 60.

References

1. Several valuable journals are available, some without charge to qualified technical people. These journals periodically furnish up-to-date summaries of computers

and associated peripherals. The following are typical:

Datamation, published monthly by F. D. Thompson Publications, Inc., P.O. Box 2000, Greenwich, Conn. 06830.

Modern Data, published monthly by Delta Publications, Inc., 129 Brighton Rd., Clifton, N.J. 07012.

Computer Design, published monthly by Computer Design Publishing Corp., P.O. Box A, Winchester, Mass. 01890.

2. See, for example, "Charles Babbage" by Philip and Emily Morrison, *Scientific American*, April 1952.
3. A readable review of computer technology is included in the Scientific American book *Information*, Freeman, San Francisco, 1966.
4. See, for example, *Concepts of Digital Logic and Computer Operations*, Chapter II, by R. C. Barron, A. T. Piccirilli, D. L. Wallace, and R. L. Ward, Computer Control Co., Inc. (presently a division of Honeywell), Framingham, Mass. (1965).
5. See, for example, *Applications Manual for Computing Amplifiers*, Philbrick Researches, Inc. (presently Philbrick/Nexus Research, a Teledyne Co.), Dedham, Mass., 2nd ed. (1966).
6. See, for example, *Logic Handbook*, 1969 Edition, Digital Equipment Corp., Maynard, Mass.
7. N. Abramson, *Information Theory and Coding*, McGraw-Hill, New York, 1963.
8. See, for example, *PDP-8/L Users Handbook*, Digital Equipment Corp., Maynard, Mass., 1968.
9. Software Writing Group, Programming Dept., Digital Equipment Corp., *Introduction to Programming*, D.E.C., 1968, page Index-10.
10. *Data Conversion Circuits and Subsystems*, Staff of Computer Control Co. (Honeywell), Framingham, Mass., 1964.
11. The authors are indebted to Dr. Peter Scullard of the Eastman Kodak Research Laboratories for this program.
12. K. Nagans and D. E. Metzler, *J. Am. Chem. Soc.* **89,** 2891 (1967).
13. G. Read and D. J. Stone, *J. Chem. Soc.* (C), 906 (1966).
14. K. Iverson, *A Programming Language*, Wiley, New York, 1962.
15. The authors are indebted to Mr. James P. Rizzo of The Lawrenceville School, Lawrenceville, N.J., for this example.

Bibliography

Assembler

1. Elements of IBM 1130 Programming, W. T. Price, Holt, Reinhart and Winston, New York, 1968.
2. Manuals provided by computer manufacturers.

FORTRAN

1. FORTRAN IV Programming and Computing, J. T. Golden, Prentice-Hall, Englewood Cliffs, N.J., 1965.
2. Computer Programming FORTRAN IV, D. M. Anderson, Appleton-Century-Crofts, New York, 1966. Written for the beginner.
3. Manuals provided by computer manufacturers.

General

Information, Scientific American, Freeman, San Francisco, 1966.
N. Abramson, *Information Theory and Coding*, McGraw-Hill, New York, 1963.

Programs

Chemical Abstracts, published by the American Chemical Society.
Ohio State University, Columbus, Ohio 43210, provides an index of computer programs.
Quantum Chemistry Program Exchange, Purdue University, Lafayette, Indiana.
User groups sponsored by various computer manufacturers.

INDEX